Lewis J. Minor
9374 Cherry Lane
E. Lansing, Mich.

METHODS OF BIOCHEMICAL ANALYSIS

Volume IV

METHODS OF
BIOCHEMICAL ANALYSIS

Edited by **DAVID GLICK**

Professor of Physiological Chemistry
University of Minnesota, Minneapolis

VOLUME IV

INTERSCIENCE PUBLISHERS, INC., NEW YORK
INTERSCIENCE PUBLISHERS LTD., LONDON

Interscience Publishers, Inc., 250 Fifth Avenue, New York 1, N. Y.
For Great Britain and Northern Ireland:
Interscience Publishers Ltd., 88/90 Chancery Lane, London, W. C. 2

PRINTED IN THE UNITED STATES OF AMERICA

PREFACE TO THE SERIES

Annual review volumes dealing with many different fields of science have proved their value repeatedly and are now widely used and well established. ·These reviews have been concerned primarily with the results of the developing fields, rather than with the techniques and methods employed, and they have served to keep the ever expanding scene within the view of the investigator, the applier, the teacher, and the student.

It is particularly important that review services of this nature should now be extended to cover methods and techniques, because it is becoming increasingly difficult to keep abreast of the manifold experimental innovations and improvements which constitute the limiting factor in many cases for the growth of the experimental sciences. Concepts and vision of creative scientists far outrun that which can actually be attained in present practice. Therefore an emphasis on methodology and instrumentation is a fundamental need for material achievement to keep in sight of the advance of useful ideas.

The current volume is the first of a series which is designed to try to meet this need in the field of biochemical analysis. The topics to be included are chemical, physical, microbiological and, if necessary, animal assays, as well as basic techniques and instrumentation for the determination of enzymes, vitamins, hormones, lipids, carbohydrates, proteins and their products, minerals, antimetabolites, etc.

Certain chapters will deal with well established methods or techniques which have undergone sufficient improvement to merit recapitulation, reappraisal, and new recommendations. Other chapters will be concerned with essentially new approaches which bear promise of great usefulness. Relatively few subjects can be included in any single volume, but as they accumulate these volumes should comprise a self-modernizing encyclopedia of methods of biochemical analysis. By judicious selection of topics it is planned that most subjects of current importance will receive treatment in these volumes.

The general plan followed in the organization of the individual chapters is a discussion of the background and previous work, a critical evaluation of the various approaches, and a presentation of the procedural details of the method or methods recommended by the author.   The presentation of the experimental details is to be given in a manner that will furnish the laboratory worker with the complete information required to carry out the analyses.

Within this comprehensive scheme the reader may note that the treatments vary widely with respect to taste, style, and point of view. It is the editor's policy to encourage individual expression in these presentations because it is stifling to originality and justifiably annoying to many authors to submerge themselves in a standard mold.   Scientific writing need not be as dull and uniform as it too often is.   In certain technical details a consistent pattern is followed for the sake of convenience, as in the form used for reference citations and indexing.

The success of the treatment of any topic will depend primarily on the experience, critical ability, and capacity to communicate of the author.   Those invited to prepare the respective chapters are scientists who have either originated the methods they discuss or have had intimate personal experience with them.

It is the wish of the Advisory Board and the editor to make this series of volumes as useful as possible and to this end suggestions will always be welcome.

DAVID GLICK

Minneapolis, Minnesota
January, 1954

CONTRIBUTORS

STANLEY R. AMES, *Research Laboratories, Distillation Products Industries, Rochester, New York*

E. M. BICKOFF, *Western Regional Research Laboratory, U. S. Department of Agriculture, Albany, California*

HAROLD M. DAVIDSON, *Tufts University School of Medicine, Boston, Massachusetts*

K. S. DODGSON, *University of Wales, Physiology Institute, Cardiff*

NORRIS D. EMBREE, *Research Laboratories, Distillation Products Industries, Rochester, New York*

WILLIAM H. FISHMAN, *Tufts University School of Medicine, Boston, Massachusetts*

ERNEST F. GALE, *Medical Research Council Unit for Chemical Microbiology, Department of Biochemistry, University of Cambridge*

PHILIP L. HARRIS, *Research Laboratories, Distillation Products Industries, Rochester, New York*

RALPH T. HOLMAN, *Department of Physiological Chemistry and Hormel Institute, University of Minnesota, Austin*

C. F. JACOBSEN, *Carlsberg Laboratory, Copenhagen*

EDNA B. KEARNEY, *Edsel B. Ford Institute for Medical Research, Detroit, Michigan*

ROBERT W. LEHMAN, *Research Laboratories, Distillation Products Industries, Rochester, New York*

J. LÉONIS, *Carlsberg Laboratory, Copenhagen*

K. LINDERSTRØM-LANG, *Carlsberg Laboratory, Copenhagen*

M. OTTESEN, *Carlsberg Laboratory, Copenhagen*

CURT C. PORTER, *Merck Institute for Therapeutic Research, Rahway, New Jersey*

ROBERT H. SILBER, *Merck Institute for Therapeutic Research, Rahway, New Jersey*

THOMAS P. SINGER, *Edsel B. Ford Institute for Medical Research, Detroit, Michigan*

E. SPENCER, *University of Wales, Physiology Institute, Cardiff*

CONTRIBUTORS

CONTENTS

DETERMINATION OF CAROTENE

E. M. BICKOFF, *U. S. Department of Agriculture*

CONTENTS (*continued*)

I. INTRODUCTION

Steenbock (74), in 1919, was the first to postulate that the vitamin A activity of vegetables was in some way related to their content of yellow pigment. Following this observation there was a period of about 10 years before it was definitely established by Euler (28) that the plant pigment known as carotene could be converted into vitamin A in the animal body and that, therefore, carotene is a provitamin A. Although numerous methods have since been proposed for the assay of this pigment in foods, feeds, animal tissues, and other natural materials, the estimation of the vitamin A activity of a particular biological material by chemical or physical determination of its carotene content is still not completely satisfactory.

Most of the older methods measured only total carotene, no allowance being made for the difference in activity of the various provitamin A carotenoids that might be present. At least 10 different naturally occurring provitamins A are known, the most important being α-, β-, and γ-carotene and cryptoxanthin. Since these isomers do not have the same biological activity (25,26,48), assays that do not determine the relative amount of each that may be present can yield only approximate provitamin A values.

Recently, the problem has become further complicated by the discovery that each of the carotenoids is capable of existing in a number of stereoisomeric forms, having widely different biological potencies (94). The error arising from failure to separate and individually determine the stereoisomers may be significant even in the case of fresh plant tissues where the carotenoids occur predominantly in the all-trans form (98). Furthermore, these isomeric changes can assume increasing importance, depending on the processing or pretreatment to which the carotenoid containing foods or feeds have been subjected. In some cases, if corrections are not made for the presence of the stereoisomers, estimates as much as 30% in excess of the true potency can result (11).

Analytical techniques based on the chemical or physical properties of the carotenes are now available for determining the relative amounts of the main provitamins A (58,77). Methods are also available for determining the relative amounts of the two main cis-trans stereoisomers of β-carotene that may be naturally present in the material (7,75), or else may have been formed during processing (80). A number of these methods have been developed to the point where they are rapid and reliable, but they have not as yet become widely adopted.

Since utilization by the animal is usually not taken into account, carotene values obtained by physical or chemical assays only represent quantities of carotene with a certain vitamin A activity. They do not indicate the actual biological potency of the material in terms of vitamin A (90). Recent work has demonstrated that the animal shows a wide variability in the utilization of carotene, depending on the form in which it is administered.

II. OCCURRENCE OF CAROTENOIDS

Carotenoids are widely distributed in the plant kingdom. All green plant tissue contains carotene as well as xanthophyll and chlorophyll. The mixture of carotenes in green plant tissues is a relatively simple one; β-carotene is the major component and it may or may not be accompanied by smaller amounts of cis isomers and by α-carotene. Recently, very small amounts of the colorless polyenes, phytoene and phytofluene, have been detected in some green tissues (95). The xanthophylls of green tissues are more complex. They exist mostly unesterified and are extremely difficult to resolve completely. Two recent reports describe the resolution of the xanthophyll complex of the fresh corn plant (58) and of fresh alfalfa (9).

Yellow plant tissues such as corn, carrots, sweet potatoes, and yams are also rich in carotenoids. Not all fruits contain these pigments, but in those species that do the great majority have a carotenoid distribution quite different from that found in green leaves (35).

Carotenoids are found in products of animal origin such as eggs, butter, milk, and cheese. They have also been found in nearly every part of the mammalian organism. It is almost certain that these carotenoids are derived from the vegetable feeding stuffs. There is no record of any mammal manufacturing a "specific" carotenoid (41).

III. CHEMICAL STRUCTURE OF PROVITAMINS A

Chemically, the carotenoids belong to a class of organic compounds known as polyenes. They all contain an aliphatic chain with attached methyl groups and a system of conjugated double bonds. For this reason, they may be regarded as being composed of isoprene units, the most common of which contain 8 such units or 40 carbon atoms.

In all provitamin A carotenoids, the arrangement of isoprene units is reversed in the center of the molecule so that the methyl groups occupy the 1,6- instead of the 1,5-position, and it is this arrangement which makes it possible for the cleavage to occur in the center, thereby producing vitamin A. The most important provitamin A from the analytical point of view is β-carotene. Its complete structure, together with the now accepted numbering for carotenoids (35), is shown below.

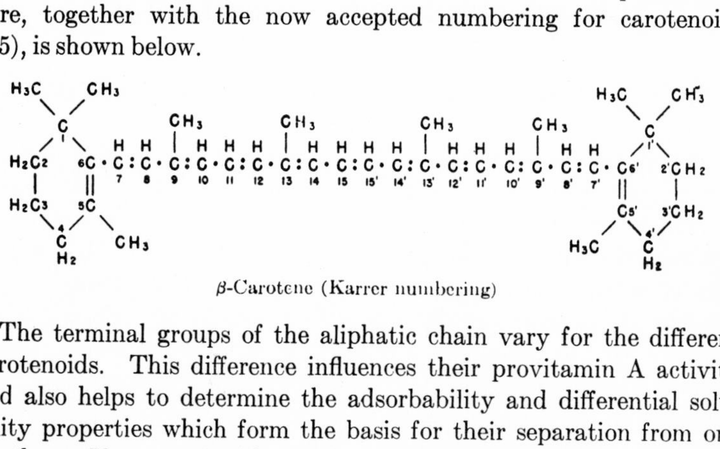

β-Carotene (Karrer numbering)

The terminal groups of the aliphatic chain vary for the different carotenoids. This difference influences their provitamin A activity and also helps to determine the adsorbability and differential solubility properties which form the basis for their separation from one another. If a carotenoid contains one unsubstituted β-ionone residue, or if the β-ionone residue contains an epoxy substituent in positions 5, 6, then the pigment will exhibit vitamin A activity.

All the provitamin A carotenoids are structurally related to one of the three isomeric carotenes, α-, β-, or γ-carotene, having the empirical composition, $C_{40}H_{56}$. α-Carotene contains a β-ionone residue on one end of the chain and an α-ionone residue on the other end. γ-Carotene has only the one β-ionone residue, the other end of the chain being open. Cryptoxanthin is 3-hydroxy-β-carotene. The structure of two of the naturally occurring vitamin A active carotenoids is still in doubt. These are aphanicin, found in the blue-green algae, and echinenone, found in the sex glands of sea-urchins.

TABLE I

The Naturally Occurring Vitamin-A-Active Carotenoids (35)

Aphanicin	γ-Carotene
Cryptoxanthin	α-Carotene,5:6-epoxide
Echinenone(= Aphanin, ? = myxoxanthin)	β-Carotene,5:6-epoxide
α-Carotene	Mutatochrome
β-Carotene	Torularhodin

Aphanicin may possibly be considered to be composed of two molecules of aphanin (3-keto-β-carotene) joined by an oxygen bridge. Echinenone may be identical with aphanin or myxoxanthin (14). Table I presents the carotenoids known at the time of writing to be vitamin A active.

IV. STEREOISOMERISM AND VITAMIN A ACTIVITY

The all-trans configuration of provitamin A carotenoids is maintained only when they are freshly extracted from natural sources or kept in the crystalline state. In solution, some of the sterically unhindered double bonds slowly change configuration, and a mixture of several cis-trans isomers is produced. This change can be brought about more rapidly when the solutions are refluxed or exposed to light in the presence of catalytic amounts of iodine. Zechmeister and coworkers have investigated this problem in detail (93).

Of the 20 possible isomers of β-carotene, fortunately, only 2 (neo-β-carotene B and neo-β-carotene U) have been found in large amount in fresh and processed plant tissues (11,17,47,98). The effect of commercial dehydration on the formation of stereoisomers has been studied at this laboratory. The results showed that the dehydration process greatly promoted the formation of cis isomers. Subsequent irradiation of the dried material or fat-soluble extracts prepared from it converted some of the cis isomers back to the all-trans form (80).

Table II presents the relative potencies of the principal stereoisomers of the four most important provitamins A. The percentages

TABLE II

Relative Potencies of Stereoisomeric Provitamins A in the Rat (94)

Stereoisomeric set	Stereochemical configuration (probable)	Current name	Biopotency in % of the all-*trans-β*-carotene potency
α-Carotene	All-trans	α-Carotene	53
	Peripheral mono-cis	Neo-α-carotene U	13
	Central-peripheral di-cis	Neo-α-carotene B	16
β-Carotene	All-trans	β-Carotene	100
	Peripheral mono-cis	Neo-β-carotene-U	38
	Central-peripheral di-cis	Neo-β-carotene B	53
γ-Carotene	All-trans	γ-Carotene[a]	27
	All-trans	γ-Carotene[b]	42
	Peripheral mono-cis	Neo-γ-carotene P	19
	Central mono-cis	(mixture)	16
	About penta-cis	Pro-γ-carotene	44
Cryptoxanthin	All-trans	Cryptoxanthin	57
	Peripheral mono-cis	Neo-cryptoxanthin U	27
	Central mono-cis	Neo-cryptoxanthin A	42

[a] ex *Pyracantha.*
[b] ex pro-γ-carotene, by iodine catalysis.

of provitamin A activities of the various carotenoids are based on all-*trans-β*-carotene = 100. Recently, it has been reported that *cis*-β-carotene C exhibits about $1/4$ to $1/5$ of the vitamin A activity of all-*trans-β*-carotene (32). At present, it is not entirely clear whether the activity of the stereoisomers is entirely inherent in the isomer or whether it is due to the transformation, *in vivo*, of at least a part of the cis-trans isomers into the natural all-trans form.

V. CORRELATION BETWEEN CHEMICAL ANALYSIS AND BIOASSAY

Graves (36) in a review article pointed out that the actual biological efficiency of yellow and orange vegetables is only 21 to 25% of the amount indicated by physical assay, while it is 70 to 100% for green vegetables. Wagner (83) has shown that as much as 96% of ingested plant carotene is excreted in the feces by man.

At present, there are no universally accepted conversion factors which may be applied to the non-biological values obtained on various types of materials. Callison (17) has shown that the bioassay values of an extract of yellow corn meal agreed well with the vitamin A potency calculated from chemical analysis, provided that hydrated lime was used as an adsorbent to separate an inactive pigment and partially active stereoisomers of β-carotene from the all-$trans$-β-carotene. It was further indicated (18) that it would be feasible to obtain a factor for each vegetable, or each class of carotene-bearing plant foods, which could be used to convert provitamin A content in terms of carotene to the equivalent international vitamin A units, derived biologically.

A conversion of this nature is necessary in order to compare with any degree of validity vitamin A values obtained by the two methods. Except for the few cases where correlations between chemical analysis and bioassays have been worked out (17,61,90), the biological assay is the only method which indicates the actual vitamin A activity of foods and feeds.

Biological assays are carried out on vitamin A depleted rats by feeding several levels of the sample in question and comparing the weight gains with those obtained by feeding known quantities of β-carotene. That quantity of food which results in weight gains similar to that produced by 0.6 μg. of the standard β-carotene contains 1 I.U. of vitamin A. Differences in utilization of carotene from various food sources are thus taken into account, although the types and relative amounts of the various provitamins present are not indicated. This method, though desirable, is tedious, time-consuming, expensive, and subject to considerable error and the variations inherent in all bioassays. Biological methods for the determination of vitamin A activity have been adequately described elsewhere (37,38,39,60,94) and will not be further discussed here.

VI. CHEMICAL ESTIMATION OF CAROTENE

1. General

In attempting to decide on a particular analytical method for a required assay, the analyst must first ascertain what degree of accuracy is required. For instance, in cases of clinical determination, it is often sufficient to determine only the total carotene content, particularly since the analytical methods are not sufficiently exact for the small quantities of material that are usually available. If a chemical determination, correlating closely with bioassay were required, it would be necessary to determine each of the provitamin A pigments present, including the relative amounts present as cis stereoisomers. In assaying products such as butter or milk, only the total vitamin A value might be required, contributed in this case partly by carotene and partly by vitamin A itself.

The preparation of vegetable material for analysis varies to a certain extent for each plant. Zscheile and Whitmore (99) point out that different plants, plant parts, or products made from plants require individual treatment and study because extraction methods, identity of pigments, and interpretation of both chromatographic columns (or other separation procedures) and characteristic absorption curves cannot be carried over arbitrarily from one material to another. All must be checked for accuracy in the application at hand.

In plants, such as tomatoes, having large lycopene content, conventional methods of assay will yield high "apparent carotene" values unless provision is made to separate the lycopene from carotene. In plant products such as corn, where a major portion of the provitamin A is present as cryptoxanthin, having considerably less vitamin A potency than β-carotene, it is necessary to separate it in order to evaluate its contribution to the total vitamin A potency of the material. Skillful sampling is also important in carotene analyses because of the great variability of the materials which are assayed. Failure to take such variations into consideration may result in data of limited value and may lead to false conclusions. A discussion of this subject, including the application of sampling techniques to various types of products, is presented in *Methods of Vitamin Assay* (2).

Perhaps it is correct to state that no single method completely satisfies the criteria of the ideal assay, namely, accuracy, rapidity, and specificity. Nevertheless, it is true that many do fulfill part of the requirements and may be satisfactory when maximum accuracy is not required. Often portions may be taken from several different procedures, and by slight modification a new and improved method may be developed or one applicable to a specific commodity.

Basically, the quantitative determination of carotene may be considered to consist of three essential steps: (1) extraction of the pigment from the plant or animal tissue with a suitable fat solvent, (2) its separation from xanthophylls and chlorophyll, if present, as well as oxidation products of carotene, and other colored impurities, and (3) measurement of the carotene content of the purified extract.

The classical method of Willstätter and Stoll (89) was employed for many years and has served as the basis for many of the later methods. A brief summary of this method is presented below.

The fresh plant material is ground finely in a mortar with quartz sand and 40% acetone. The ground material is then filtered and washed with 30% acetone until the filtrate comes through clear. The extracted material is finally washed with pure acetone and filtered a second time. The combined acetone extract is then treated with ether and the acetone-ether solution saponified with methyl alcoholic potash; then the acetone is removed from the ether solution by washing with water. The ether extract is evaporated to dryness with vacuum, the residue taken up in petroleum ether, and the extract poured into a separatory funnel. Xanthophyll is then removed from the carotene by washing first with 85% methanol and then 90% and finally 92% methanol until the washings are colorless. The xanthophyll which is present in the alcohol phase is then brought into ether solution. Both the carotene and xanthophyll solutions are washed free of methanol with water, dried and brought to volume and the concentrations are determined colorimetrically with a 0.2% solution of potassium dichromate as the colorimetric standard.

Although numerous modifications of the Willstätter and Stoll method have appeared, in most essentials later extraction methods have offered·no strikingly new contributions. The purification procedure employing phasic separation between methanol and petroleum ether for separation of the carotene from the other pigments was widely used for some time, especially for grass and forage, and still finds some application where β-carotene constitutes all or nearly all of the provitamin A fraction. However, the chromatographic adsorption method, originally pioneered by Tswett, consisting of the fractionation of the carotenoids upon a suitable adsorption column, is much more generally applicable and more specific. In the following section, each of the three basic steps which together constitute the chemical assay will be discussed in some detail.

2. Details of Technique

A. EXTRACTION OF THE PIGMENTS

A great many solvents have been suggested for extracting carotene from biological materials. These include acetone, alcohol, petroleum ether, and mixtures of petroleum ether with acetone or alcohol. The methods involving cold extraction have some points of difference which allow a choice to be made based on the types of materials to be analyzed and upon the final degree of purification desired.

As originally pointed out by Willstätter, it is often necessary to grind the sample together with the extractant in order to quantitatively extract the carotene. Zscheile (4) adds magnesium carbonate to the extractant during this operation in order to neutralize vegetable acids which may serve to promote a rapid enzymic destruction of carotene. Some workers recommend a one-minute scald with boiling water to inactivate enzymes and prevent oxidation which occurs rapidly when the cells are ruptured (53). If it is not possible to analyze green tissues immediately, they should be frozen and stored at temperatures below freezing.

The importance of special care in the handling of extracts of plant materials is further emphasized by the interesting observation that photochemical destruction of carotene occurs in the presence of chlorophyll in acetone or petroleum ether. Both light and chlorophyll are necessary for the reaction which has been found to be a function of time. Chlorophyll takes part in the reaction and does not act as a catalyst. Sodium cyanide partially inhibits the photochemical reaction (62).

For disintegrating the tissue, some still find it satisfactory to grind the sample with quartz in a small beaker using a flattened stirring rod (19). Others prefer more elaborate devices for macerating the tissue. Berkhout and Jongen (5) have designed a cylinder with a plunger in which dried, ground samples are extracted by grinding 10 to 500 mg. for 3 minutes in a cold mixture of 3 parts benzene to 2 parts of petroleum ether with a pinch of ground glass added.

Wherever possible, it is more convenient to disintegrate the tissue with the solvent in a blending device such as the Waring blendor. Callison (18) blends cooked vegetables in 1:1 mixture of acetone and absolute methanol and allows them to stand for 24 hours at 0°C. The residue is then filtered and washed with acetone-methanol. To avoid the splashing that may result with consequent loss of sample,

Moore (57) found that a mixture consisting of 100 ml. of 95% alcohol and 75 ml. of petroleum ether produced a foam in a Waring Blendor which prevented spashing of the solvent and was very effective in extracting carotene from a variety of fresh, green materials, silages, and hays. Results obtained with this method compared favorably with a method (55) which required grinding the sample with sand in a mortar and refluxing for 1 hour with alcohol. Moore's method has the disadvantage that the alcohol must be removed from the extract if chromatography is to be employed for purification of the carotene.

The splashing in the blendor may also be controlled by use of a close-fitting baffle. In the writer's laboratory, a stainless steel or aluminum plate, cut to fit the shape of the bowl, and attached to the top cover by a threaded bolt, is employed. The baffle fits about $1/_3$ of the way down from the top of the bowl when the cover is in place.

The relatively cumbersome transfers encountered in the use of such a blendor may be readily overcome by working with aliquots for subsequent operations. Pepkowitz (63) has suggested that a measured portion of the filtered extract be taken for assay, thus eliminating the need for quantitative transfer of the entire extract. This technique may be further simplified by taking an aliquot, by means of a pipette, directly from the blendor bowl for subsequent operations (10). Some (2) prefer extraction with the solvent, such as acetone, on a fritted glass funnel. This has the advantage of elimination of transfers of the material and enables one to work with small volumes.

Quantitative extraction is always facilitated by first reducing the material to as fine a state as is convenient. For dried material, this may be accomplished by passage through a grinding mill. Fresh or moist materials may first be sliced or minced. For dried samples, extraction techniques which employ a preliminary rehydration of the material are rapid and may permit more quantitative extraction of the pigments (10,27). Using 85% acetone, Davidson (24) extracted ground hay that had been moistened, frozen, and thawed and recovered 99% of the fat-soluble pigments of various samples.

For extraction of carotene from dried peas, Franklin (29) recommended a 16-hour leaching with a 2:1 mixture of light petroleum ether and acetone. The A.O.A.C. procedure for carotene in dried alfalfa offers a similar procedure as an alternate method of extraction to their 1-hour hot reflux procedure (1). Little if any oxidation or isomerization occurs in the procedures which employ a cold extraction in the dark (79). To further retard oxidation, it has been suggested (19) that antioxidants be added together with the meal and extractant.

Because control laboratories need a method for the determination of carotene which will furnish results within 2 or 3 hours of sampling, it has been stated that an overnight extraction procedure is too long for efficient control work (21). Therefore, a 1-hour hot reflux procedure is often preferred to hasten the extraction of the carotene. However, a rehydration procedure can eliminate the necessity for hot reflux and the entire assay can be completed in $1/2$ hour (10).

As compared with the older A.O.A.C. procedure which required boiling in 12% alcoholic KOH, refluxing the sample with a 2:1 mixture of petroleum ether and acetone is a satisfactory method for extracting the carotene. However, a mixture of 3 solvents (toluene, ethyl alcohol, and ethyl acetate) was shown to be an even more efficient extractant than either of the other methods (23) when applied to dried alfalfa, corn, corn products, and mixed feeds. Carotene assays on a limited number of fresh grass and silage samples indicated that the method may also be useful and applicable when working with material of this type.

In general, heating should be avoided during the extraction step if it is at all possible, since carotene will both oxidize and isomerize rapidly when exposed to heat and light (93). The extent and degree of isomerization will depend on the relative amount of stereoisomers initially present and upon the degree of illumination during the hot extraction (80). In extracts from fresh tissues, where the carotene is predominantly in the all-trans form, heating causes formation of cis isomers with consequent decrease in color intensity (79). In processed plant tissues, where the carotene may already be close to the equilibrium mixture of cis-trans and all-trans isomers, heating in the presence of light can cause a reisomerization of some of the partially cis isomers back to the all-trans form with consequent increase in total apparent absorption (11).

Hot extraction may sometimes be necessary in the analysis of materials with a high fat content, such as dairy products and mixed feeds. Hot extraction in conjunction with alkali (65) results in disintegration of the tissue as well as saponification of the fats, thus facilitating complete removal of the pigment. Many of the older techniques employed such a hot reflux with alcoholic KOH to extract the carotene. Modifications of this procedure have included preliminary digestion with aqueous KOH, followed by direct extraction with alcohol (54). In many cases, saponification at room temperature has been utilized in order to avoid the deleterious effect of heating (47).

Occasionally, provitamin A may be present in natural materials combined as an ester or protein complex. In natural material, particularly animal tissues where the hydroxylated carotenoid may be present as an ester, saponification is necessary to liberate it. Separation from its simple linkage with protein may be effected either by rapid heating to 40–60°C. (88), or by the use of quaternary ammonium salts such as lauryl dimethylbenzylammonium bromide (50).

B. SEPARATION OF THE PIGMENTS

(1) **Phasic Separation.** Borodin in 1883 (15) first showed that the carotenoid pigments could be separated into two fractions: (a) a petroleum ether soluble fraction, and (b) an alcohol soluble fraction This method was further developed and improved upon by Willstätter and Stoll (89). Until about 10 to 15 years ago, it had been the most widely used method for separating the biologically active carotene from the non-active pigments.

The solvents which are most generally employed are petroleum ether as the upper or "epiphasic" layer and aqueous methanol (85–95%) as the lower or "hypophasic" layer. The carotenes, their epoxides, monoketo- or monohydroxy-derivatives, or xanthophylls with their hydroxy group esterified or methylated remain in the epiphase. The xanthophylls containing two or more free hydroxy or keto groups remain in the hypophase. If the pigment composition is relatively simple and little decomposition has occurred, the method works fairly well. However, it has been shown by Peterson (64) and others that certain non-carotenoid chromogens are not removed from the petroleum ether phase, especially on samples in which the carotene has undergone some decomposition.

Furthermore, lycopene tends to remain in the petroleum ether phase, thus giving high "apparent carotene" values to materials containing this pigment. Cryptoxanthin, being a hydroxylated carotenoid, is not completely extracted from the hypophase, so that low "apparent carotene" assays will be obtained from materials, such as corn, which are rich in this provitamin.

White and Zscheile (86) have investigated the partition behavior of carotenoids between hexane and alcohols other than methanol. Diacetone alcohol was more effective than methanol, giving a more quantitative, clear-cut separation of the xanthophylls and other non-biologically active pigments from the provitamin A pigments. However, because phasic separations do not always make clear-cut separations of the various pigments, and also because they are laborious and not readily applicable to rapid, routine assay, they have been largely replaced by chromatographic methods for quantitative assay (59).

(2) Chromatographic Adsorption Analysis. Chromatography has now become the most widely used method for the purification of the carotenoid extracts. Using a properly activated adsorbent, the separation of the carotenes from the xanthophylls and other non-carotene pigments becomes a relatively simple matter. Furthermore, there is no other method that is so helpful in the separation and identification of the closely related carotenes. Even minor differences in structure between the various pigments allow for the development of distinct adsorption zones when petroleum ether solutions are poured through a column of properly activated adsorbent. These zones may be separated mechanically or eluted individually by the flowing chromatographic technique. The absorption spectrum of a pigment together with its adsorptive power or relative position on a chromatographic column gives a good indication of its identity.

Tswett (82) introduced methods of analyzing for carotene, based on the fact that powdered sugar, calcium carbonate, and inulin do not adsorb carotenes but do adsorb the other plant pigments from a solution of the pigments in petroleum ether. Since the early days of Tswett, improved techniques have been developed by a great many workers in the field. Many variations of adsorbent and eluant are available to achieve the required separations of the pigments. Precautions and conditions which must be observed in the preparation and effective use of adsorption columns have been described by Miller (52) and Zechmeister (92). It is desirable to have an adsorbent which is sufficiently active to achieve a sharp and clear-cut separation of the pigments. However, if the adsorbent is too active, it may also be too retentive and not allow a quantitative elution of the carotenes. Also, there is increased possibility for oxidation of the carotene to occur. On the other hand, an adsorbent which is less activated and permits a more nearly quantitative removal of adsorbed pigments may have lost much of the power of selective adsorption frequently necessary in the separation of very closely related carotenes.

Wilkes (87) has suggested the following requirements for the ideal adsorbent. It should be inexpensive and readily obtained commercially; should be easily packed into the adsorption column; should not contract from the column walls if drawn dry of solvent; should not require special activation or special storage precautions; and should allow a rapid flow of solvent through the column and rapid development of the chromatogram. All non-carotene pigments should be adsorbed and firmly held in the columns, while the carotenes should not be appreciably adsorbed but should wash through the column with the solvent. Of the wide variety of adsorbents that have been proposed at various times for purification of carotene extracts, only a few have met wide acceptance and none meets all the requirements of the ideal adsorbent.

Magnesium Oxide. Mixtures of magnesium oxide and filter aid have been introduced which have many of the desired properties. The work of Strain (76) is especially noteworthy in this regard. Experiments carried out by Strain in collaboration with the Westvaco Chlorine Products Division of Food Machinery and Chemical Company, Newark, California, showed that magnesia prepared by dehydration of the hydroxide is a very active adsorbent. The adsorptive capacity of the magnesia for carotenes was found to vary with the temperature at which the hydroxide was dehydrated. By comparison of samples prepared in different ways, a preparation was selected that exhibited great adsorptive capacity yet caused a minimum decomposition of the carotenes. This magnesia is now commercially available and is sold under the trade name of Micron Brand Magnesium Oxide No. 2641. The carotene method recommended by the Association of Vitamin Chemists (2) uses this material as the basis of the purification procedure. A more active preparation which retains the xanthophylls, chlorophylls, and degradation products of the carotenes more firmly, but still permits quantitative elution of the carotenes, is also manufactured by the same company and sold under the trade name Micron Brand Magnesium Oxide No. 2642. This adsorbent is employed in the Official Method for Carotene of the Association of Official Agricultural Chemists.

Micron brand magnesia has the disadvantage that it is too fine a powder to be used without a filter aid. Austin and Shipton (3) have found several commercial brands of magnesia, which after activation have sufficiently rapid flow rates so that admixture with a filter aid is not required. These include B.D.H. ("Heavy"), Hopkins and Williams ("Heavy"), and Howard and Co. ("Heavy"). These are the only brands of "Heavy" magnesias that these authors have tested, and they state that it is probable that others may be equally suitable.

Wall and Kelley (84) have shown that with a 1:3 adsorbent mixture of magnesia (Micron brand No. 2641) and Super-Cel and 2 to 5% acetone in petroleum ether as eluant, the separation of the biologically active pigments from the other carotenoids is rapid, clearcut, and gives great accuracy and reproducibility. In addition, it also permits the study of the pigment system occurring in the product assayed. Callison (18) has used a 1:3 mixture of magnesia and Super-Cel for vegetable extracts and eluted α-carotene with petroleum ether and β-carotene with 2% ethanol in petroleum ether. By decreasing the amount of Super-Cel in the adsorbent mixture, the individual pigments become more distinct and isomers which occur in small amounts may be observed. Magnesia, however, will not separate the stereoisomers of β-carotene from one another (4).

Aluminum Oxide. Partially hydrated alumina is one of the best and most widely used adsorbents (78). Its employment in the United States is not as extensive as it is in other parts of the world. In England, the Carotene Method of the Society of Public Analysts employ a 1:1 mixture of activated alumina and sodium sulfate as an alternate adsorbent to bone meal. The product, sold by Merck, standardized according to Brockmann (16), although expensive is manufactured under very exacting conditions, assuring a uniform and reproducible material from one batch to the next. Aluminum Ore Co. (East St. Louis, Illinois) is now supplying a minus 80 mesh activated alumina, special for chromatographic analysis, which contains particles ranging from 80 to 300 mesh. With respect to its adsorptive properties, this alumina is fairly similar to that standardized according to Brockmann. The writer has described its application to the purification of carotene extracts (13) and has indicated its special applicability to the determination of carotene in vegetable oils without the necessity for a prior saponification of the oil. For some time, Baker Chemical Company, Phillipsburg, New Jersey, has also sold an activated alumina known as "Hydralo" that is manufactured for them by the Aluminum Ore Company.

The separation of vitamin A from carotenoids can be accomplished because the latter, in petroleum ether solution, are less strongly adsorbed than vitamin A on activated alumina and are washed through the column, leaving the colorless vitamin on the adsorbent (42,43).

Bone Meal. The product called commercial feeding bone meal, sterilized bone flour, or steamed bone flour has been shown by Mann (51) to be a most satisfactory adsorbent for quantitative estimation of carotene. It was found to be extremely adsorbent for the xanthophyllic pigments, as well as the sterols in egg yolk but, when properly activated, readily allows a quantitative elution of the carotene. The adsorbent column of bone meal has the further advantage that, once it is properly prepared and set up, it may be used many times in succession. It may also be employed for the separation of carotene from vitamin A. Bone meal especially prepared for carotene chromatography can now be purchased. It is employed in the Official Method for Carotene of the Society of Public Analysts in England.

Calcium Phosphate. Dicalcium hydrogen phosphate was suggested as an adsorbent for separating carotene from other pigments by Moore (55). When suitably activated, it is an excellent adsorbent for purification of carotene extracts. It has been widely used in this country and is still employed in a number of laboratories. It has the disadvantage that the commercially obtained material must be first activated by boiling with potassium hydroxide, water washed, and then dried at 100°C. Moore (56) has also found that the activated phosphate will sometimes retain the carotene on the column, when freshly activated. However, it is claimed that after a few days exposure to room temperature this particular property is lost. Calcium phosphate has the further disadvantage that slight traces of polar solvents such as alcohol or acetone will elute impurities along with the carotene. This requires that all polar solvents used in the extraction of the carotene from the plant or animal tissue must be completely removed prior to chromatography. This material was employed in this laboratory for most routine analyses until about 10 years ago (14,27). However, because of the drawbacks mentioned above, it has now been replaced by magnesia for all routine assay work (10,79).

Soda Ash. This adsorbent was originally recommended by Kernohan (49), who claimed that it retained non-carotene chromogens and allowed the carotene to pass through unadsorbed. However,

Cooley and coworkers (22) found that samples of sodium carbonate from some sources did not retain all the non-carotene pigments. It has been reported that only one technical grade of soda ash (Wyandotte light soda ash, Wyandotte Chemical Corp., Michigan Alkali Division, Wyandotte, Michigan) has been found to have the proper adsorptive properties (87). In the writer's experience with this adsorbent, higher "apparent carotene" values were always obtained than with either dicalcium phosphate or magnesia for a given plant extract. It is therefore recommended that all samples of this product be carefully tested for retention of non-carotene chromogens prior to its employment in carotene assay procedures. The activity of the adsorbent will change unless it is protected from atmospheric moisture.

Magnesium Carbonate. This adsorbent has been proposed by Kemmerer (46). However, he pointed out that some lots might be too retentive. He suggested the use of U.S.P. light $MgCO_3$ that will adsorb less than 5% of carotene when tested by the following method: Place one gram of the $MgCO_3$ in a glass tube 5–8 mm. wide and about 15 cm. tall, constricted at one end and plugged with a wad of cotton. Pass through it a solution of purified carotene containing 1.0–1.5 p.p.m. of carotene. Wash with the petroleum ether and determine the carotene in the filtrate. If the $MgCO_3$ is too retentive of carotene, try another lot.

Kieselguhr. Wilkes (87) found that heat-treated diatomaceous earths, which have been widely used as filter aids and diluents in preparing adsorbents for chromatographic purposes, possess in themselves a large number of the desired properties of adsorbents for the chromatographic determination of carotene. Hyflo-Super-Cel (Johns-Manville) was found to be the strongest adsorbent of those tested for the carotenoid pigments and was therefore the preferred material. Used in an adsorption column in proper amounts, it separated almost all non-carotene pigments from a petroleum ether solution of plant pigments while allowing the carotenes to pass through the column almost unadsorbed.

Hyflo-Super-Cel is claimed to be especially well adapted to the separation of cryptoxanthin from carotene. The cryptoxanthin does not pass through the chromatographic column but forms a band on the column at some distance from the xanthophyll, thus permitting ready separation and elution of the cryptoxanthin. Lycopene, however, cannot be separated from carotenes by this adsorbent.

Wilkes reports that Hyflo-Super-Cel is inexpensive, uniform in properties, and exceptionally stable. After storage in open sacks for 5 years it was found to be as active as newly manufactured material. As the heat-treated siliceous earths are comparatively weak adsorbents, they are more strongly affected by traces of polar solvents such as acetone and methanol than are the mixtures of magnesium oxide and diatomaceous earth.

Recently Wiseman (91) reported that carotene was destroyed when dissolved in petroleum ether and placed in contact with Celite such as Hyflo-Super-Cel. The amount of carotene destroyed increased with time of contact, decreased humidification, and temperature. Addition of 0.5% acetone or pretreatment of the Celite with concentrated NH_4OH vapors exerted a protective action.

Lime. Both quicklime and slaked lime are active and selective adsorbents (44). Their adsorptive capacity lies between that of activated alumina and magnesia and that of the alkaline earth carbonates. The activity of most technical preparations of these compounds is subject to enormous variation due possibly to the presence of impurities and to the method of preparation. In a survey made by the writer of approximately seventy commercially available hydrated limes for their suitability for use in a chromatographic procedure for carotene stereoisomers (7), it was found that these products differed greatly in permeation rates and separating powers. Nevertheless, this adsorbent can be successfully employed to separate closely related members of the various stereoisomeric sets. Thus in a recent paper Zechmeister and Pinchard (96) report the successful isolation of various members of the *Pyracantha* pigment, which includes representatives of the α-carotene, β-carotene, γ-carotene, and lycopene sets. The adsorbent was Sierra Hydrated Lime, United States Lime Products Corp., Los Angeles, California. Calcium hydroxide has also been successfully employed by Thompson and coworkers (81) for separation and quantitative determination of carotene, cryptoxanthin, and vitamin A from dried eggs (see Section VII.5).

Calcium Carbonate. Tswett often used calcium carbonate as a mild adsorbent for leaf pigments. Like other adsorbents, this carbonate exhibits great variations in its adsorptive properties. The presence of very small quantities of moisture greatly diminishes the activity of all preparations. In order to obtain even moderately active preparations, the powdered material should be dried at about 150°C.

E. M. BICKOFF

immediately before use. A recent paper describes a procedure for the quantitative determination of carotene using this adsorbent to purify the carotene extract (31).

C. MEASUREMENT OF THE PURIFIED CAROTENE

(1) **Spectrophotometric Methods.** In using spectrophotometric methods, certain precautions must be observed rigidly. The spectrophotometer must provide adequate spectral isolation and be capable of permitting reproducible and accurate measurements of extinction coefficients. The solutions must be purified of substances having interfering absorption. The solvent selected and used must be reproducible in purity and composition. The extinction coefficients, at appropriately selected wave length positions of characteristic absorption, must be carefully determined from the most highly purified standards obtainable. The extinction coefficients for all-*trans*-β-carotene, all-*trans*-α-carotene, neo-β-carotene B, and neo-β-carotene U have been obtained from highly purified crystalline preparations at this laboratory (see Table III).

TABLE III

Wave Length Positions of Maximum and Minimum Absorption, and Corresponding Specific Absorption Coefficient,[a] of Carotene Isomers in Iso-octane

	Isomer			
	All-*trans*-α-carotene	All-*trans*-β-carotene	Neo-β-carotene U	Neo-β-carotene B
		Maximum		
Wave length, mμ	446	451	447	443
α-Preparation 1[a]	267–267	252–251	239–238	192–194
α-Preparation 2	267–269	252–251	237–237	187–189
Average	267	251	238	191
		Minimum		
Wave length, mμ	462	468	462	462
α-Preparation 1	184–184	203–203	184–185	149–151
α-Preparation 2	184–185	204–202	184–183	147–149
Average	184	203	184	149
		Maximum		
Wave length, mμ	474	479	474	470
α-Preparation 1	244–243	220–221	207–206	154–156
α-Preparation 2	245–245	220–221	205–206	150–150
Average	244	221	206	153

[a] Specific absorption coefficient: optical density referred to solution depth of 1 cm. and concentration of 1 g./liter.

(2) Colorimetric Methods. While a spectrophotometer, suitably calibrated and operated, is inherently capable of the most accurate results (34), a properly calibrated colorimeter can also yield satisfactory analytical data. The colorimeter may be calibrated directly by means of standard solutions or indirectly with extracts whose absorbance has been determined spectrophotometrically.

Calibration with Standard Solutions. Frequently it is necessary to recalibrate or check electrical instruments, and in the case of optical colorimeters a standard solution is required for comparison with the unknown solution. The carotene used for preparation of the standard solution should be purified by recrystallization (30) and its homogeneity verified by chromatography. According to Cooley (21), the addition of 10 to 50 times as much tocopherol as there is carotene present will stabilize standard solutions of carotene completely for as long as 12 weeks at 20°C. in diffuse daylight. A calibration curve is obtained for use with a photoelectric colorimeter by plotting the absorbance against concentration for a series of dilutions, employing the 440 mμ filter.

The use of potassium dichromate solutions for calibration of colorimeters is of doubtful reliability because the dichromate absorption spectrum is so different from that of β-carotene and its stereoisomers that small differences in wave length of the pass band of the colorimeter filter may introduce significant differences in calibration between different instruments. The maximum light absorption for a potassium dichromate solution is at a much lower wave length (390 mμ) than for a carotene solution. In a comparative evaluation (8), a group of 440 mμ colorimeter filters of the same manufacture gave a range greater than 5% in the relative ranking of a dichromate and a carotene solution when examined in a particular colorimeter of that manufacture. It has been suggested that a 14.5 mg. per cent solution of azobenzene in ethanol be used for color comparisons with carotene solutions (69).

Indirect Calibration with Spectrophotometer. Crystalline β-carotene may be the ideal material for colorimetric calibration, except for the inconvenience of preparation of authentic material of high purity in most control laboratories (30) and the necessity of verifying the purity of the commercially available material (20). The writer considers that, in the absence of concern for the different nutritive values of the several beta-carotene stereoisomers, the indirect calibration of the colorimeter proposed by Comar (20) by means of chromatographed carotene extracts whose absorbance has been determined at 451 mμ (12) on a spectrophotometer has great superiority for both convenience and reliability in inter-laboratory comparisons.

The general procedure is as follows: The worker prepares an extract in the manner decided upon for the colorimetric analysis. From the original extract a series of known dilutions is made which covers the optium $\log_{10} I_0/I$ range of the colorimeter to be used. The absorbancy of each dilution is measured on the colorimeter, and an aliquot of the original extract is measured on a spectrophotometer which is known to be satisfactory for absolute measurements on the system under study. The concentration of each of the dilutions used for the colorimetric measurement can then be calculated from the spectrophotometric value, and the calibration curve constructed.

D. STEREOISOMERIC ANALYSIS

(1) **Chromatographic Methods.** Since stereoisomers of all-*trans*-β-carotene have reduced nutritional value, it is evident that the presence of appreciable proportions of stereoisomers may lead to considerable error in estimating vitamin A activity from β-carotene analysis unless the relative amounts of the isomers are taken into account. Since α-carotene is not present in products such as alfalfa, broccoli, apricots, and sweet potatoes and since β-carotene is the predominant form in most foods containing carotene, methods for determining the approximate stereoisomer composition of β-carotene can have wide applicability.

Slowness in adopting chromatographic methods for evaluating the neo-β-carotene content of carotene extracts has been due to the difficulty of quantitatively separating the closely related stereoisomers. Polgár and Zechmeister (66) showed that the components of an isomerized β-carotene solution could be resolved on a hydrated lime column with an acetone-hexane mixture as a developer. However, the neo-β-carotene B zone remained in contact with the all-trans form, making it necessary to extrude the column and separate the bands mechanically. The adsorbed pigments were eluted from each of the separate segments with petroleum ether containing alcohol.

Kemmerer and Fraps (47) applied this technique to various plant materials. Their method was included in the A.O.A.C. collaborative study on carotene. The difficulty of separating the bands quantitatively led to conflicting results from different laboratories

(45), and it was recommended that the method be further studied and simplified before adoption.

Work at this laboratory has been aimed at developing a comparatively rapid, reliable, liquid chromatogram procedure for separating β-carotene extracts. In attempting to improve the degree of separation of the isomers on the developed column, the writer studied the relative efficiency of a number of solvent mixtures used as developers and found that certain aromatic ethers, such as p-cresyl methyl ether, were superior to most of the more common developers (6). Significant variables affecting the chromatographic separation included adsorbent, developer, adsorbate, size of column, and method of packing. From this study, a procedure was developed for the stereoisomeric analysis of β-carotene extracts (7). The method is sufficiently simple to make its routine application practical. It has been successfully implied to both fresh and dehydrated alfalfa (11).

In this procedure (see Section VII.6), the β-carotene extract is separated by chromatographing on a hydrated lime column into three fractions consisting primarily of neo-β-carotene B, all-*trans*-β-carotene, and neo-β-carotene U. If colored oxidation products of β-carotene are present, they remain firmly adsorbed near the top of the column.

(2) Spectrophotometric Method. The earlier work on β-carotene stereoisomers recognized only the presence of neo-β-carotene B (33). In this work alumina was used as an adsorbent and, under the conditions employed, the neo-β-carotene U (which is spectroscopically not very different from the all-*trans*-β-carotene) was included in the upper, more blurred part of the β-carotene zone and did not separate from it. Working on the assumption that purified carotene extracts contain only all-*trans*-β-carotene and neo-β-carotene B, Beadle and Zscheile (97) in 1942 developed a spectrophotometric analysis for both pigments in a single solution. Using this technique, they were able to show that carotene extracts of fresh vegetables may contain up to 20% or more of neo-β-carotene B. They confirmed their spectrophotometrically obtained results by employing chromatography of the purified extracts on alumina.

Subsequent work (66) has shown that the two-component system of Beadle and Zscheile consisted primarily of (*1*) neo-β-carotene B and (*2*) a mixture of all-*trans*-β-carotene and neo-β-carotene U. Thus, Went, LeRosen, and Zechmeister (85), using calcium hydroxide as the adsorbent, found that tomatoes contained neo-β-carotene U in

addition to neo-β-carotene B. In the same year, Polgár and Zechmeister (66) reported these two pigments in extracts of pumpkin,
squash, carrots, etc., and stated that they were formed by spontaneous isomerization.

The isolation and spectrophotometric characterization of the three
most abundant stereoisomers (12,40) of β-carotene provided the
background for the development of a spectrophotometric method of
analysis for the three isomers. Since approximately 95% of β-caro-
tene occurs as the all-trans, neo-B, and neo-U isomers in an equilibrium mixture at 25°C. (7,66), β-carotene solutions were treated
as containing three light-absorbing components with absorption
curves essentially those of the pure isomers. The method should be
applicable to extracts of β-carotene from any source, but for each
source a procedure must be established for preparing the extracts
free of impurities which may interfere with the spectrophotometric
measurements. Details of the procedure are presented in Section
VII.7.

VII. PROCEDURAL DETAILS FOR VARIOUS MATERIALS

1. Total Carotene in Fresh Plant Material (Bickoff, Livingston, and Van Atta (10))

A. PRINCIPLE OF THE METHOD

The carotene is rapidly extracted with acetone in a Waring Blendor.
To avoid lengthy transfers, an aliquot of the whole extract is taken
directly from the blendor bowl for subsequent operations. The
extracted carotene is purified by chromatography, and the total
carotene in the purified extract is then determined colorimetrically.
The method has been employed in this laboratory on alfalfa, lettuce,
and green peas. The same extraction procedure has been found
applicable to a variety of garden vegetables (63) and can probably
be employed with most green plant materials, although this should
be verified in each case.

B. ASSAY PROCEDURE

The freshly harvested material is sampled and a 10 g. portion is
transferred to the bowl of a Waring Blendor and disintegrated at high

speed for 1 minute in the presence of 100 ml. of acetone. A 5 ml. aliquot of the acetone extract is taken and added to 5 ml. of hexane and 3 ml. of water in a 50 ml. separatory funnel. Gently swirling the funnel for a minute transfers most of the acetone into the lower water layer which is then withdrawn and discarded.

The entire hyperphase is chromatographed on a column 12 mm. in diameter, packed to 70 mm. in height with an equal-parts mixture by weight of magnesium oxide (No. 2642, Westvaco) and filter aid. The carotene is eluted with a mixture of 1 part acetone and 9 parts hexane until 25 ml. is collected in a volumetric flask. The optical density (absorbance) of the solution is read at 440 mμ in a suitably calibrated colorimeter or spectrophotometer. The carotene content in the original plant material is determined from the aliquot of the acetone extract taken. The moisture content of the sample is assumed to have become part of the volume of the final acetone extract.

C. REPRODUCIBILITY OF METHOD

The standard deviation from the mean for 12 replications was 1.7%.

D. COMMENTS

To avoid loss of solvent during the blending operation, the time of blending should be kept to a minimum and a tightly fitted baffle should be employed within the bowl (see Section VI.2.A). To prevent the pipette from becoming clogged with small particles of solid material when the aliquot is taken from the bowl, a small wad of cotton may be affixed to the tip by means of a small rubber band.

2. Total Carotene in Dehydrated Plant Material

A. REHYDRATION PROCEDURE (10)

A procedure similar to that employed for fresh plant tissue may also be employed for dehydrated material following a rehydration. The details are as follows: A 2.00 g. sample of meal is placed on a No. 1 Whatman filter paper and washed with hot water (500 ml. at 50°C.). Vacuum is used to move the water through the meal. The volume of water absorbed by the filter paper and the rehydrated meal is ascertained by weighing before and after rehydration. The filter paper and sample are then transferred to a blendor bowl and the assay is conducted exactly as described above for fresh plant tissue.

The carotene content in the original dehydrated meal sample is determined from the aliquot of the acetone extract taken, allowing for the water absorbed by the sample and the filter paper.

B. OVERNIGHT EXTRACTION PROCEDURE (79)

This is a modification of the A.O.A.C. method for carotene (8). Because of increased simplicity, it lends itself better to the routine determination of large numbers of samples. It also eliminates one of the potential sources of error, inherent in the A.O.A.C. method, namely, the possibility of incomplete elution of carotene from the column. In a collaborative study by forty-six laboratories comparing the A.O.A.C. procedure with this proposed modification (67), almost all reported lower values by A.O.A.C.; 10 reported values from 12 to 20% lower, 8 reported values from 20 to 35% lower, and one reported an even lower value.

The details of the procedure are as follows: A 1 to 2 g. sample of meal ground to 40 mesh is allowed to soak overnight in the dark at room temperature in a 100 ml. stoppered volumetric flask with 30 ml. of a mixture of 3 parts acetone and 7 parts hexane. After standing approximately 16 hours, the extract is diluted to 100 ml. with hexane, and 5 ml. aliquot is chromatographed on a column 12 mm. in diameter, packed to 40 mm. in height with an equal parts mixture by weight of magnesium oxide (No. 2642, Westvaco) and filter aid. The carotene is eluted with a mixture of 1 part acetone and 9 parts hexane until 25 ml. is collected in a volumetric flask. The optical density of the solution is read at 440 mμ in a colorimeter or spectrophotometer and the carotene content determined by means of a calibration curve or by use of absorption coefficients for β-carotene.

3. Rapid Method for Carotene in Vegetable Oils (Bickoff and Williams (13))

A. PRINCIPLE OF THE METHOD

The more rapid methods for the determination of carotene in oils depend upon measurement of the light transmission of a solution of the oil in a suitable solvent and may be subject to error when colored products result from storage of the carotene solution. It has been found that aluminum oxide can be used for separating carotene from other chromogens in oil, whereas other adsorbents tested including calcium phosphate, soda ash, and magnesium oxide were not directly applicable to oil solutions, as the presence of the oil interfered with the adsorption of the non-carotene chromogens.

B. ASSAY PROCEDURE

Tswett Tubes (internal diameter 11 mm.) are packed with 12 g. of aluminum oxide (80 mesh activated especially for chromatographic analysis, manufactured by the Aluminum Ore Company, East St. Louis, Illinois) by applying gentle suction and tamping with a flattened glass rod until columns uniformly of about 10 cm. height are obtained.

One gram of the vegetable oil solution of carotene is weighed into a 100 ml. volumetric flask and made up to volume with petroleum ether. A 10 ml. aliquot of this solution is run onto the column. After all the solution has passed into the aluminum oxide, the column is developed and the carotene is simultaneously eluted with the required amount of petroleum ether containing 2% acetone. Application of pressure or suction is not necessary.

As the commercial preparation of aluminum oxide may vary somewhat in activity from one lot to another, a preliminary determination of the volume of eluant is required. The required calibration may be readily made as follows: A 10 ml. aliquot of a petroleum ether solution of crystalline carotene, containing 0.1 g. of oil (without added carotene)/ml. of solution, is run onto the column. Several columns are prepared in this manner. Columns are then washed with various amounts of 2% acetone in petroleum ether to determine the minimum amount of eluant needed to remove all the carotene. This volume is then used in the analysis of the carotene-enriched vegetable oil for eluting the carotene and leaving the other colored impurities on the column.

The carotene eluate is caught in a 100 ml. volumetric flask and made to volume, and the carotene concentration is determined colorimetrically with a 440 mμ filter. This measures β-carotene together with any α- or neo-β-carotenes that may be present.

C. COMMENTS

Columns prepared from the first three lots of aluminum oxide tested required 45 ml. of eluant to remove the carotene, while columns prepared from the fourth lot tested required 65 ml. The alumina must be protected against adsorption of moisture to keep its activity constant.

The method can also be used to separate carotene from other pigments in a petroleum ether solution that is free of oil. More eluant is needed to remove carotene from the column when no oil is present. The volume of eluant required may be readily determined as described above by use of a petroleum ether solution containing no oil. The volume of eluant required for columns prepared from various lots of alumina ranged from 75 to 90 ml.

4. Carotene and Vitamin A in Milk (Sobel and Rosenberg (70))

A. PRINCIPLE OF THE METHOD

This method is based on the fact that both vitamin A and carotene will react with activated 1,3-dichloro-2-propanol (henceforth referred to as GDH) to give stable colored solutions, having absorption maxima sufficiently different from one another to permit their employment for the simultaneous determination of both carotene and vitamin A in the presence of one another. Thus, vitamin A reacts with GDH to give a violet color having a maximum absorption at 550 mμ which remains constant at 25°C. for 2 to 10 minutes. The relationship between light absorption and concentration at 550 mμ is such that Beer's law is obeyed up to a concentration of 25 I. U. of vitamin A in 5.0 ml. of solution.

GDH reacts with carotene under the same conditions to produce two maxima, one at 500 and a second at 625 mμ, as well as one minimum at 550 mμ. This minimum coincides with the maximum for vitamin A, while the other maxima are almost at the minima for the vitamin. The green color is stable for 6 to 15 minutes, and the relationship between the concentration of carotene and light absorption at 550 mμ obeys Beer's law (72). Above 630 mμ the vitamin A color no longer absorbs light, whereas the carotene color continues absorbing light beyond this point. Thus, by taking readings at two wave lengths, 555 and 800 mμ, one can evaluate both β-carotene and vitamin A, as the optical densities are additive (73). A similar method for determination of vitamin A and carotene in blood serum has also been developed (71).

B. ASSAY PROCEDURE

One milliliter of milk is pipetted into a 0.375 x 4 inch test tube, 1 ml. of 1 N potassium hydroxide in 90% ethanol is added, the contents of the tube are mixed, and the tube is placed in a 60°C. water bath (or in a 60° oven in a vessel of water) for 35 minutes. The tube is removed and allowed to cool to room temperature. Two milliliters of reagent grade petroleum ether is added, and the tube is stoppered with a size 00 stopper pre-extracted with petroleum ether and shaken for 10 minutes. (A shaking machine is normally used.) After shaking, the tube is centrifuged for approximately 30 seconds to separate the phases sharply. The supernatant petroleum ether extract is aspirated with a fine-tipped rubber bulbed dropper and placed in a 0.5 x 4 inch test tube. The saponified milk sample is shaken with two succeeding 1 ml. aliquots of petroleum ether, allowing 5 minutes for each shaking. The supernatant petroleum ether extract is collected as previously.

The extract is evaporated to dryness by placing the tube in a 40°C. to 50°C. water bath and running a slow stream of nitrogen into it. One milliliter of reagent grade chloroform is added to bring the dried extract into solution. This solution is placed in a 25°C. water bath, and 4 ml. of GDH (prepared from glycerol dichlorohydrin, Eastman Kodak, Pract., by distilling with approximately 1% by weight of antimony trichloride at 10 to 40 mm. pressure, and discarding the first and last fractions) is added. The contents of the tube are mixed with a flat-tipped stirring rod. Two minutes after the initial mixing the solution is transferred to the 5.0 cm. light path cuvette. The absorption of the solution is read at a wave length dial setting of 550 mμ (with the 555 mμ filter in the filter housing) against a blank consisting of 1 ml. of reagent grade chloroform and 4 ml. of activated GDH. The wave length dial is then set to 800 mμ; the 555 mμ filter is replaced with the Coleman PC-5 filter and the absorption is read 4 minutes after the initial mixture of the reagents.

The absorption at 800 mμ will give the carotene content from a carotene calibration chart. The carotene content permits evaluation of the interference due to carotene at 555 mμ from a carotene interference chart. The optical density due to carotene interference at 555 mμ is subtracted from the total optical density at this wave length, and the resultant optical density permits evaluation of vitamin A content per milliliter from a vitamin A calibration chart.

The volume of the 1,3-dichloro-2-propanol-chloroform mixture is 5.0 ml. Because the horizontal cuvette has a capacity of less than 3 ml., sample and reagent aliquots may be reduced to six tenths of the above volumes. Where the analysis of milk samples of unusually low vitamin A content is not expected, it is possible to use the short light path (1.3 cm. cuvettes) or else reduce the amount of milk sample taken to as little as 0.25 ml.

Preparation of Calibration Charts

Vitamin A. The vitamin A reference graph is prepared with standards in chloroform solution ranging from 0.2 to 5.0 μg. of vitamin A per ml. All reagents are preheated to 25°C. before use. To 1 ml. of standard in a glass-stoppered cylinder is added 4 ml. of 1,3-dichloro-2-propanol. The contents are mixed by inversion and placed in a 25°C. water bath for 2 minutes. The absorption of the pink color produced is read in the 5.0 cm. cuvette against a blank consisting of 1 ml. of chloroform and 4 ml. of GDH. The wave length dial of the spectrophotometer is set at 550 mμ with the 555 mμ filter in the filter housing. Optical densities are plotted against vitamin A concentration per milliliter. If 1 ml. of milk is used as a starting sample, the chart may be used to evaluate directly the vitamin A content of 1 ml. of milk.

Carotene. This chart is prepared in the same manner as the vitamin A chart. The wave length dial is set at 800 mμ with the Coleman filter PC-5 in the filter housing. Optical densities due to concentrations of 1.0 to 10.0 μg. of carotene per ml. of chloroform are read 4 minutes after reagent mixture.

Carotene Interference. This chart is prepared in the same manner as the vitamin A chart. The carotene concentrations prepared above for the carotene calibration chart are read at the 550 mμ setting with the 555 mμ filter in the filter housing.

This graph is used to correct the vitamin A reading for carotene interference as follows: Carotene content is evaluated with the carotene calibration chart. The optical density which this amount of carotene gives at 555 mμ is found on the carotene interference graph. This optical density is subtracted from the total optical density read at 555 mμ.

With the corrected optical density, vitamin A content is evaluated from the vitamin A calibration chart. For convenience, all three graphs are drawn with common axes on the same sheet of coordinate paper.

C. COMMENTS

By saponifying and extracting the milk sample in a single test tube, and by employing horizontal cuvettes with a 5.0 cm. light path, sample volumes for each determination were reduced from the normally required 10 to 100 ml. to as little as 0.25 to 1.0 ml. A comparative study of this method and a method using larger volumes of milk showed higher values for this method. Added vitamin A was quantitatively recovered. Comparing the GDH with an antimony trichloride method of analysis showed similar values. Saponification of small milk samples was found to be absolutely necessary in order to extract the vitamin A-containing lipid completely from fresh milk.

5. Carotene and Vitamin A in Whole Dried Eggs (Thompson *et al.* (81))

A. PRINCIPLE OF THE METHOD

By proper control of conditions, the unsaponifiable fraction of dried eggs may be adsorbed on a column of calcium hydroxide and upon development with a mixture of 60% benzene and 40% petroleum ether a sharp separation of the carotenoids and of vitamin A can be made. The carotenoids are eluted from the column in the following order: β-carotene, cryptoxanthin, vitamin A, lutein, and zeaxanthin. The provitamins may then be determined colorimetrically. Vitamin A is determined by the antimony trichloride reagent. Values obtained by the chemical method agree within 10% with those obtained by bioassay.

B. ASSAY PROCEDURE

A 5.0 g. sample is weighed into a 125 ml. Erlenmeyer flask and 20 ml. of absolute methanol and 5 ml. of saturated aqueous KOH are added. The contents are stirred with a glass rod until complete suspension of the sample is effected. The flask is then heated on a steam bath for 10 minutes, or until all solid particles are disintegrated. The hydrolyzate is then cooled and transferred with 70 ml. of water (in three portions of 30, 20, 20 ml.) to a 500 ml. separatory funnel.   The first extraction is made with 35 ml. of peroxide-free ethyl ether and the four subsequent extractions with 25–30 ml. portions.   The last extractions should be almost colorless.   The pooled ether extract is washed 5 times with 25 ml. portions of water, then dried over 20 g. of anhydrous sodium sulfate for 1 hour at room temperature.   The filtered ether extract is evaporated to approximately 15 ml. under reduced pressure in a 50°C. water bath and then transferred to a 25 ml. volumetric flask with dry petroleum ether.   If the solution still contains some moisture, as indicated by cloudiness, it should be dried with a small amount of sodium sulfate.

In the chromatographic separation, 10 ml. of this solution is adsorbed on a column (20 x 135 mm.) of 3 parts of calcium hydroxide and 2 parts of Hyflo-Super-Cel.   The chromatogram is developed with a mixture of 60% benzene (thiophene-free) and 40% dry petroleum ether.   The two lowest bands, containing β-carotene and cryptoxanthin, are eluted separately.   The vitamin A fraction is collected until the lutein begins to give a yellow color to the eluate. If the column is properly packed, the β-carotene and cryptoxanthin bands are easily distinguished.   The lutein band should be sharp as it nears the bottom of the column.   Fifty to eighty I. U. of vitamin A and 150–200 gamma of total carotenoids (as β-carotene) can be handled satisfactorily with this column.   A total volume of 250–500 ml. of combined β-carotene, cryptoxanthin, and vitamin A eluate gives the optimum dilution.

After removing the solvent from the β-carotene and cryptoxanthin fractions, these are taken up in 10 ml. of petroleum ether and the yellow color measured by means of an Evelyn photoelectric colorimeter, with the 440 mμ filter.

These solutions are then recombined with the vitamin A fraction and the solution is evaporated under reduced pressure at 50°C. to approximately 15 ml.   This solution is then transferred to a 25 ml. volumetric flask with redistilled chloroform.   Ten milliliters of this solution is evaporated to dryness in a colorimeter tube and the residue is taken up in 2.0 ml. of chloroform.   The tube is placed in the colorimeter, 8.0 ml. of antimony trichloride reagent is added and the blue color measured at 620 mμ within 5–10 seconds.

This total blue color is corrected for the presence of β-carotene and cryptoxanthin by reference to a previously prepared correction curve relating the blue color of these compounds with their yellow color as measured at 440 mμ.   For this purpose as well as for the calculation of the concentration of cryptoxanthin, this provitamin A is considered equivalent to β-carotene.

C. COMMENTS

Since small amounts of vitamin A were found in the β-carotene and cryptoxanthin fractions, it was necessary to add these fractions back to the vitamin A eluate before reacting with antimony trichloride. β-Carotene and cryptoxanthin were shown experimentally to give only 7 and 11%, respectively, of the blue color given by vitamin A on reaction with antimony trichloride. Therefore, the effects of the β-carotene and the cryptoxanthin on the total blue color development were so small as to be negligible.

6. Chromatographic Determination of β-Carotene Stereoisomers in Alfalfa (Method of Bickoff and Thompson (11))

A. PRINCIPLE OF THE METHOD

The purified β-carotene extract from plant tissue is separated by means of the flowing chromatogram procedure into three fractions consisting primarily of neo-β-carotene B, all-*trans*-β-carotene, and neo-β-carotene U.

B. ASSAY PROCEDURE

(1) **Preparation of Chromatographic Column.** The chromatographic tube is 9 mm. inside diameter and 28 cm. in length with the upper end flared to a diameter of 2.5 cm. to form a convenient funnel for the addition of the adsorbent. The tube is constricted at the lower end and sealed to a capillary tube having a bore of 1 mm. and a length of 16 cm. The column, mounted by means of an adapter and rubber stopper in a 1 liter flask, is packed with hydrated lime to a depth of 10 cm., while the pressure is reduced at the lower end to 100 to 200 mm. of Hg by means of an aspirator. The adsorbent is added in 5 to 10 separate portions with gentle tapping of the side of the column to obtain uniform packing.

(2) **Extraction.** Ten grams of alfalfa meal is soaked in 25 ml. of petroleum ether (b.p. 88–99°C.) for 15 minutes in the dark and then filtered. Good quality dehydrated meal will yield about 40 μg. of carotene per milliliter of extract. For fresh or frozen alfalfa, 20 g. is ground in a Waring Blendor with 200 ml. of acetone for 30 seconds.

It is then filtered rapidly through a coarse sintered glass filter and added to 25 ml. of petroleum ether in a 500 ml. separatory funnel. The acetone is removed with about 5 separate washes with water and the extract dried over sodium sulfate. After drying, it is ready for stereoisomeric analysis.

(3) **Chromatography.** A sufficient quantity of the carotene extract (preferably 1 ml.) is added to the dry column to give about 40 μg. of carotene. The chromatogram is developed with a solution of 1.5% p-cresyl methyl ether in petroleum ether (b.p. 88–99°C.). By means of a Fisher Filtrator or equivalent, maintained at an absolute pressure of 100 to 200 mm. Hg, the eluate is collected directly in 25 ml. volumetric flasks. The bands of the stereoisomers are eluted from the column in the following order: neo-β-carotene B, all-*trans*-β-carotene, neo-β-carotene U. The neo-B fraction contains all the eluate leaving the column before the leading boundary of the all-trans zone reaches the bottom of the column. Further eluate is collected as the all-trans fraction until the leading boundary of the neo-U zone reaches the column outlet. The elution of the neo-U fraction is accelerated by addition to the column of 15 ml. of 5% acetone in petroleum ether when the collection of the all-trans fraction is nearly completed.

(4) **Colorimetric Analyses.** As soon as each fraction is collected, the solution in the flask is made up to volume with petroleum ether and the absorbancy is measured at once in a photoelectric colorimeter with a 440 mμ filter. If D_b, D_t, and D_u are the absorbancies of the neo-B, all-trans, and neo-U fractions, respectively, and B, T, and U represent micrograms of isomer present in the fraction, then

$$B = 0.78KD_b$$
$$T = KD_t$$
$$U = 0.95KD_u$$

The value of K is determined by measuring the absorbancies of petroleum ether solutions of crystalline all-*trans*-β-carotene. The factors 0.78 and 0.95 in the above equations were determined from measurements in an Evelyn colorimeter on solutions of pure neo-B, all-trans, and neo-U isomers. These calibrations have not been checked with other types of colorimeters.

(5) **Comments.** (a) It is desirable that the time required to develop the chromatogram be kept as low as possible, both for economy of time and to minimize the possibility of re-isomerization of any

band during the procedure. The development time is determined by the manner in which the column is prepared as well as by the properties of the adsorbent and developing solution. The tightness of packing of the column affects both the development time and the degree of separation of the zones. Tightly packed columns usually give well-defined zones but require 2 to 3 hours for development. Packing the column uniformly under vacuum with a minimum of tamping results in more diffuse zones, but the speed of development is increased so that all three major zones can be collected in 40 to 60 minutes. Columns packed with mixtures of hydrated lime and diatomaceous earth in ratios of 3:1, 2:1, and 1:1 developed increasingly rapidly (68) but were considered unsatisfactory because of diffuseness and resulting low color intensities of the bands.

Increase in packed length of the column increases the separation of the bands but requires longer development times. Analyses by the procedure described, using 7.5, 10, and 12 cm. effective column length, showed a slight difference in results for the first two, but no difference for the last two. The intermediate column length is accordingly recommended.

(b) The total amount of carotene added to a column is more important than its concentration in determining the degree of separation of the isomers. However, it is preferable to add the desired quantity in a volume of 1 ml. or less to produce compact, well-defined bands. Increasing the amount of carotene on the column from 20 to 1000 μg. gives successively poorer separations. With very small quantities of carotene, the bands are quite pale. Thus, it is necessary to choose sufficient carotene to produce easily visible bands. A quantity of 40 μg. is recommended.

(c) It is recommended that the hydrated lime or calcium hydroxide employed meet the following performance characteristics when an iodine-isomerized petroleum ether solution of crystalline β-carotene is analyzed by this procedure: (1) V_c, the rate of flow of developing solvent through the column when a state of constant flow has been reached, should be at least 2 mm. per minute; (2) the time required to develop the column to the point where the neo-U zone is beginning to leave the column should not exceed 90 minutes; (3) there should be no obvious overlapping of the neo-B and all-trans bands in the developed column. These specifications are rather arbitrary and are intended only as a guide in deciding whether a particular product is suitable for routine analytical use. At least nine different limes tested were found to meet these requirements (7). Columns prepared with the most satisfactory adsorbents clearly separate the neo-B and all-trans bands by at least 5 mm., have flow rates (V_c) of at least 5 mm. per minute, and require only 30 minutes for the development time mentioned. Many commercial samples were found to be unsatisfactory.

(d) Since light has a very pronounced effect on the isomerization, the light intensity during analysis should not be greater than 2–4 foot candles.

(e) On the basis of the finding that extraction of alfalfa meal for periods from 15 minutes to 25 hours yielded constant isomer ratios, it was decided that a quantitative extraction is not necessary. A 15 minute soaking of the meal in petroleum ether gives sufficient carotene for stereoisomeric analysis. Such extracts can be chromatographed directly on hydrated lime without a preliminary separation of the carotenes from the chlorophylls and xanthophylls.

7. Spectrophotometric Determination of β-Carotene Stereoisomers in Alfalfa (75)

A. PRINCIPLE OF THE METHOD

Since approximately 95% of β-carotene occurs as the all-trans, neo-B, and neo-U isomers in an equilibrium mixture at 25°C. (7,66), β-carotene solutions are treated here as containing three light-absorbing components with absorption curves essentially those of the pure isomers. The development of the chromatographic procedure, described above, and the characterization of the three most abundant stereoisomers (12) provided the background for the development of the spectrophotometric method. Empirically adjusted absorptivities for iso-octane solutions of β-carotene isomers were determined by means of which spectrophotometric results could be obtained which agreed closely with chromatographic analysis. Since the spectrophotometric measurements and calculations require less than 30 minutes per sample, the spectrophotometric procedure is much faster than the chromatographic separation of the isomers on a lime column. However, the chromatographic procedure must be considered more reliable since it is less likely to give erroneous results owing to the presence of impurities absorbing radiation in the cis peak region. The method should be applicable to suitably prepared extracts of β-carotene from any source, but for each source a procedure must be established for preparing the extracts free of impurities which may interfere with the spectrophotometric measurements.

B. ASSAY PROCEDURE

Five grams of alfalfa meal is soaked in 20 ml. of iso-octane (2,2,4-trimethyl pentane) for 15 minutes in the dark. The meal is removed by coarse filtration and the extract transferred to a chromatographic column 12 mm. diameter x 70 mm. in height, packed with a 1:1 mixture of magnesia (Westvaco No. 2642) and filter aid. This step need not be quantitative. The column is washed with 100 ml. iso-octane which is discarded. Carotene is eluted with 25 ml. of 1:9 acetone–iso-octane mixture. The acetone is removed by swirling in a separatory funnel 5 times with 25 ml. portions of water. The approximate concentration is checked by measuring the absorbance at 450 mμ using a specific absorption coefficient of 250 l. per g. cm. The concentration is then adjusted to some level between 3 and 4 mg. per liter. The absorbancies of this solution are then carefully measured at 26 ± 1°C. on a Beckman Model DU spectrophotometer at 470 and 490 mμ in 1 cm. path cells and at 340 mμ in 5 cm. cells using the following slit widths: 0.10 mm. at 340 mμ, 0.020 mm. at 470 mμ, 0.015 mm. at 490 mμ. Reduce the absorbancy at 340 mμ to 1 cm. path value. Calculate the concentration in mg. per liter of the three main β-carotene stereoisomers from the following equations:

$$B = 20.307A_1 - 3.636A_2 + 2.969A_3$$
$$T = 4.708A_1 - 6.244A_2 + 14.729A_3$$
$$U = -19.757A_1 + 14.087A_2 - 17.308A_3$$

where B, T, and U are the concentrations of neo-β-carotene B, all-trans-β-carotene, and neo-β-carotene U in the solution having 1 cm. path absorbancies of A_1, A_2, and A_3 at wave lengths 340, 470, and 490 mμ, respectively.

Sample Calculation. A solution as diluted for spectrophotometric analysis showed absorbancies of 0.666 and 0.379 at 470 and 490 mμ in 1 cm. path cells and an absorbancy of 0.615 at 340 mμ in a 5 cm. path cell. Substituting these values in the above equations for B, T, and U gives concentrations of 1.20, 2.00, and 0.39 mg. per liter for the neo-B, all-trans, and neo-U isomers, respectively, corresponding to an isomer composition of 33% neo-β-carotene B, 56% all-*trans*-β-carotene, and 11% neo-β-carotene U.   For total carotene content, either of the procedures of Section VII 2 may be used.

C. COMMENTS

Since the results are rather sensitive to errors in the measured absorbancies, care must be taken to minimize both wave length and photometric errors.   The wave length scale of the instrument should be frequently checked using the mercury arc lamp available from the manufacturer for that purpose.   The wave length settings should be carefully made to the appropriate calibrated wave length dial positions corresponding accurately to the specified wave length values. This is particularly true for the 490 mμ readings because of the rapid change with wave length of the absorption coefficients of the carotene isomers in this region.   Changes in wave length calibration of the instrument due to variations in ambient temperature of more than a few degrees can be significant.

Wave length errors can be eliminated by employing the mercury arc source for the photometric measurements.   Equations to be used in calculating the concentrations of the isomers for this procedure are given in the original publication (79).   The results obtained using the mercury lamp for photometric measurements are probably somewhat more reliable, but use of the tungsten lamp is more convenient.

If only 1 cm. path cells are available, the extract should be diluted to produce an absorbancy between 0.2 and 0.8 at 340 mμ.   Since the absorption coefficients used in this procedure were adjusted to give results in accord with those obtained using the chromatographic procedure described in Section VII.6, it is essential that, if this procedure is used with a spectrophotometer other than the Beckman DU, equivalent spectral slit widths must be used.

It is recommended that stereoisomeric analysis of samples also be made by the chromatographic procedure of Section VII.6 until experience with this spectrophotometric procedure has shown that reliable results are obtained for the type sample being analyzed.

References

1. Association of Official Agricultural Chemists, *Official Methods of Analysis*, 8th ed., Washington 4, D. C., 1955.
2. Association of Vitamin Chemists, Inc., *Methods of Vitamin Assay*, 2nd ed., Interscience, New York-London, 1951.
3. Austin, C. R., and Shipton, J., *J. Council Sci. Ind. Research, 17,* 115 (1944).
4. Beadle, B. W., and Zscheile, F. P., *J. Biol. Chem., 144,* 21 (1942).
5. Berkhout, H. W., and Jongen, G. H., *Chem. Weekblad, 45,* 333 (1949).
6. Bickoff, E. M., *Anal. Chem., 20,* 51 (1948).
7. Bickoff, E. M., Atkins, M. E., Bailey, G. F., and Stitt, F., *J. Assoc. Offic. Agr. Chemists, 32,* 766 (1949).
8. Bickoff, E. M., Livingston, A. L., and Bailey, G. F., *J. Assoc. Offic. Agr. Chemists, 37,* 509 (1954).
9. Bickoff, E. M., Livingston, A. L., Bailey, G. F., and Thompson, C. R., *J. Agr. Food Chem., 2,* 563 (1954).
10. Bickoff, E. M., Livingston, A. L., and Van Atta, G. R., *J. Assoc. Offic. Agr. Chemists, 35,* 826 (1952).
11. Bickoff, E. M., and Thompson, C. R., *J. Assoc. Offic. Agr. Chemists, 32,* 775 (1949).
12. Bickoff, E. M., White, L. M., Bevenue, A., and Williams, K. T., *J. Assoc. Offic. Agr. Chemists, 31,* 633 (1948).
13. Bickoff, E. M., and Williams, K. T., *Ind. Eng. Chem., Anal. Ed., 15,* 266 (1943).
14. Bickoff, E. M., and Williams, K. T., *Ind. Eng. Chem., 36,* 320 (1944).
15. Borodin, L., *Bull. acad. imp. sci. (Petrograd), 9,* 512; *Botan. Zentr., 41,* 577 (1883).
16. Brockmann, H., and Schodder, H., *Ber., 74,* 73 (1941).
17. Callison, E. C., Hallman, L. F., Martin, W. F., and Orent-Keiles, E., *J. Nutrition, 50,* 85 (1953).
18. Callison, E. C., Orent-Keiles, E., Frenchman, R., and Zook, E. G., *J. Nutrition, 37,* 139 (1949).
19. Carotene Panel of Sub-Committee on Vitamin Estimations, *Analyst, 75,* 568 (1950).
20. Comar, C. L., *Ind. Eng. Chem., Anal. Ed., 18,* 626 (1946).
21. Cooley, M. L., *J. Assoc. Offic. Agr. Chemists, 35,* 487 (1952).
22. Cooley, M. L., Christiansen, J. B., and Schroeder, C. H., *Ind. Eng. Chem., Anal. Ed., 17,* 689 (1945).
23. Cooley, M. L., and Koehn, R. C., *Anal. Chem., 22,* 322 (1950).
24. Davidson, J., *J. Sci. Food Agr., 5,* 1 (1954).
25. Deuel, H. J., Jr., Johnston, C., Sumner, A., Polgár, A., Schroeder, W. A., and Zechmeister, L., *Arch. Biochem., 5,* 365 (1944).

26. Deuel, H. J., Jr., Sumner, E., Johnston, C., Polgár, A., and Zechmeister, L., *Arch. Biochem.*, *6*, 157 (1945).
27. Dutton, H. J., Bailey, G. F., and Kohake, E., *Ind. Eng. Chem.*, *35*, 1173 (1943).
28. Euler, B. von, Euler, H. von, and Hellström, H., *Biochem. Z.*, *203*, 370 (1928).
29. Franklin, D., Lyons, F. B., and Wheeler, T. S., *Analyst*, *75*, 49 (1950).
30. Fraps, G. S., and Kemmerer, A. R., *Chem. Eng. News*, *19*, 846 (1941).
31. Fulop, L., *Bull. Fac. Hort. and Viticult.*, *Univ. Agr. Sci.*, *Budapest*, *10*, 152 (1944); *Chem. Abstr.*, *44*, 5494d (1950).
32. Garbers, C. F., Eugster, C. H., and Karrer, P., *Helv. Chim. Acta*, *37*, 382 (1954).
33. Gillam, A. E., and El Ridi, M. S., *Biochem. J.*, *30*, 1935 (1936).
34. Goldring, L. S., Hawes, R. C., Hare, G. H., Beckman, A. O., and Stickney, M. E., *Anal. Chem.*, *25*, 869 (1953).
35. Goodwin, T. W., in Paech, K., and Tracey, M. V., eds., *Modern Methods of Plant Analysis*. Vol. III, Springer-Verlag, Berlin, 1955.
36. Graves, H. C. H., *Chemistry & Industry*, *61*, 8 (1942).
37. Gridgeman, N. T., *The Estimation of Vitamin A*, Lever Brothers and Uni. Lever Ltd., London (1944).
38. György, Paul, *Vitamin Methods*, Vol. II, Academic Press, New York (1951).
39. Heilbron, I. M., Jones, W. E., and Bacharach, A. L., *Vitamins and Hormones*, *2*, 155 (1944).
40. Jones, F. T., and Bickoff, E. M., *J. Assoc. Offic. Agr. Chemists*, *31*, 776 (1948).
41. Karrer, P., and Jucker, E., *Carotenoids*, Elsevier Publishing Co., Inc., trans. and revised by E. A. Brande, Elsevier Publishing Co., New York (1950).
42. Karrer, P., and Schopp, K., *Helv. Chim. Acta*, *15*, 745 (1932).
43. Karrer, P., and Schopp, K., *Helv. Chim. Acta*, *17*, 693 (1934).
44. Karrer, P., and Walker, O., *Helv. Chim. Acta*, *16*, 641 (1933).
45. Kemmerer, A. R., *J. Assoc. Offic. Agr. Chemists*, *28*, 563 (1945).
46. Kemmerer, A. R., *J. Assoc. Offic. Agr. Chemists*, *29*, 18 (1946).
47. Kemmerer, A. R., and Fraps, G. S., *Ind. Eng. Chem., Anal. Ed.*, *15*, 714 (1943).
48. Kemmerer, A. R., and Fraps, G. S., *J. Biol. Chem.*, *161*, 305 (1945).
49. Kernohan, G., *Science*, *90*, 623 (1939).
50. Kuhn, R., and Bielig, H. J., *Ber.*, *73*, 1080 (1940).
51. Mann, T. Barton, *Analyst*, *68*, 233 (1943).
52. Miller, E. S., *Botan. Gaz.*, *96*, 447 (1935).
53. Mitchell, H. A., and Hauge, S. M., *J. Biol. Chem.*, *163*, 7 (1946).
54. Moon, F. E., *J. Agr. Sci.*, *29*, 295 (1939).
55. Moore, L. A., *Ind. Eng. Chem., Anal. Ed.*, *12*, 726 (1940).
56. Moore, L. A., *Ind. Eng. Chem., Anal. Ed.*, *14*, 707 (1942).

57. Moore, L. A., and Ely, R., *Ind. Eng. Chem., Anal. Ed.*, *13*, 600 (1941).

58. Moster, J. B., Quackenbush, F. W., and Porter, J. W., *Arch. Biochem. Biophys.*, *38*, 287 (1952).

59. Nelson, E. M., *J. Assoc. Offic. Agr. Chemists*, *28*, 544 (1945).

60. Nelson, E. M., and de Witt, J. B., *Biol. Symposia*, *12*, 1 (1947).

61. Orent-Keiles, E., Callison, E. C., Schaevitz, J., and Frenchman, R., *Science*, *103*, 498 (1946).

62. Pepkowitz, L. P., *J. Biol. Chem.*, *149*, 465 (1943).

63. Pepkowitz, L. P., and Gardner, J., *Chemist Analyst*, *32*, 33 (1944).

64. Peterson, W. J., *Ind. Eng. Chem., Anal. Ed.*, *13*, 212 (1941).

65. Peterson, W. J., Hughes, J. W., and Freeman, H. F., *Ind. Eng. Chem., Anal. Ed.*, *9*, 71 (1937).

66. Polgár, A., and Zechmeister, L., *J. Am. Chem. Soc.*, *64*, 1856 (1942).

67. Quackenbush, F. W., *J. Assoc. Offic. Agr. Chemists*, *35*, 736 (1952).

68. Roth, W. A., and LeRosen, A. L., *Anal. Chem.*, *20*, 1092 (1948).

69. Schmalfuss, H., *Fette u. Seifen*, *25*, 734 (1950).

70. Sobel, A. E., and Rosenberg, A. A., *Anal. Chem.*, *21*, 1540 (1949).

71. Sobel, A. E., and Snow, S. D., *J. Biol. Chem.*, *171*, 617 (1947).

72. Sobel, A. E., and Werbin, H., *J. Biol. Chem.*, *159*, 681 (1945).

73. Sobel, A. E., and Werbin, H., *Ind. Eng. Chem., Anal. Ed.*, *18*, 570 (1946).

74. Steenbock, H., *Science*, *50*, 352 (1919).

75. Stitt, F., Bickoff, E. M., Bailey, G. F., Thompson, C. R., and Friedlander, S., *J. Assoc. Offic. Agr. Chemists*, *34*, 460 (1951).

76. Strain, H. H., *J. Biol. Chem.*, *105*, 523 (1934).

77. Strain, H. H., *J. Biol. Chem.*, *127*, 191 (1939).

78. Strain, H. H., *Chromatographic Adsorption Analysis*, Interscience, New York-London 1942.

79. Thompson, C. R., and Bickoff, E. M., *J. Assoc. Offic. Agr. Chemists*, *34*, 219 (1951).

80. Thompson, C. R., Bickoff, E. M., and Maclay, W. D., *Ind. Eng. Chem.*, *43*, 126 (1951).

81. Thompson, C. R., Ewan, M. A., Hauge, S. M., Bohren, B. B., and Quackenbush, F. W., *Ind. Eng. Chem., Anal. Ed.*, *18*, 113 (1946).

82. Tswett, M., *Ber. Bot. Ges.*, *29*, 630 (1911).

83. Wagner, K. H., *Klin. Wochschr.*, *32*, 87 (1954).

84. Wall, M. E., and Kelley, E. G., *Ind. Eng. Chem., Anal. Ed.*, *15*, 18 (1943).

85. Went, F. W., LeRosen, A. L., and Zechmeister, L., *Plant Physiol.*, *17*, 91 (1942).

86. White, J. W., and Zscheile, F. P., *J. Am. Chem. Soc.*, *64*, 1440 (1942).

87. Wilkes, J. B., *Ind. Eng. Chem., Anal. Ed.*, *18*, 702 (1946).

88. Willstätter, R., and Escher, H. H., *Z. Physiol. Chem.*, *64*, 47 (1910).

89. Willstätter, R., and Stoll, A., *Untersuchungen über Chlorophyll*, Berlin, 1913; English translation by Schertz, F. M., and Merz, A. R., Science Press, Lancaster, Pa., 1928.

90. Wilson, R. H., Ambrose, A. M., DeEds, F., Dutton, H. J., and Bailey, G. F., *Arch. Biochem.*, *10*, 131 (1946).
91. Wiseman, H. G., Stone, S. S., Savage, H. L., and Moore, L. A., *Anal. Chem.*, *24*, 681 (1952).
92. Zechmeister, L., *Carotenoide*, Julius Springer, Berlin, 1934.
93. Zechmeister, L., *Chem. Revs.*, *34*, 267 (1944).
94. Zechmeister, L., *Vitamins and Hormones*, *7*, 57 (1949).
95. Zechmeister, L., and Karmaker, G., *Arch. Biochem. and Biophys.*, *47*, 160 (1953).
96. Zechmeister, L., and Pinchard, J. H., *J. Am. Chem. Soc.*, *69*, 1930 (1947).
97. Zscheile, F. P., and Beadle, B. W., *Ind. Eng. Chem.*, *Anal. Ed.*, *14*, 633 (1942).
98. Zscheile, F. P., Beadle, B. W., and Kraybill, H. R., *Food Research*, *8*, 299 (1943).
99. Zscheile, F. P., and Whitmore, R. A., *Anal. Chem.*, *19*, 170 (1947).

DETERMINATION OF VITAMIN A

Norris D. Embree, Stanley R. Ames, Robert W. Lehman, and
Philip L. Harris, *Distillation Products Industries*

CONTENTS (*continued*)

I. INTRODUCTION

1. General Properties

Vitamin A is an unsaturated alcohol, $C_{20}H_{29}OH$, with the following structural formula:

Vitamin A   (Axerophthol, vitamin A₁)

3,7-Dimethyl-9-(2,6,6-trimethyl-1-cyclohexen-1-yl)-2,4,6,8-nonatetraen-1-ol

The carbon atoms are numbered by the Geneva System as given in *Chemical Abstracts, 1954 Subject Index.*

It is an essential nutrient for man and other vertebrates, and is found in blood and many other tissues, particularly the liver.

While details for handling vitamin A will be given in specific analytical procedures, an analyst should keep in mind the following properties:

Vitamin A is: soluble in fats and fat solvents; insoluble in water, but sometimes quite difficult to extract from aqueous emulsions; unstable to light, even to artificial room illumination when diluted to a few micrograms per milliliter; stable in alkali; unstable in acids and on acidic or acid-activated adsorbents; unstable to oxygen or oxidizing agents. Vitamin A esters are more stable to oxidation, but less stable to refluxing in alcohol or other polar solvents. Solvents that may contain peroxides, such as ethers, should be redistilled before use, and oils for diluents for bioassay should have no peroxides or other evidence of rancidity.

Vitamin A occurs in animal tissues, mostly as fatty acid esters, but some unesterified vitamin A may be associated. Commercial vitamin A from natural sources comes from marine livers; it includes the liver oil itself, "natural ester" concentrates prepared by molecular distillation or by extraction, concentrates of unesterified vitamin A prepared by saponification, and vitamin A acetate concentrates made by acetylating the unsaponifiable fraction. Commercial synthetic vitamin A is usually esterified to produce the acetate or the palmitate.

2. Analytical Properties

A. INTERNATIONAL UNIT OF VITAMIN A

The basic properties of vitamin A for analytical use are now reasonably established. The foundation for official assays was set in 1950 when the World Health Organization followed the suggestion of the Vitamin Advisory Board of the XIV edition of the U. S. Pharmacopeia by defining one International Unit to be the activity of 0.344 μg. of crystalline all-*trans*-vitamin A acetate which is equivalent to 0.3 μg. of vitamin A alcohol (84).

The reference standard for biological assay is a solution of crystalline vitamin A acetate of appropriate strength (see Section III.1.A.2). For physicochemical assay, various official methods have been developed based on the ultraviolet absorption properties of pure vitamin A.

B. ULTRAVIOLET ABSORPTION

Enough is known about the ultraviolet absorption of various crystalline vitamin A preparations for most practical purposes, but the uncertainties remaining are interesting and should be kept in mind. The first trouble is that no two investigators report *exactly* the same results on the same compounds in the same solvents; this may be due to slight differences in the spectrophotometers, the samples, and the techniques. Another trouble is the differences in the spectra when measured in different solvents. Also leading to problems are the *cis*-isomers of vitamin A with slightly different spectra and lower biopotencies.

A convenient set of ultraviolet data for vitamin A alcohol and vitamin A acetate is shown in Table I. The actual values are a per cent or so different from some other equally qualified investigations; the set chosen showed the best selection of solvents.

The official reference vitamin A is the all-*trans* form; it is the dominant form in most natural and synthetic products and its acetate is the only one that has been crystallized. Neovitamin A, later found to be 2-*cis*-vitamin A, was discovered by Robeson and Baxter to constitute about one-third of the vitamin A in fish liver oil (see Section III.1.-A.4). Work on vitamin A aldehydes in the visual process by Wald's laboratory has shown the importance of other isomers (see Section II.6.C). In Table II are presented some ultraviolet and biological data showing the differences in the isomers. While the isomers are of considerable scientific interest, the commercial problem has appeared to be reasonably simple; only the two forms, all-*trans*-vitamin A and neovitamin A, have been considered to predominate in commercial fish liver oils and synthetic vitamin A. The ultraviolet absorption of

TABLE I

Ultraviolet Absorption Data[a] from Cama, Collins, and Morton (22)

Solvent	Wave length of max. absorption, mμ	$E(1\%, 1$ cm.)[b] at max. absorption	Conversion factor[c]
Vitamin A Alcohol			
Ethanol	324	1800	1850
iso-Propanol	325.5	1835	1820
cyclo-Hexane	326.5	1745	1910
Light petroleum	324.5	1830	1820
Vitamin A Acetate			
Ethanol	326	1550	1880
iso-Propanol	326	1535	1895
cyclo-Hexane	328	1515	1920
Light petroleum	325	1595	1825

[a] Specialists should consider other recent literature and should watch for publications of extensive collaborative assays now under way. Commercial analysts should use "official conversion factors" discussed in Sections III.1.A.c and III.1.B.

[b] For the purposes of vitamin A analysts, $E(1\%, 1$ cm.) is the quotient obtained by dividing the optical density in a 1 cm. cell of the solution being tested by the concentration of the solution calculated in grams per 100 ml. (see Section III.1.A).

[c] The conversion factor is the quotient obtained by dividing the potency in units per gram (in this table, the calculated values of 3,333,000 I. U./g. for the alcohol and 2,907,000 I. U./g. for the acetate) by the value of $E(1\%, 1$ cm.).

TABLE II

Properties of Isomers[a] of Vitamin A Acetate

	M.p., °C.	U. V. absorption in ethanol		Biopotency (6)	
		λmax. mμ (69)	$E(1\%, 1$ cm.) max. (69)	Units per gram	as % of all-*trans*
All-*trans*	57.5–58	326	1565	(2,907,000)	(100)
Neovitamin A (2-*cis*)	(Oil)	328	1435	2,200,000	75
6-*cis*	(Oil)	323	1200	630,000	22
2,6-Di-*cis*	(Oil)	324	1112	690,000	24
Neovitamin A$_b$ (4-*cis*) (62a)	(Oil)	322 (6)	950 (est.)[b] (6)	680,000[c]	23

[a] Numbering of *cis* bonds by Geneva System.

[b] Subsequently, Wald *et al.* (83) reported a value of $E(1\%, 1$ cm., 319 mμ) = 1220.

[c] Referred to in ref. (6) as "2,4-di-*cis*-vitamin A acetate."

neovitamin A is penalized about enough by the "Morton-Stubbs" correction (see Section III.1.A.4) to make up for its lower inherent biological potency.

C. ANTIMONY TRICHLORIDE REACTION

While the ultraviolet assay method dominates the commercial analytical picture, there are many uses for the sensitive colorimetric procedure originated by Carr and Price.   The blue color produced by reacting a chloroform solution of vitamin A with strong chloroform solutions of antimony trichloride has a value for $E(1\%, 1$ cm.) (620 mμ) of about 5000.   The amount of color is substantially the same for each isomer, and, on a stoichiometric basis, for the esters.   Unfortunately, many substances give interfering reactions, and the reaction at best gives a color that fades in a few seconds.   Standardization is now feasible by using a solution of pure vitamin A as a control.

D. FLUORESCENCE

Vitamin A has a distinctive green fluorescence of considerable value for qualitative identification, such as control of chromatographing (see Section III.3.B.1), location of vitamin A in tissues (37,64), and recognition of vitamin A$_2$ bearing livers (72).   Fluorescence responses of dilute solutions give a linear response with concentration (77), but various forms of natural and synthetic vitamin A give different slopes (49).

3. Substances Related to Vitamin A

There are many substances related in structure to vitamin A and having one or both of the following complications: (1) they have biological action related to vitamin A, or (2) they interfere with a physicochemical assay method.   Thus a variety of homologs, des-methyl analogs, and variations such as the corresponding acids and hydrocarbons will have properties similar enough to those of vitamin A to enrich the biological aspects of synthetic organic research programs for many years.   The substances listed below are chosen as being the most important of natural materials of this class (or of products arising from handling or mishandling commercial synthetic vitamin A).

A. CAROTENES

Carotene and other carotenoids are the most prominent group of compounds with properties that interfere with both biological and physicochemical assay of vitamin A.   Some methods of analysis for them and for their mixtures with vitamin A are given in Sections IV.5 and 7, and in the chapter "Determination of Carotene" (14).

B. VITAMIN A ALDEHYDES

The terminal carbinol group of vitamin A is readily converted to an aldehyde group by appropriate chemical or enzyme action. Isomers of vitamin A aldehyde are important in some of the processes of vision (see Section II.6.C). The high activity of some of the aldehydes by the usual vitamin A bioassay is shown in Table III. The chemical analysis of vitamin A aldehyde is still a research project, but purified preparations can often be recognized by the ultraviolet spectra or the antimony trichloride reaction product [all isomers give a blue color with a maximum at 664 mμ and values of 3470 to 3500 for $E(1\%, 1$ cm.) (68)].

C. ANHYDROVITAMIN A

Anhydrovitamin A is a hydrocarbon readily prepared by acid-catalyzed dehydration of unesterified vitamin A or by refluxing vitamin A esters in alcohol (73). It has absorption maxima at 351, 371, and 392 mμ with a value of 3650 for $E(1\%, 1$ cm.) (371 mμ) in ethanol. Its antimony trichloride reaction product is the same as that for vitamin A, but its biological activity is less than one per cent that of the vitamin. The presence of anhydrovitamin A is usually obvious upon an examination of the complete ultraviolet spectrum. It can

TABLE III
Properties of Isomers[a] of Vitamin A Aldehyde

| | M.p. (68), °C. | U. V. absorption in ethanol | | Biopotency (7) | |
		λmax. mμ (68)	$E(1\%, 1$ cm.) max. (68)	Million units per gram	Conversion factor
All-*trans* (retinene)	57, 65	381	1530	3.05	1991
2-*cis* (neoretinene) (neoretinene *a*)	77	375	1250	3.1	2497
6-*cis* (isoretinene *a*)	64	373	1270	0.64	524
2,6-Di-*cis* (isoretinene *b*)	49, 85	368	1140	0.58	510
Neoretinene *b* (4-*cis*) (62a)	64.5	376	857	1.6	1874

[a] Numbering of double bonds by Geneva System. Trivial names according to Wald *et al.* (83).

be readily separated by chromatography or solvent distribution from most vitamin A preparations. We do not know if it occurs naturally but it often shows up in lower grades of natural and synthetic vitamin A. The analyst should be sure not to produce some accidentally during his own manipulations. Controlled dehydration can be used to identify vitamin A (see Section III.1.D).

D. VITAMIN A₂

Vitamin A$_2$ (72) absorbs ultraviolet light in the vitamin A region, having maxima at 351 mμ and 287 mμ. It gives a strong antimony trichloride reaction color with a maximum at 693 mμ, and its biological potency is 40% that of vitamin A. It is a major constituent of the vitamin A in some fresh water fish, but is usually negligible in commercial fish liver oils with the exception of oils from halibut and related fish. A method for estimating the content of vitamin A$_2$ in such oils has been based upon careful cross comparison of spectral measurements (22). A chromatographic method for separating vitamin A$_2$ from vitamin A has been developed (19), as well as a method for separating the anhydrovitamins (30) (termed "cyclized vitamin A" at the time of the reference).

E. KITOL

A biologically inactive substance, kitol has a broad absorption band at 290 mμ with a value of 700 for $E(1\%, 1$ cm.) (25). Its ultraviolet absorption sometimes leads to a serious interference with the vitamin A determination of liver oils, especially whale liver oil. Spectral correction methods (see Section III.1.A) are often satisfactory but large quantities need to be removed by a careful chromatographic method of the type shown in Section III.3.B. Kitol has the interesting property of yielding vitamin A upon molecular distillation or other short exposure to high temperatures (31).

II. BIOASSAY PROCEDURES

1. Introduction

The various procedures for the bioassay of vitamin A may be grouped into several categories. A deficiency of vitamin A leads to certain physiological abnormalities which can be cured by the administration of vitamin A. These include depressed growth, vaginal cornification, xerophthalmia, and histological changes in the medulla. Another group of bioassay procedures falls into the category of measuring vitamin A following its absorption; these include the analysis of liver and of blood for vitamin A. A third category consists of *in vitro* tests based on the synthesis of rhodopsin from opsin and neoretinene *b*, and is specific for vitamin A aldehydes. A fourth category includes measurement of growth depression and of bone fragility produced by excessive amounts of vitamin A.

The most commonly used bioassays are growth, liver storage, and vaginal smear. About 1000 times as large a dose of vitamin A is fed in the liver-storage bioassay as in the growth bioassay, with the vaginal-smear bioassay intermediate. In spite of this disparity of the doses administered, these three bioassays give comparable results (4,6,61,62). Some underlying physiological response of the animal to vitamin A must therefore be common to the several bioassay procedures.

2. General Bioassay Considerations

A. METABOLISM OF VITAMIN A

Bioassay results will depend on the form of vitamin A administered and on its mode of metabolism. Vitamin A alcohol is apparently absorbed through the intestinal wall as such. Differentiation between isomers probably depends on the intestinal wall, which controls the rate of absorption. Esters of vitamin A, whether natural or synthetic, appear to be hydrolyzed prior to or during absorption. Vitamin A aldehydes are reduced to vitamin A alcohols. All-*trans* and neovitamin A aldehydes are isomerized apparently during the digestive process to an equilibrium mixture of 2 parts all-*trans* and 1 part 2-mono-*cis*-isomers. Following absorption, the *in vivo* interconversion proceeds as described by Harris *et al.* (40) and Ames *et al.* (7). In the case of other derivatives of vitamin A, the rate of metabolic conversion to vitamin A probably determines the biopotency.

B. EXPERIMENTAL ANIMALS

Rats and chicks are used as experimental animals for the bioassay of vitamin A. Rats are preferred because they are well standardized and procedures for handling, supplementing, and treating them have been thoroughly investigated. Chicks are used particularly for the evaluation of products and supplements to be used in poultry feeds.

The use of both male and female animals in the same bioassay introduces needless variation. Males grow more rapidly than female animals, but females appear to store more vitamin A. Male rats are generally used.

Employing litter-mates and balancing treatments within litters has been recommended so as to segregate litter differences and to reduce the number of experimental animals. In practice we have found it more economical of animals, time, and expense, as well as much more convenient, to ignore litter differences. Animals are assigned at random to the various experimental treatments.

C. METHODS OF ADMINISTERING SUPPLEMENTS

In any bioassay procedure, the relative biopotency is the ratio of the response to the test material and the response to the reference standard. Obviously, if the reference standard is allowed to deteriorate or is otherwise mishandled, the test material will have an apparently higher biopotency. Extreme care must be taken to determine the response to the reference standard under identically the same conditions as the test material.

Most supplements are administered orally, either as oil solutions or as dry preparations. Oil solutions of vitamin A can be administered either as oil dilutions, as aqueous suspensions, or as emulsions in a colloidal sol. The type and quantity of the oil used as the diluent affect the utilization of vitamin A or carotene. Tocopherol and hydroquinone are used as antioxidants for vitamin A in the diluent oil. The tocopherol level is important, since it affects the magnitude of the growth and liver-storage response to vitamin A. We use deodorized, refined cottonseed oil (Wesson) for diluting vitamin A for bioassay. It contains a sufficient amount (about 75 mg./100 ml.) of tocopherols to eliminate the need for additional vitamin E supplementation. This oil, with the addition of 0.1% hydroquinone, is reasonably stable.

Administration of oil dilutions of vitamin A orally by dropper is quite satisfactory. The weight per drop of diluent oil is determined and doses of 2 or 4 drops per rat are readily administered. Aqueous suspensions of vitamin A are introduced into the stomach. Use of a hypodermic syringe with a blunted 13-ga. needle renders supplementation by this procedure a convenient and rapid operation.

Low-potency, dry supplements containing vitamin A can be fed as a separate dietary supplement in a small dish. To encourage rapid consumption, the rats are deprived of food before the supplement is fed. We prefer to prepare suspensions of dry material in colloidal sols, such as 2% aqueous Methocel, and orally inject such suspensions quantitatively into the rat's stomach. In the case of chicks, the supplement is weighed into a small gelatin capsule and orally inserted into the chick's crop. Many vitamin A bioassays are conducted by mixing the vitamin A-containing material in the diet. But the dangers of rapid destruction of vitamin A, and especially the reference standard, by dietary ingredients cannot be overemphasized. It is necessary to mix the diet fresh at least every other day and store the diet under refrigeration when not being fed. Uneaten diet should be discarded daily. When the vitamin A preparation is mixed in the diet, the problems of availability and stability are confounded. It is necessary to separately determine the stability of the preparation. Only after determining the stability of the vitamin A in the feed can its biopotency when mixed in the diet be ascertained.

Besides oral supplementation, vitamin A can be assayed by either intraperitoneal or intramuscular injection, or by topical application. Oil dilutions of vitamin A administered in these ways will result in a lesser response than when fed orally.

3. Growth Bioassay

A. GENERAL REMARKS

In the curative growth bioassay, experimental animals are depleted of their vitamin A stores until they no longer grow on the test diet. Graded levels of vitamin A are administered and the growth response measured. The growth response is a linear function of the log of the dose (see Fig. 1).

The curative growth bioassay for vitamin A is very difficult to control because of many factors which affect the growth response. However, it is the only vitamin A bioassay which has been recognized as "official" by the *United States Pharmacopeia* XIII and XIV (80, 81). In its "official" form it is a "pass or fail" procedure and makes no provision for calculating the biopotency of the test material. These defects have been discussed at length and modifications presented by Bliss (78) and György (39).

The growth bioassay for vitamin A has several advantages. The procedure using rats has been well standardized. Since the animals are supplemented with only a few units per day, low-potency samples may be tested without prior concentration. For most purposes,

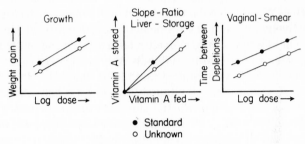

Fig. 1. Biological assays for vitamin A.

however, the disadvantages outweigh the advantages, particularly for a routine bioassay program. Growth bioassays are expensive and very time consuming; 2 to 3 months are required. They are subject to extensive variation; a standard error of the relative potency of

TABLE IV

Modified U.S.P. Vitamin A-Free Diet

Component	Composition, %
Vitamin test casein	18
Salt mixture (U.S.P. XIV)	4
Dried brewers' yeast	7.8
Liver concentrate, N.F.X	0.2
Refined cottonseed oil	5.0
Corn starch	43
Cerelose	22

B-vitamins are pre-mixed with a portion of the vitamin test casein and fat-soluble vitamins are added to the cottonseed oil to supply the following amounts/kg. of diet:

thiamin HCl, 10 mg.   nicotinic acid, 50 mg.
riboflavin, 10 mg.   p-aminobenzoic acid, 100 mg.
pyridoxine HCl, 10 mg.   d-biotin, 0.2 mg.
d-calcium pantothenate, 30 mg. folic acid, 2 mg.
choline chloride, 1.0 g.   vitamin B_{12} (cryst. U.S.P.), 0.02 mg.
i-inositol, 500 mg.   vitamin D, 3000 units
menadione, 5 mg.   tocopherol, 150 mg.

$\pm 12\%$ is considered excellent and ± 15 to $\pm 20\%$ not uncommon. One serious defect is that no provision is made in the statistical treatment for rats not surviving at least 3 weeks of the 4-week experimental period. If the activity of the unknown is overestimated, there will be a substantial number of deaths on the low doses. This probably results in a serious overestimation of the calculated growth response.

The composition of the vitamin A-free basal diet has been extensively investigated. Ideally, it should be devoid of vitamin A and complete in all other nutrients. As employed in our laboratories (see Table IV), the U.S.P. XIV vitamin A-test diet has been modified so that carbohydrate is supplied as a mixture of starch and glucose rather than starch alone. In addition, the diet has been fortified with liver extract and all the known vitamins, except vitamin A, to prevent the development of concurrent vitamin deficiencies. The tocopherol content of the diet has been demonstrated to exert a marked effect on the growth response to vitamin A so the level of this vitamin is controlled.

The following procedure is employed in many laboratories and embodies most of the recommendations of the Animal Nutrition Research Council (78).

B. PRETREATMENT

Male rats with low vitamin A reserves are placed at weaning on the vitamin A depletion diet (see Table IV) and water *ad libitum*. The weanling rats should weigh between 35 and 50 g. If a stock colony is available, the nursing mothers should be placed on the vitamin A depletion diet when the pups are 14 days old. If rats are obtained commercially, they should be specified as "suitable for vitamin A bioassay."

The rats are housed individually and weighed twice weekly until their weight tends to remain stationary. They are then weighed daily. A rat is considered to be depleted when it meets all of the following criteria: (*1*) its net gain in 4 days is 1 g. or less; (*2*) on at least 2 of the 4 days the rat failed to gain; (*3*) it has reached depletion in not less than 18 nor more than 45 days.

C. SUPPLEMENTS

The rats are supplemented orally with the vitamin A preparations using a calibrated dropper (about 25 mg./drop). A standard solution of all-*trans*-vitamin A acetate as described in Section III.1.A.2 is diluted with refined cottonseed oil containing 0.1% hydroquinone so that one drop contains 1 unit. The unknown is assigned an "estimated potency" and it is then diluted in the same manner.

D. BIOASSAY

Monday and Thursday are designated as "record days." The rats are weighed and all supplements administered on the record days. Rats depleting between record days are supplemented at depletion with 1 unit of vitamin A for each day until the next record day, designated the "initial record day."

As they become depleted, rats are assigned to the experimental groups so as to randomize differences in depletion weight, depletion time, and litters. The experimental groups receive weekly supplements of 6 units or 12 units per rat of the standard, or similar levels of the unknown. Rats in the negative control group receive no supplement and should die before the end of the bioassay. Each group should consist of at least 10 animals, preferably more. On the initial record day and on each of the 7 following record days, each rat is weighed and supplemented with one-half the weekly dose (3 and 6 units, respectively). If two-thirds of the rats in any group do not survive the bioassay period, that group is eliminated and the bioassay is computed as described elsewhere (39). In addition, each rat is weighed on the 27th, 28th, and 29th days. The average of these three weights is recorded as the weight on the "final record day." If the rat dies on the 29th day, the average of the weights on the 27th and 28th days is the weight on the "final record day."

E. CALCULATION OF POTENCY

If a rat dies before the 21st day, it is discarded. If a rat dies during the 4th week and failed to gain during any one of the first 3 weeks, it is discarded. If a rat gains weight during each of the first 3 weeks and loses weight or dies during the 4th week, the mean weekly gain (y) is calculated as follows:

$$y = \frac{(-3)\,(\text{initial wt.}) + (-1)\,(\text{wt. 7th day}) + (+1)\,(\text{wt. 14th day}) + (+3)\,(\text{wt. 21st day})}{10}$$

The mean weekly gain of all other surviving rats (most of the animals) is calculated as follows:

$$y = \frac{(-2)\,(\text{initial wt.}) + (-1)\,(\text{wt. 7th day}) + (+1)\,(\text{wt. 21st day}) + (+2)\,(\text{final wt.})}{10}$$

From the mean weekly gains the total gains (T_d) are computed for each treatment and are denoted by T_{1r}, T_{2r}, T_{1u}, and T_{2u}. The total gains for the combined reference ($T_r = T_{1r} + T_{2r}$) and the combined unknown ($T_u = T_{1u} + T_{2u}$) groups are calculated. The numbers of animals (N_d) in each group are denoted by N_{1r}, N_{2r}, N_{1u}, and N_{2u}. The numbers of animals in the combined reference ($N_r = N_{1r} + N_{2r}$) and combined unknown ($N_u = N_{1u} + N_{2u}$) groups are calculated. The number of animals in the two reference groups must be equal ($N_{1r} = N_{2r}$) and the number of animals in the two unknown groups must be equal ($N_{1u} = N_{2u}$). However, N_{1r} does not necessarily equal N_{1u}. Since the dosage levels are in the ratio of 1:2, the dosage interval is 2. The log of the dosage interval is therefore 0.3010.

$$\text{The assay slope } (b) = \frac{1}{0.3010} \left(\frac{T_{2r} - T_{1r} + T_{2u} - T_{1u}}{0.5\,(N_r + N_u)} \right)$$

The log of the "relative potency" (log RP) (unknown compared with standard) is:

$$\log \text{RP} = \frac{1}{b} \left(\frac{T_u}{N_u} - \frac{T_r}{N_r} \right)$$

The relative potency (RP) is the antilog of log RP. The biopotency of the unknown equals the relative potency multiplied by the estimated potency.

The standard deviation of the assay (s) is computed from the gain in grams per week for individual rats (y) on all dosage levels, as follows:

$$s = \sqrt{\frac{\text{Sum }(Sy^2) - \text{Sum } T_d^2/N_d}{N_r + N_u - 4}}$$

The standard error of the log of the relative potency ($SE_{\log RP}$) is computed as follows:

$$SE_{\log RP} = \frac{s}{b} \sqrt{\frac{1}{N_r} + \frac{1}{N_u} + \frac{(T_u/N_u - T_r/N_r)^2}{B^2 - s^2 t^2}}$$

where $B^2 = \dfrac{(T_{2r} - T_{1r} + T_{2u} - T_{1u})^2}{N_r + N_u}$ and t is the 0.975 point of

Student's distribution with degrees of freedom equal to $N_r + N_u - 4$.* If $B^2 - s^2t^2$ is negative, the bioassay is so lacking in precision that 95% confidence intervals are meaningless and the assay must be repeated.

Approximate 95% confidence intervals† are determined as antilog $(\log RP + tSE_{\log RP})$ and antilog $(\log RP - tSE_{\log RP})$. The upper and lower confidence intervals are usually expressed in terms of potencies by multiplying by the estimated biopotency of the unknown oil. The interpretation of the 95% confidence intervals is that 19 times out of 20 the actual potency would be expected to fall between these limits.

Detailed calculations of a typical growth bioassay are presented in the example (Table V).

TABLE V

Example of Growth Bioassay for Vitamin A

In this bioassay, the reference oil (r) and unknown (u) were each fed at daily dosage levels of 1.0 and 2.0 I. U.   Assumed potency of the unknown was 250,000 I. U./g. $(N_{1r} = N_{2r}$ and $N_{1u} = N_{2u})$.

Dose-group index (d)	No. of animals (N_d)	Total gains (T_d)	Sy^2	$T_d{}^2/N_d$
1r	10	87.3	958.93	762.13
2r	10	189.1	3884.09	3575.88
1u	10	77.3	800.67	597.53
2u	10	169.3	3203.03	2866.25
Totals	40		8846.72	7801.79

$N_r = 20$; $T_r = 276.4$; $N_u = 20$; $T_u = 246.6$
Log dose interval $= \log 2 = 0.3010$

$$b = \frac{1}{0.3010} \left(\frac{189.1 - 87.3 + 169.3 - 77.3}{0.5(20 + 20)} \right) = 32.19$$

$$\log RP = \frac{1}{32.19} \left(\frac{246.6}{20} - \frac{276.4}{20} \right) = -0.046288 = \bar{1}.953712$$

---

* If $N_r + N_u - 4 = 30$, then $t = 2.04$; if $N_r + N_u - 4 = 40$, then $t = 2.02$; if $N_r + N_u - 4 = 50$, then $t = 2.01$; and if $N_r + N_u - 4 = 60$, then $t = 2.00$.

† In bioassays with slopes of high precision, the approximate 95% confidence intervals will agree very closely with the exact 95% confidence intervals.   Exact 95% confidence intervals can be computed and are equal to:

$$\text{antilog} \left[\left(\frac{B^2}{B^2 - s^2t^2} \right) \log RP \pm (t) (SE_{\log RP}) \sqrt{\frac{B^2}{B^2 - s^2t^2}} \right]$$

RP = antilog ($\overline{1}.953712$) = 0.8989 or 89.89%
Biopotency = 250,000 $\times$ 0.8989 = 224,700 I. U./g.

Bioassay Precision

$$s = \sqrt{\frac{8846.72 - 7801.79}{20 + 20 - 4}} = \sqrt{29.026} = 5.388$$

t with 36 degrees of freedom = 2.03

$$B^2 = \frac{(189.1 - 87.3 + 169.3 - 77.3)^2}{20 + 20} = 938.96$$

$$SE_{\log RP} = \frac{5.388}{32.19} \sqrt{\frac{1}{20} + \frac{1}{20} + \frac{(246.6/20 - 276.4/20)^2}{938.96 - (29.026)(2.03)^2}} = 0.05365$$

Approx. 95% Confidence Intervals

$\begin{cases} \text{antilog} \ (-0.04629 + (2.03)(0.05365)) = \text{antilog} \ 0.06262 = 1.1551 \\ \text{antilog} \ (-0.04629 - (2.03)(0.05365)) = \text{antilog} \ -0.15520 = 0.6995 \end{cases}$
$\begin{cases} 250,000 \times 1.1551 = 288,800 \ \text{I. U./g.} \\ 250,000 \times 0.6995 = 174,900 \ \text{I. U./g.} \end{cases}$

4. Liver-Storage Bioassay

A. GENERAL REMARKS

The liver-storage bioassay for vitamin A, originally devised by Guggenheim and Koch (38), has been finding increasing application in recent years. It is based on the fact that substantial amounts (65–70%) of large doses of vitamin A are deposited in the liver (see Fig. 1). The liver-storage of vitamin A is a linear function of the dose. Recently, the liver-storage bioassay was modified further and the procedures applicable to the slope-ratio statistical analysis successfully employed (4).

An important difference between the growth and the liver-storage bioassays is that a much larger quantity of vitamin A is fed in the liver-storage bioassay. Liver storage of vitamin A is directly proportional to the dose over a range from 500 to 10,000 units of vitamin A fed. Convenient working levels are 1000 and 2000 units of total vitamin A administered in three daily doses. The potency of the test material as it is fed should be greater than 5000 units per gram to avoid excessive administration of oil. However, low-potency materials can be bioassayed by first saponifying (Section III.3.A) the sample and the reference standard, and then administering oil dilutions of the unsaponifiable fractions.

Since the slope-ratio liver-storage bioassay involves a different measure of physiological response than the growth bioassay, its agreement with the growth bioassay on a comparative basis has been tested. The results obtained by liver-storage bioassay correspond to those by growth bioassay on a wide variety of vitamin A derivatives and isomers (4,6,7).

The slope-ratio liver-storage bioassay is both rapid and precise. It can be completed within a 10-day period. Its precision is far superior to that of the growth bioassay; the estimated standard error of the relative potency in the slope-ratio liver-storage procedure has been reported to be about ±3% (4).

A detailed slope-ratio liver-storage bioassay procedure follows:

B. PRETREATMENT

Male rats with low vitamin A reserves are placed at weaning on the vitamin A depletion diet (Table IV) and water *ad libitum*. The rats are maintained on this diet no longer than 20 days. If signs of vitamin A deficiency begin to develop before supplements are ready, the rats should be supplemented with small quantities of vitamin A (about 5 units per day). Following a depletion period of at least 9 days, rats will have no detectable vitamin A in the lipid extracts of their livers.

C. SUPPLEMENTS

The rats are supplemented orally with the vitamin A preparations using a calibrated dropper (about 25 mg./drop). A standard solution of all-*trans*-vitamin A acetate, as described in Section III.1.A.2, is diluted with refined cottonseed oil containing 0.1% hydroquinone so that one drop contains 166.7 units. The vitamin A potency of the unknown is estimated and is diluted in the same manner.

D. BIOASSAY

At the end of the depletion period, the rats are divided into equal groups (about 10 per group) assigned to each of 5 dosage schedules. In addition to a negative control group (o) receiving no vitamin A supplement, the standard is fed at levels of 1000 and 2000 units (1r and 2r) and the assay oil at two similar levels (1u and 2u). Two drops or four drops are given each day to each rat on three consecutive days, resulting in a total dose of six drops or twelve drops of the standard or unknown. Forty-eight hours after the third supplement, the animals are killed. The entire liver is carefully removed, blotted, and stored at $-15°C$. until analyzed. The entire rat liver is assayed for its vitamin A content as described in Section V.6. Results are recorded as total units of vitamin A per liver (y) based on the blue color value.

E. CALCULATION OF POTENCY

The vitamin A contents of the individual rat livers (y) are tabulated and the numbers of animals (N_d), the totals (T_d), the means $(\bar{y}_d)$, the sums of the squares (Sy^2), and T_d^2/N_d are determined for each group. When the mean liver stores are below 50 units, the standard deviation of the combined analytical procedure and bioassay variation is about ± 10 units. Thus, the sums of the squares of the "o" group are estimated to be $n \times 10^2$. When the mean liver storage of the "o" group is greater than 50 units, the sums of the squares calculated in the usual manner are employed.

Since the design includes 5 equal groups, the standard deviation of the assay (s) is:

$$s = \sqrt{\frac{\text{Sum } (Sy^2) - \text{Sum } T_d^2/N_d}{N - 5}}$$

The departures of the two dose-response lines from linearity are measured by the two quantities L_r and L_u, which are calculated and tested for significance as follows:

$$L_r = \bar{y}_o + \bar{y}_{2r} - 2\bar{y}_{1r} \qquad L_u = \bar{y}_o + \bar{y}_{2u} - 2\bar{y}_{1u}$$

$$SE_L = \sqrt{\frac{30s^2}{N}}$$

$$t = \frac{L_r \text{ or } L_u \text{ (whichever is greater)}}{SE_L} \text{ with } N-5 \text{ degrees of freedom}$$

If the deviation from linearity (L_r or L_u) is significant (see footnote, page 58), as determined by the t-test, the assay should be discarded.

The two regression lines of slopes b_r and b_u, which must share a common y-intercept (a), are calculated as follows:

$$a = \bar{y}_o - \frac{(L_r + L_u)}{7}$$

$$b_r = \frac{\bar{y}_{2r} - \bar{y}_o}{2} + \frac{(6L_u - L_r)}{70} \qquad b_u = \frac{\bar{y}_{2u} - \bar{y}_o}{2} + \frac{(6L_r - L_u)}{70}$$

The relative potency (RP) of the assay oil in terms of the reference standard, and its approximate standard error (SE_{RP}) are calculated according to the following equations:

$$RP = \frac{b_u}{b_r} \qquad \text{approx. } SE_{RP} = \sqrt{\frac{2s^2}{7N(b_r)^2}(8RP^2 - 9RP + 8)}$$

The relative potency multiplied by the estimated potency yields the biopotency of the unknown material. Approximate 95% confidence intervals are determined as $RP + tSE_{RP}$ and $RP - tSE_{RP}$ (see footnote, page 58). The upper and lower confidence intervals are usually expressed in terms of potencies.

Detailed computations of a typical liver-storage bioassay are presented in the example (Table VI).

TABLE VI

Example of Liver-Storage Bioassay for Vitamin A

In this bioassay, the reference oil (r) and unknown (u) were each fed at total dosage levels of 1000 and 2000 I.U. The negative control group received no supplement. Assumed potency of the unknown was 333,300 I. U./g. ($N_o = N_{1r} = N_{2r} = N_{1u} = N_{2u}$).

Dose-group index (d)	No. of animals (N_d)	Liver storage		Sy^2	T_d^2/N_d
		Mean ($\bar{y}_d$)	Total (T_d)		
0	10	0	0	1,000	—
1r	10	630.8	6,308	4,001,022	3,979,086
2r	10	1356.7	13,567	18,461,563	18,406,348
1u	10	599.2	5,992	3,605,922	3,590,406
2u	10	1212.8	12,128	14,823,394	14,708,838
Totals	50			40,892,901	40,684,678

$$s = \sqrt{\frac{40{,}892{,}901 - 40{,}684{,}678}{50 - 5}} = \sqrt{4649.4} = 68.18$$

Linearity

$L_r = 0 + 1356.7 - 2 \times 630.8 = 104.1$
$L_u = 0 + 1212.8 - 2 \times 599.2 = 14.4$

$$SE_L = \sqrt{\frac{30 \times 4649.4}{50}} = \sqrt{2789.64} = 52.82$$

$$t = \frac{104.1}{52.80} = 1.971$$

Regression

$$a = 0 - \frac{104.1 + 14.4}{7} = -16.93$$

$$b_r = \frac{1356.7 - 0}{2} + \frac{(6 \times 14.4 - 104.1)}{70} = 678.6$$

$$b_u = \frac{1212.8 - 0}{2} + \frac{(6 \times 104.1 - 14.4)}{70} = 615.1$$

Relative Potency

$$RP = \frac{615.1}{678.6} = 0.9065 \text{ or } 90.65\%$$

Biopotency $= 333{,}300 \times 0.9065 = 302{,}200$ I. U./g.

Bioassay Precision

$$\text{Approx. } SE_{RP} = \sqrt{\frac{2 \times 4649.4}{7 \times 50 \times 678.6 \times 678.6}[8(0.9065)^2 - 9(0.9065) + 8)]}$$

$$= \sqrt{0.0003698} = 0.0192$$

Approx. 95% Confidence Intervals with 45 degrees of freedom (t = 2.01)

$$\begin{cases} 0.9065 + 2.01 \times 0.0192 = 0.9451 \\ 0.9065 - 2.01 \times 0.0192 = 0.8679 \end{cases}$$

$$\begin{cases} 333{,}300 \times 0.9451 = 315{,}000 \text{ I. U./g.} \\ 333{,}300 \times 0.8679 = 289{,}300 \text{ I. U./g.} \end{cases}$$

5. Vaginal-Smear Bioassay

A. GENERAL REMARKS

Rats on a vitamin A-deficient diet show a persistence of cornified cells in the vagina (32). Supplementation with large amounts of vitamin A causes a quick resumption of the normal smear picture. Pugsley and co-workers (65) have established the method on a quantitative basis using ovariectomized rats. Removal of the ovaries insures against misinterpreting the response. The vaginal-smear bioassay has a low standard error and for this reason is preferred over the growth-type bioassay. In addition, vaginal cornification is specific for vitamin A and therefore should be less subject to extraneous factors.

In the vaginal-smear bioassay the response approximates a linear function of the logarithm of the dose over a dosage range from about 25 to 250 units. Thus, the exact dosage administered does not have to be as carefully chosen as in the growth bioassay. The procedure for performing the vaginal-smear bioassay in rats as modified by Murray and Campbell (62) is given in detail as follows:

B. TREATMENT OF ANIMALS

Weanling female albino rats are fed the maintenance diet and water *ad libitum*. The "maintenance diet" consists of the vitamin A-free diet (Table IV) supplemented with 200 units of vitamin A per kilogram of diet using a dry stabilized vitamin A preparation containing no more than 1 I. U. per particle.

When vaginal introitus occurs (3–4 weeks) the female rats are ovariectomized as follows: The animals are anesthetized with ether and an incision made with scissors at a point midway between the last rib and the hip bone. The incision starts approximately 1.5 cm. from the spinal vertebrae and is carried ventrally for approximately 1 cm. A similar but shorter incision is then made through the muscles. The ovary and surrounding fat are withdrawn with forceps and cut off with scissors. Bleeding may be minimized by clamping with hemostatic forceps prior to removal of the ovary. The end of the fallopian tube is then returned to the abdominal cavity and the incision in the muscle closed with a simple suture. The skin is then united with two additional sutures. The ovary of the other side is removed through a separate incision in a similar manner. The operation is not difficult and need not take more than 6–7 minutes. Mortality from infection is negligible, it being only necessary to wash instruments and the site of the incision with a mild germicidal agent. It may be found desirable to shave the site of the incision.

One week following the operation, the rats are shifted to the vitamin A-free diet. Vaginal smears are made daily from each rat and the smear examined under low power. Each smear is scored as follows: (*1*) mostly squamous cells, (*2*) mostly squamous cells with a few leucocytes, (*3*) mostly leucocytes with a few squamous cells, and (*4*) mostly leucocytes. The four stages of the vaginal smears are diagrammed in Figure 2. Rats in stage 1 for 2 successive days, or in stages 1 and 2 for 3 sucessive days, are considered to be depleted. Those in stages 3 and 4 are not yet depleted and are examined daily until they show depletion smears.   Any rat showing a loss in weight of 10 g. or more is excluded from the group.

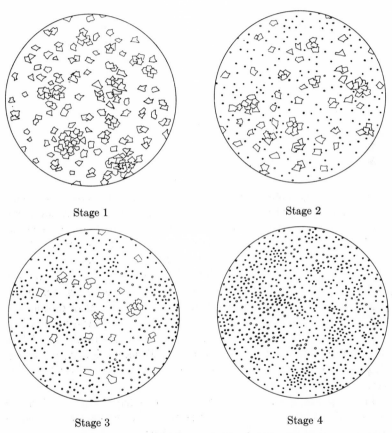

Stage 1   Stage 2

Stage 3   Stage 4

Fig. 2. Four stages of vaginal smears. Smears indicating depletion: Stage 1, mostly squamous cells; Stage 2, mostly squamous cells with a few leucocytes. Smears indicating nondepletion: Stage 3, mostly leucocytes with a few squamous cells; Stage 4, mostly leucocytes.

As they are depleted, the rats are randomly segregated into groups of at least 10 rats each, housed individually, continued on the vitamin A-free diet, and bioassay supplementation started immediately.

C. SUPPLEMENTS

The vitamin A supplements are administered twice daily (early morning and late afternoon) for two successive days in a volume of 0.1 ml. Using a tuberculin syringe with a blunted 19-gauge needle, the supplements are orally injected directly into the rat's stomach. If necessary, supplements as large as 0.4 ml. can be administered twice daily for 5 successive days. It is essential that all levels of all oils be administered in exactly the same volumes and numbers of doses.

Reference groups receive dilutions of a standard solution of all-*trans*-vitamin A acetate (see Section III.1.A.2) in refined cottonseed oil. The unknown preparation is assigned an "estimated" potency and is diluted in the same fashion. The negative control group receives doses of corn oil containing no vitamin A.

D. BIOASSAY

In each assay there must be one negative control group, 3 groups receiving the reference standard, and 3 groups receiving the unknown. The "reference" groups are supplemented with total doses of about 25, 50, and 100 I. U. (dose levels must be in the proportion of $1:2:4$). The "unknown" groups receive these same total doses.

Commencing with the day following the last dose, all rats are smeared daily. In all but the negative control animals, smears in stages 3 or 4 will be obtained within the first 2 days after dosing. A greater delay than this indicates that the dosage level was too low and the assay must be repeated using higher levels of vitamin A. Daily smearing is continued for each rat until it shows depletion smears. Negative control rats should show depletion smears throughout the assay period (many will die).

The response of each rat is the number of days elapsing from the first day of dosing to the day of depletion. The vaginal smears change from stages 1 or 2 to 3 or 4 and return to 1 or 2.

As soon as the rats are again depleted, they are returned to the maintenance diet until needed for the next bioassay. The rats can be employed for 3 or 4 assays.

E. CALCULATION OF POTENCY

The total responses in days (T_d) are computed for each group and are denoted by T_{1r}, T_{2r}, T_{3r}, T_{1u}, T_{2u}, and T_{3u}. The total days for the

combined reference $(T_r = T_{1r} + T_{2r} + T_{3r})$ and the combined unknown $(T_u = T_{1u} + T_{2u} + T_{3u})$ groups are calculated. The numbers
of animals (N_d) are recorded for each group and are denoted by N_{1r},
N_{2r}, N_{3r}, N_{1u}, N_{2u}, and N_{3u}. The numbers of animals in the combined
reference $(N_r = N_{1r} + N_{2r} + N_{3r})$ and the unknown $(N_u = N_{1u} +
N_{2u} + N_{3u})$ groups are calculated. The numbers of rats in the three
reference groups must be equal $(N_{1r} = N_{2r} = N_{3r})$ and the numbers of
animals in the three unknown groups must be equal $(N_{1u} = N_{2u} =
N_{3u})$. However, N_{1r} does not necessarily equal N_{1u}. Since the dosage
levels are in the ratio of $1:2:4$, the dosage interval is 2. The log of
the dosage interval is therefore 0.3010.

$$\text{The assay slope } (b) = \frac{1}{0.3010}\left(\frac{T_{3r} - T_{1r} + T_{3u} - T_{1u}}{N_{1r} + N_{3r} + N_{1u} + N_{3u}}\right).$$

The log of the relative potency (log RP) (test material compared
with standard) is:

$$\log \text{RP} = \frac{1}{b}\left(\frac{T_u}{N_u} - \frac{T_r}{N_r}\right)$$

The relative potency (RP) is the antilog of log RP. The biopotency
of the unknown equals the relative potency multiplied by the estimated potency.

The standard deviation of the bioassay (s) is computed from the
responses for each individual rat (y) in days on all dosage levels, as
follows:

$$s = \sqrt{\frac{\text{Sum } (Sy^2) - \text{Sum } (T_d^2/N_d)}{N_r + N_u - 6}}$$

The standard error of the log of the relative potency is computed
as follows:

$$\text{SE}_{\log \text{RP}} = \frac{s}{b}\sqrt{\frac{1}{N_r} + \frac{1}{N_u} + \frac{(T_u/N_u - T_r/N_r)^2}{B^2 - s^2t^2}}$$

where $B^2 = \dfrac{(T_{3r} - T_{1r} + T_{3u} - T_{1u})^2}{N_{1r} + N_{3r} + N_{1u} + N_{3u}}$ and t is determined with degrees
of freedom equal to $N_r + N_u - 6$ (see footnote, page 58). If $B^2 -
s^2t^2$ is negative, the bioassay is so lacking in precision that 95% con-
fidence intervals are meaningless and the assay must be repeated.

Approximate 95% confidence intervals (see footnote, page 58) are determined as antilog (log RP + $t\mathrm{SE}_{\log \mathrm{RP}}$) and antilog (log RP − $t\mathrm{SE}_{\log \mathrm{RP}}$). The upper and lower 95% confidence intervals are multiplied by the estimated potency of the unknown to convert them to 95% confidence intervals in I. U./gram.

Detailed calculations of a typical vaginal-smear bioassay are presented in the example (Table VII).

TABLE VII

Example of Vaginal-Smear Bioassay for Vitamin A[a]

In this bioassay the reference oil (r) and unknown (u) were each fed at total dosage levels of 29, 58, and 116 I. U. Assumed potency of the unknown was 10,000 I. U./g. ($N_{1r} = N_{2r} = N_{3r}$ and $N_{1u} = N_{2u} = N_{3u}$).

Dose-group index (d)	No. of animals (N_d)	Total days (T_d)	S_{y^2}	T_d^2/N_d
1r	9	90	912.0	900.0
2r	9	126	1,770.0	1,764.0
3r	9	160	2,854.0	2,944.4
1u	10	102	1,048.0	1,040.4
2u	10	140	1,978.0	1,960.0
3u	10	188	3,564.0	3,534.4
Totals	57		12,126.0	12,143.2

[a] Data courtesy of T. K. Murray and J. A. Campbell, Dept. of National Health and Welfare, Ottawa, Canada.

$N_r = 27$; $T_r = 376$; $N_u = 30$; $T_u = 430$
Log dosage interval = log 2 = 0.3010

$$b = \frac{1}{0.3010}\left(\frac{160 - 90 + 188 - 102}{9 + 9 + 10 + 10}\right) = 13.639$$

$$\log \mathrm{RP} = \frac{1}{13.639}\left(\frac{430}{30} - \frac{376}{27}\right) = +0.02987$$

RP = antilog (+0.02987) = 1.0712 or 107.12%
Biopotency = 10,000 × 1.0712 = 10,710 I. U./g.

Bioassay Precision

$$s = \sqrt{\frac{12,126.0 - 12,043.2}{27 + 30 - 6}} = \sqrt{1.6235} = 1.2744$$

t with 51 degrees of freedom = 2.01

$$B^2 = \frac{(160 - 90 + 188 - 102)^2}{9 + 9 + 10 + 10} = 640.42$$

$$SE_{\log RP} = \frac{1.2744}{13.639} \sqrt{\frac{1}{27} + \frac{1}{30} + \frac{(430/30 - 376/27)^2}{640.42 - (1.6235)(2.01)^2}} = 0.02483$$

Approx. 95% Confidence Intervals

$\begin{cases} \text{antilog } [+0.029870 + (2.01)(0.02483)] = \text{antilog } + 0.07978 = 1.2016 \\ \text{antilog } [+0.029870 - (2.01)(0.02483)] = \text{antilog } - 0.02004 = 0.9549 \end{cases}$

$\begin{cases} 10,000 \times 1.2016 = 12,020 \text{ I. U./g.} \\ 10,000 \times 0.9549 = 9,550 \text{ I. U./g.} \end{cases}$

6. Bioassays Based on Other Biological Responses

The growth, liver-storage, and vaginal-smear bioassays are of primary importance. In addition, there are a number of other biological responses which either have been or potentially could be employed for vitamin A bioassay.

A. VITAMIN A DEFICIENCY CONDITIONS

Many physiological abnormalities occur in vitamin A deficiency. Of these, growth depression was first discovered and has formed the basis of many different bioassay procedures. Growth bioassays are of two types: The curative growth bioassay has been presented in detail in Section II.3. The prophylactic or preventive bioassay consists of supplementing partially depleted animals with graded doses of vitamin A and determining the levels necessary to prevent the development of a vitamin A deficiency. In another modification described by Sherman and Todhunter (74), rats are depleted of vitamin A until they cease to gain weight. Then they are supplemented with single graded levels of vitamin A, whereupon they start to grow. The response is the time from the beginning of supplementation until the animal returns to its original depletion weight.

Xerophthalmia is a characteristic symptom of vitamin A deficiency in rats. Graded doses of vitamin A are administered to rats on a vitamin A-free diet and the dose either preventing or curing xerophthalmia ascertained. Comparison of the response of the unknown with that of a standard preparation approximates the relative effectiveness of the unknown material. Because of substantial biological variation and difficulty of identifying borderline cases of xerophthalmia, this bioassay is seldom used and cannot be recommended.

Prevention of other characteristics of vitamin A deficiency forms the basis of several other prophylactic bioassays for vitamin A. The appearance of vaginal cornification has been discussed in detail in Section II.5. Irving and Richards (46) found that degeneration of the medulla occurs with remarkable consistency in vitamin A deficiency in rats. This degeneration in the central nervous system can be identified histologically and is progressive. Graded supplements are fed for 35 to 50 days to rats on a vitamin A-free diet. The rats are killed and their medullas sectioned. Daily doses of about 1.5 units of vitamin A prevent the appearance of histological abnormalities. This procedure has been extensively investigated by Coetzee (26), who found it to be more precise than the growth bioassay.

B. CHEMICAL ANALYSIS OF VITAMIN A

The liver-storage procedure (see Section II.4) is typical of bioassays in which vitamin A is administered and, after a designated time interval, the vitamin A content of a body tissue determined. In clinical investigations, an increase of vitamin A in the blood following supplementation is widely employed. The response is determined by withdrawing samples at appropriate time intervals and determining the vitamin A content (see Section V.5). Concentration of vitamin A is plotted against time. The area under the curve representing the increase in vitamin A content over basal values is the measure of response. This procedure has been adapted to the study of certain pathological conditions in humans in which vitamin A metabolism or absorption is impaired. Almquist (2) has reported that, for rats, lambs, cattle, and fowl, the blood plasma levels are linearly related to the log of the liver vitamin A content as well as to the log of the dietary vitamin A intake.

The vitamin A content of the egg is a measure of the vitamin A status of the hen. Graded doses of vitamin A are fed to hens receiving a vitamin A-free diet. The egg yolks are analyzed for vitamin A (see Section V.7). This procedure has not been extensively investigated. Potentially it is of considerable interest since it determines the overall effectiveness with which the vitamin A supplement is metabolized, absorbed, transported, and secreted in the egg yolk.

C. *In vitro* FORMATION OF RHODOPSIN

This reaction is of great value in identifying the various isomers of vitamin A. Rhodopsin, the light-sensitive pigment of rod vision, consists of a protein ("opsin") and vitamin A aldehyde (retinene) (43,44,45).   Opsin and retinene can react *in vitro* to form rhodopsin, identifiable by its characteristic absorption maximum at 500 mμ. The *in vitro* system is not complex, consisting of vitamin A alcohol, opsin, alcohol, dehydrogenase, and diphosphopyridine nucleotide, all in aqueous digitonin solution.   The difficulty of preparing opsin limits the usefulness of this procedure.   Formation of rhodopsin is specific for the isomeric vitamin A aldehyde isomer designated neo-retinene *b* (4-mono-*cis*-vitamin A aldehyde) (62a).   All-*trans*-vitamin A aldehyde and neovitamin A aldehyde do not form rhodopsin.   The two isomeric aldehydes with 6-*cis* double bonds can also be differentiated by this procedure.   6-Mono-*cis*-vitamin A aldehyde reacts with opsin to form isorhodopsin with a characteristic absorption maximum at 487 mμ.   2,6-Di-*cis*-vitamin A aldehyde does not react with opsin.   The all-*trans*- and neo-isomers can be isomerized to yield neoretinene *b* (forming rhodopsin) and the 2,6-di-*cis*-isomer can be isomerized to yield 6-mono-*cis*-vitamin A aldehyde (forming isorhodopsin).

D. VITAMIN A TOXICITY

Administration of massive doses of vitamin A (150,000 units or more/kg. body wt./day) leads to characteristic abnormalities.   The depression of growth and the increased fragility of the leg bones are sufficiently consistent that they could be employed for the bioassay of high potency vitamin A preparations (8).   The force required to break the bone is linearly related to the log of the dose.   Bioassays based on hypervitaminosis A are of no interest to the routine analyst but have proved very useful in certain research problems.   For example, bone fragility is a convenient means of distinguishing hypervitaminosis A from toxic manifestations of other substances accompanying vitamin A in a mixture.

III. PHYSICOCHEMICAL PROCEDURES

1. Spectrophotometric Procedures

A. GENERAL CONSIDERATIONS

Most official vitamin A assay procedures throughout the world depend on measuring the specific absorbance, $E(1\%, 1$ cm.), and multiplying it by a "conversion factor" to obtain "potency." The expression, $E(1\%, 1$ cm.), was formerly called "extinction coefficient," or "E value." It is the absorbance, formerly termed "optical density," of a solution, measured in a 1 cm. cell, divided by its concentration in grams per 100 ml. Table I shows conversion factors ranging from 1820 to 1920.

Prior to 1950 there was a great deal of argument about conversion factors. Most fish liver oils contain quite a bit of irrelevant absorption. That is, they contain substances other than vitamin A that contribute to the specific absorbance at 325 mμ but have no vitamin A activity. Thus, when the biopotency of a typical oil is divided by its specific absorbance a conversion factor of about 1600 is obtained. The factor 1600 was official in the *British Pharmacopeia* (17) until 1953 (18). Earlier, when bioassays were conducted in this country against the U.S.P. Cod Liver Oil Reference Standard in various degrees of deterioration, conversion factors ran from 2000 to 3000. A figure of 2000 was official in the A.O.A.C. Methods of Analysis, 1945 (10).

This argument has been resolved in recent years by three developments. (a) Fairly good methods have been developed for evaluating the amount of irrelevant absorption present in the oil. (b) Crystalline vitamin A of high purity has been obtained and has been well characterized biologically and spectrophotometrically. (c) The potency of crystalline vitamin A has been officially defined, and spectrophotometric methods have been established for its estimation.

1. Irrelevant Absorption. R. A. Morton and A. L. Stubbs (59) developed a simple mathematical calculation which estimates the amount of real vitamin A in an impure sample from the shape of its ultraviolet absorption curve. The irrelevant absorption is assumed to follow a straight line, at least across a narrow range near the vitamin A absorption peak. The absorbance observed at any wave length (A_λ) is assumed to be the sum of that due to vitamin A plus that due to irrelevant absorption. Thus:

$$A_\lambda = E_{\text{Vit. A}} \times C + a + b \times \lambda$$

This equation has three "unknowns," the concentration of vitamin A, (C), and the constants, a and b, of the straight line equation of the irrelevant absorption. Solving the equation simultaneously at three wave lengths gives an estimate of C. Official procedures have been adopted in which three wave lengths are selected (the peak and one on either side about 10 to 15 mμ from the peak) and the $E_{\text{vit. A}}$ at each wave length is defined. This leads to a correction equation of the form:

$$A_{\text{corrected}} = k_1(A_{\lambda_1}) - k_2(A_{\lambda_2}) - k_3(A_{\lambda_3})$$

where the k's and λ's are prescribed.

2. Standard Preparation. Crystalline β-carotene was the International Standard for vitamin A from about 1930 to 1950. During that time the United States Pharmacopeia issued three different lots of cod liver oil to be used as bioassay standards. Their biopotencies were assigned by collaborative assays against β-carotene. In 1948 the U. S. Pharmacopeia adopted as a Standard a capsulated cottonseed oil solution containing 3.44 mg. of crystalline all-*trans*-vitamin A acetate in each gram. This was assigned a potency of 10,000 U.S.P. units per gram. Thus, 1 unit of vitamin A was said to be equivalent to 0.344 μg. of vitamin A acetate (or 0.300 μg. of vitamin A alcohol). This U.S.P. standard solution was later adopted as an International Standard in 1950, but its distribution was discontinued in 1952 (85).

There has been a growing realization of a need for a higher potency vitamin A reference standard for use in checking physicochemical assay procedures. Therefore, in 1957 the U. S. Pharmacopeia issued a revised version of this vitamin A acetate solution in cottonseed oil at a defined potency of 100,000 U.S.P. units of vitamin A per gram—ten times the concentration of the earlier standard. The new reference standard offers a convenient, stable form of vitamin A which is spectrophotometrically pure, and much easier to handle than crystalline vitamin A.

3. W.H.O. Recommendations. In 1950 the Expert Committee on Biological Standardization of the World Health Organization made recommendations (84) for a vitamin A assay which are summarized as follows:

Since $E(1\%, 1 \text{ cm.})$ for vitamin A alcohol is 1750 and $E(1\%, 1 \text{ cm.})$ for vitamin A acetate is 1525, and since the unit is defined as 0.3 μg. vitamin A alcohol or 0.344 μg. vitamin A acetate, then the official conversion factor [potency divided by $E(1\%, 1 \text{ cm.})$] must be 1900. Because most materials contain irrelevant absorption this factor can only be applied when:

(a) the absorption peak is in the range 325–328 mμ, and the shape of the absorption curve agrees closely with that of pure vitamin A

$(E/E_{max.}$ from 310 mμ to 350 mμ must be within 0.02 of that of pure vitamin A alcohol or acetate), or

(b) irrelevant absorption has been corrected by a geometric procedure (59). If the absorption peak is outside the range 325–328 mμ, impurities must first be removed by purification procedures such as saponification and chromatography. (The exact placement of the absorption peak depends upon the solvent. See also Comments under Section III.1.B.)

4. Neovitamin A. Commercial fish liver oils and some synthetic vitamin A preparations appear to contain about one-third of their vitamin A as neovitamin A (the 2-*cis* isomer). As indicated in Table II, neovitamin A has about 75% the biopotency of all-*trans*-vitamin A; it has a lower specific absorbance; and its ultraviolet absorption curve is shifted about 3 mμ toward the longer wave lengths from that of all-*trans*-vitamin A. Because of these slight differences in its spectrophotometric properties, neovitamin A is discounted about 25% by the Morton-Stubbs correction. By coincidence, the corrected values correspond with those found on bioassay. Therefore, preparations that contain neovitamin A should properly be assayed by a procedure that employs the Morton-Stubbs correction.

It is often of interest to determine the actual neovitamin A content of a preparation. The original procedure described by Robeson and Baxter (67) is quite satisfactory and is included in Section III.2.A.3. The Hjarde chromatographic procedure described in Section III.3.B.2 has been used to separate neovitamin A from all-*trans* by using a longer calcium phosphate column than usual (19).

B. UNITED STATES PHARMACOPEIA PROCEDURE FOR VITAMIN A ASSAY

The U.S.P. procedure (82) requires saponification of all preparations, measurement in isopropanol, and correction of absorbance by a specified Morton-Stubbs equation. The U.S.P. XV assay for vitamin A is as follows:*

Complete the assay promptly and exercise care throughout the procedure to avoid undue exposure to oxidizing agents, to actinic light, and to other conditions that destroy vitamin A. The use of non-actinic glassware avoids destruction by light.

* The use of portions of the text of the *United States Pharmacopeia*, Fifteenth Revision, official December 15, 1955, is by permission received from the Board of Trustees of the United States Pharmacopeial Convention. The said Board is not responsible for any inaccuracies of the text thus used.

Special Reagents.

Isopropyl Alcohol. Redistill, if necessary, to meet the following requirements for spectral purity: When measured in a 1 cm. quartz cell against water it shows an absorbance not greater than 0.05 at 300 mμ and not greater than 0.01 between 320 mμ and 350 mμ.

Ether. Freshly distilled ethyl ether, discarding the first and last 10% portions. (*Warning:* To avoid danger of explosion, add a few milligrams of zinc dust and potassium hydroxide; do not distill completely to dryness.)

Potassium Hydroxide Solution (1 in 2). Freshly prepared by dissolving 10 g. potassium hydroxide pellets in 10 g. distilled water.

Saponification.

Transfer to a saponification flask an amount of the sample, accurately measured and expected to contain not less than the equivalent of 0.15 mg. of vitamin A (500 U.S.P. units), but not more than 1 gram of fat. Boil under a reflux condenser, in an *all-glass* apparatus, with 30 ml. of ethanol and 3 ml. of potassium hydroxide solution (1 in 2) for 30 minutes. Cool the solution, and add 30 ml. of water. Transfer the resulting solution to a separatory funnel and extract with four successive, 30 ml. portions of ether. Combine the ether extracts and wash by swirling gently with 50 ml. of water. Repeat the washing more vigorously until the last washing gives no color with phenolphthalein. Transfer the washed ether extract to a 250-ml. volumetric flask, and add ether to volume.

Procedure.

Evaporate a 25-ml. aliquot of the ether solution of the unsaponifiable extract to about 5 ml. Without the application of heat, remove the remaining ether in a stream of inert gas or by vacuum. Dissolve the residue in sufficient isopropyl alcohol to give an expected concentration of the equivalent of 3 to 5 μg. of vitamin A in each ml., or such that it will give an absorbance in the range 0.4 to 0.8 at 325 mμ. Determine the absorbances of the resulting solution at the wave lengths 310 mμ, 325 mμ, and 334 mμ, using a spectrophotometer suitable for measurements in the ultraviolet, fitted with matched quartz cells.

Calculation.

Calculate the content of vitamin A by the formula: A (corrected) $\times 5.7 \div (L \times C) = $ mg. of vitamin A per gram, capsule, or tablet, in which A (corrected) $= 7A_{325} - 2.625A_{310} - 4.375A_{334}$, and A is the absorbance measured at the wave length indicated by the subscript, L is the length of the absorption cell in cm., and C is the amount of sample expressed as gram, capsule, or tablet, represented in each 1000 ml. of the final isopropyl alcohol dilution of the sample under assay. Each mg. of vitamin A (alcohol) represents 3333 U.S.P. units of vitamin A.

Confidence Interval.

The range of the limits of error, indicating the extent of discrepancy to be expected in the results of different laboratories at $P = 0.05$, is approximately $\pm 8\%$.

Comments.

This calculation is based on the 1900 conversion factor (it is buried in the formula, which uses concentration in terms of g./1000 ml., and which yields mg. instead of units).

The 1950 W.H.O. recommendations did not specify the solvent in which specific absorbances of 1750 and 1525 are obtained for pure (all-*trans*) vitamin A alcohol and acetate. These values are probably suitable for cyclohexane, which has been commonly used in most countries except the United States.

The U.S.P. procedure measures vitamin A alcohol in isopropanol. From Table I the conversion factor should be 1820 rather than 1900, a discrepancy of 4%. Also, the correction equation is based, not on the properties of pure vitamin A alcohol, but on those of the unsaponifiable fraction (obtained in collaborative assay) of a 10,000 u./g. solution of vitamin A acetate. Pure vitamin A alcohol measured in isopropanol gives absorbance readings which lead to a corrected peak absorbance about $3\frac{1}{2}\%$ higher than the uncorrected. The two errors are additive, so that it is possible, with perfect technique, to obtain U.S.P. potencies for, say, crystalline vitamin A acetate, that are nearly $7\frac{1}{2}\%$ higher than the defined potency of that ester. In practice, however, values are hardly ever this high. The average analyst seems to lose about 4% of the vitamin A during saponification, although this varies widely between different laboratories. Also, spectrophotometers differ; and the Morton-Stubbs equation magnifies these differences, and random errors, by several times. All this leads to the statement in U.S.P. XV regarding a "Confidence Interval" of $\pm 8\%$.

C. BRITISH PHARMACOPEIA PROCEDURE FOR VITAMIN A ASSAY

The 1953 *British Pharmacopeia* (18) followed the W.H.O. recommendations for a conversion factor of 1900, but specified some of the critical points, such as absorbance ratios at various wave lengths for vitamin A alcohol and acetate in cyclohexane. These are given in Table VIII. Vitamin A ester preparations too impure to meet the criteria in Table VIII are assayed by multiplying the *corrected* extinction by the conversion factor, 1900. The correction formula (for cyclohexane) is:

$$E_{327.5 \text{ corrected}} = 7(E_{327.5} - 0.405E_{312.5} - 0.595E_{337.5})$$

Preparations which require saponification before assay are corrected by a formula based on the properties of vitamin A alcohol (also in cyclohexane):

$$E_{326.5 \text{ corrected}} = 7(E_{326.5} - 0.422E_{312.5} - 0.578E_{336.5})$$

Comments.

The W.H.O. idea is perhaps too optimistic that "spectrophotometrically pure" preparations can be recognized by the shape of the absorption curve. It is tempting to use uncorrected measurements for pure preparations because the "limits of error" are about $\pm 1\%$ instead of $\pm 8\%$. But the difficulty comes in recognizing the pure preparations from the impure. In order to allow reasonable leeway for spectrophotometer differences and random errors, limits of 0.02 have been set on the absorbance ratios. The limits cannot be set any closer than this. Yet there is room enough within this narrow range for preparations having as much as 14% impurity.

TABLE VIII

Relative Extinctions in Cyclohexane

Wave length (mμ)	Vitamin A acetate	Wave length (mμ)	Vitamin A alcohol
300	0.555	300	0.553
312.5	0.857	312.5	0.857
327.5 (max.)	1	326.5 (max.)	1
337.5	0.857	336.5	0.857
345	0.695	345	0.667
360	0.299	360	0.260

D. MODIFICATIONS OF SPECTROPHOTOMETRIC PROCEDURES FOR SPECIAL SITUATIONS

Spectrophotometric measurements are useful even on crude materials if irrelevant absorption can be properly evaluated. For example as a control procedure in the plant, margarine manufacturers can measure the amount of vitamin A added to a batch of margarine oil by measuring a solution of the fortified oil in one cell against one of the unfortified oil in the other cell (56,66).

Similarly, procedures have been proposed for destroying the vitamin A in part of the sample, then using this as a control for measuring the vitamin A in the untreated sample. One of these procedures uses ultraviolet irradiation to destroy the vitamin A (12,55) (see Section IV.5). Of course, the success of this procedure depends on destroying *all* of the vitamin A without changing the irrelevant absorption. This is said to be uncertain when applied to margarine assay (66).

Another procedure uses sulfuric acid to destroy the vitamin A. This procedure, developed by Fox and Mueller (33), was specifically designed to correct for tocopherol in multivitamin pharmaceutical products. This is necessary because the ultraviolet absorption curve for tocopherol is not linear across the vitamin A region, causing the Morton-Stubbs calculation to overestimate the amount of irrelevant absorption.

A technique first proposed by Embree and Shantz (30) and later used by Ames and Harris (3) depends on the conversion of vitamin A in the sample to anhydrovitamin A. Part of the sample is treated with alcoholic HCl to form anhydrovitamin A, and the treated sample is measured in a spectrophotometer against the untreated portion as a control. The difference curve in the region of 390 mμ gives the amount of anhydrovitamin A formed. This procedure is perhaps not very precise, but it is useful where others fail because of extreme amounts of irrelevant absorption. It is quite specific for vitamin A, and the sharp triple peak of the anhydrovitamin is unmistakable.

2. Colorimetric Procedures

A. ANTIMONY TRICHLORIDE BLUE COLOR DETERMINATION

1. "Standard Curve" Procedure. In 1926, Carr and Price developed an assay procedure for vitamin A based on its reaction with a chloroform solution of antimony trichloride to form a blue color (peak absorbance at 620 mμ). This reaction is quite sensitive, and is useful for impure materials containing too much irrelevant absorption for spectrophotometric measurements. The details of a suitable procedure are as follows:

Apparatus.

Photoelectric Photometer. A direct reading, critically damped instrument, such as the Evelyn, equipped with a 620 mμ filter and specially selected and interchangeable test tubes or colorimeter tubes.

Automatic Pipette. 10 ml. for dispensing antimony trichloride solution. It should deliver rapidly through an opening 3 to 4 millimeters in diameter.

Reagents.

Antimony Trichloride Solution. Prepare by dissolving 20 g. of antimony trichloride in sufficient chloroform to make 100 ml. Filter.

Vitamin A Reference Standard. A solution of purified vitamin A acetate crystals in cottonseed oil. The U.S.P. Standard is suitable (see Section III.1.A.2).

Preparation of Calibration Curve.

Dilute an accurately weighed portion of the Vitamin A Reference Standard in chloroform so that 2 ml. of the solution will give an absorbance of about 0.8 in the colorimeter upon addition of 10 ml. of antimony trichloride solution. From this solution make a series of dilutions in chloroform that are 80%, 60%, 40%, and 20% of this concentration.

Determine the absorbances (as directed below under Procedure) of the blue color formed when 2 ml. aliquots of each of these five solutions are treated with 10 ml. of antimony trichloride solutions.

Using rectangular coordinate paper, plot the best fitting smooth curve through the origin and the five absorbances obtained with the known quantities of vitamin A. Do not attempt to draw a straight line. This calibration curve should be checked at frequent intervals, particularly when solutions are renewed.

Procedure.

Prepare a solution of the sample for assay in chloroform of such concentration that 2 ml. will have an absorbance of about 0.4 in the photoelectric photometer when treated with 10 ml. of antimony trichloride solution.

To a colorimeter tube add 2 ml. of chloroform and 10 ml. of antimony trichloride solution and set the instrument for 100% transmittance. Place another tube in the colorimeter. Add exactly 2 ml. of the solution for assay, add rapidly 10 ml. of antimony trichloride solution, and take a steady absorbance reading within 5 seconds. (Absorbance = 2 − log of per cent transmittance.) From the calibration curve find the concentration of vitamin A which corresponds to the absorbance observed for the assay sample.

2. Increment Modification of Antimony Trichloride Determination. The procedure given above is inhibited by large amounts of fat or other diluents. (For example, inhibition can just be detected in a cottonseed oil solution containing 1000 units of vitamin A per gram.) To correct for inhibition, Oser (63) has recommended the use of an internal standard. Three readings are taken, one on the standard, one on the "unknown," and one using 1 ml. of each solution. A procedure incorporating this modification is as follows:

Preparation of Calibration Curve.

Prepare a calibration curve as directed in the procedure above except that the stock solutions of the Vitamin A Reference Standard must be made to have twice the concentration per 100 ml. To the colorimeter tube add 1 ml. of vitamin A solution, 1 ml. of chloroform, and 10 ml. of antimony trichloride solution.

Procedure.

Prepare solutions of the sample for assay, and of the vitamin A reference standard, in chloroform such that 1 ml. plus 1 ml. of chloroform plus 10 ml. of antimony trichloride solution will give an absorbance of about 0.2. The absorbance of the blue color formed in Tube 4, below, must equal that from the calibration curve for the weight of Standard used.

To a series of colorimeter tubes add the following:

	Tube 1	Tube 2	Tube 3	Tube 4
Chloroform solution of sample for assay	—	1 ml.	1 ml.	—
Chloroform solution of vitamin A reference standard	—	—	1 ml.	1 ml.
Chloroform	2 ml.	1 ml.	—	1 ml.

Note: The absorbance in Tube 3 must not exceed 0.5.

Place Tube 1 in the colorimeter, add 10 ml. of antimony trichloride solution, and set the instrument for zero absorbance (100% transmittance). Place Tube 2 in the colorimeter, add rapidly 10 ml. of antimony trichloride solution, and take steady absorbance reading, A_u, within 5 seconds. Place Tube 3 in colorimeter, add rapidly 10 ml. of antimony trichloride solution and take steady absorbance reading, $A_{(u + s)}$, within 5 seconds.

Calculation.

N_s = units vitamin A in each ml. of chloroform solution of vitamin A reference standard, calculated from weight of standard.

N_u = units vitamin A in each ml. of chloroform solution of sample for assay corresponding to absorbance reading, A_u, from calibration curve.

$N_{(u + s)}$ = units vitamin A in each ml. of the chloroform solution of sample for assay with added increment of vitamin A reference standard solution corresponding to absorbance reading, $A_{(u + s)}$, from calibration curve.

W = amount of sample, expressed as grams, represented in each ml. of final chloroform dilution of sample under assay.

$$\frac{N_u \times N_s}{(N_{(u+s)} - N_u) \times W} = \text{units of vitamin A per gram}$$

If inhibition is known to be absent, the simple "standard curve" procedure should be used since it is much more precise.

3. Determination of Neovitamin A. Unless a Morton-Stubbs correction procedure is used, either spectrophotometric or colorimetric assays should be corrected for the presence of neovitamin A. The proportion of neovitamin A to all-*trans* can be determined by reacting the sample with maleic anhydride then determining the antimony trichloride blue color. After 16 hours at 25°C., all-*trans*-vitamin A exhibits only 2% vitamin A recovery while neovitamin A gives 90% recovery. The procedure (22,67) is as follows:

Pipette into a 10 ml. amber volumetric flask a 5 ml. aliquot of benzene solution of vitamin A containing approximately 1250 total units. Make to volume with a solution of maleic anhydride in benzene (10 g. per 100 ml.). Mix and store at 25°C. for 16 hours. Dilute an aliquot of this solution and measure its antimony trichloride blue color using the procedure in Section III.2.A.1. Calculate the percentage of neovitamin A (based on total vitamin A) in the sample by the following formula:

$$\% \text{ neovitamin A} = \frac{R - R_1}{R_2 - R_1} \times 100$$

where R = recovery of vitamin A in the test sample, $R_1 = 2$ and $R_2 = 90$.

The above formula is for vitamin A ester. For vitamin A alcohol the recoveries are 83% for neovitamin A and 3% for all-*trans*, so that in the formula $R_1 = 3$ and $R_2 = 83$.

B. GLYCEROL DICHLOROHYDRIN PROCEDURE

A different, though related, colorimetric procedure (76) uses the reaction of vitamin A with activated glycerol dichlorohydrin (GDH). The reagent is activated by adding HCl or antimony trichloride then distilling. The color complex formed has an absorption maximum at 550 mμ rather than 620. It does not fade as rapidly, but is less intense; $E(1\%, 1$ cm.) is about 1000 vs. 5000 for antimony trichloride. The GDH procedure has appealed to many analysts because the reagent is not as corrosive nor as difficult to handle as antimony trichloride solution and the more stable color has obvious advantages. However, the color does fade fairly rapidly, often dropping to half its intensity in a very few minutes—the activation is quite critical and cannot be reproduced from batch to batch—and inhibition is a much more serious problem with GDH than with antimony trichloride. Often samples which can be assayed readily by antimony trichloride cannot be assayed at all by GDH.

An application of the GDH procedure to blood is given in Section IV.5. A similar application (9) showed that only vitamin A, and no vitamin A aldehyde, was present in livers of rats fed vitamin A aldehyde. Vitamin A aldehyde gives a complex with GDH with an absorption peak at 660 mμ. Since vitamin A alcohol gives a peak at 550 mμ, the two can be determined simultaneously in mixtures.

3. Purification Procedures

A. SAPONIFICATION

Saponification is often necessary in order to remove materials which interfere with the spectrophotometric procedure, such as in cod liver oil or in multivitamin pharmaceutical preparations, or to concentrate the sample in preparation for a colorimetric procedure, as in the case of margarine, milk, etc. The saponification procedure detailed in the U.S.P. XV assay is a good one for fish oils and pharmaceutical products. A modification of this which is useful for fats such as margarine follows:

Procedure.

Accurately weigh approximately 10 grams of the fat into a 250 ml. flask connected to a reflux condenser with a ground glass joint. Do not use rubber stoppers or corks. Add 50 ml. of alcoholic alkali (10 g. of KOH per 100 ml. of solution) and reflux for 15 minutes.

Cool, add 150 ml. of water, transfer to a 500 ml. separatory funnel, and extract successively with 125, 100, and 75 ml. portions of freshly redistilled ethyl ether. Pool the extracts and wash them once with 100 ml. of water, once with 50 ml. of 0.5 N KOH, and then with successive 75 to 100 ml. portions of water until the wash solution is colorless to phenolphthalein. Allow to stand 15 minutes, drain out the last droplets of water, transfer the washed ether extract to an Erlenmeyer flask, and swirl with 3 to 5 grams of anhydrous sodium sulfate. Decant into another Erlenmeyer flask, rinsing the sodium sulfate thoroughly with ether to remove all traces of vitamin A. Evaporate to a volume of about 10 ml., transfer to a 25 or 50 ml. volumetric flask, rinsing the Erlenmeyer flask thoroughly with ether, and complete the evaporation in the volumetric flask *in vacuo* or under inert gas. Dilute to the mark with chloroform and assay by the antimony trichloride procedure.

B. CHROMATOGRAPHY

1. General Considerations. Chromatography offers a fairly efficient way to remove irrelevant absorption from vitamin A. However, there are difficulties. If the adsorbent is sufficiently strong to give good separations, some vitamin A is usually destroyed—probably by dehydration to anhydrovitamin A. If the adsorbent is sufficiently weak to be safe, separations are not cleancut. Thus, standardization of the adsorbent is most critical.

The usual precautions need to be taken. Columns may be packed dry, under suction, by tamping successive portions with a flat tipped rod; or a slurry may be poured into the tube and packed by filtration. The adsorbent must always be kept covered with solvent in the tube to avoid channeling. The vitamin A solution is preferably added to the column in a minimum volume of non-eluting solvent (usually petroleum ether), and then followed with small portions of the same solvent. Then the chromatogram is developed with a mild-eluting solvent. The vitamin A band may be followed by means of its characteristic light green fluorescence under ultraviolet radiation—but it is easily destroyed by excessive radiation. Alternatively, a large number of fractions are collected and the vitamin A located by treating aliquots of these with antimony trichloride.

Several chromatographic procedures have been proposed, each for a specific type of problem. Three of these procedures are quite generally used, and are described. The first and second procedures are specifically designed to remove extraneous absorption so that spectrophotometry can be applied. The third procedure removes materials that interfere with the antimony trichloride colorimetric assay. A fourth procedure, which we shall not describe fully here, uses dicalcium phosphate to separate all-*trans*-vitamin A, neovitamin A, and vitamin A$_2$ in cod liver oil (19).

2. **Hjarde Procedure for Bulk Vitamin A.** In 1950, Hjarde proposed (42) chromatographic procedures which have since been adopted in several European countries as a step in official spectrophotometric vitamin A assays. Either alumina or calcium phosphate may be used; but the adsorptivity must be adjusted (57) by a standard procedure. Alumina (Brockman) is mixed with 4 to 8% of its weight of water and allowed to stand at least 20 hours before use. Dibasic calcium phosphate is mixed with 5% its weight of dibasic sodium phosphate in 8 times its weight of water and boiled for 15 minutes. It is then filtered, washed with 5 volumes of water, dried 48 hours at 110°C., then stored 24 hours at 50% relative humidity (over saturated potassium thiocyanate).

The sample is prepared for assay by saponification; that part of the U.S.P. procedure (Section III.1.B) is quite satisfactory. The unsaponifiable fraction (300 to 400 μg. of vitamin A) in petroleum ether is added to the column (12 x 90 mm.). When the adsorbent is alumina, the chromatogram is developed with successive solutions of ethyl ether in petroleum ether, of gradually increasing concentration from 2% to 10% (v./v.). When the adsorbent is calcium phosphate, the eluting solvent is 4% ethyl ether in petroleum ether. The vitamin A fraction is measured spectrophotometrically.

3. **Boldingh and Drost Procedure** (16) **for Margarine.** This is currently being studied by the A.O.A.C. referee (58) as a possible official procedure for margarine. It requires two chromatographic columns, the first of water-weakened alumina, the second of alkali-treated alumina. A forecut from the first column is discarded, then the remaining material is fractionated on the second column. For the first column, alumina is heated for 6 hours at 600°C., cooled, sifted through 180 mesh, shaken with 2% of its weight of water and stored overnight or longer. It is packed in a 5 x 240 mm. tube. For the second column, alumina is mixed with an equal part of 10% aqueous sodium hydroxide, allowed to stand 1 hour, then dried in a vacuum oven, 15–20 mm. Hg, first at 30–40°C., finally for 1 hour at

100°C. It is packed into a 5 x 100 mm. tube. The unsaponifiable fraction (Section III.3.A) from 10 g. of margarine is added to the first column in petroleum ether. The chromatogram is developed with 5 ml. portions of petroleum ether containing 0%, 4%, 8%, and 12% ethyl ether. The eluate collected up to this point is discarded. The second column is attached and the eluate from the first column is passed continuously through the second column. Both columns are eluted with 5 ml. portions of petroleum ether containing 16%, 20%, and 24% ethyl ether. Finally, a 36% ethyl ether solution is passed through both columns until the vitamin A band has passed through the second column. The final eluate is collected in 1 ml. fractions. The vitamin A band is located by a qualitative antimony trichloride test on one-drop aliquots from each fraction. Equal aliquots of the fractions containing vitamin A are combined, and diluted for spectrophotometric measurement.

There is still some doubt whether the Morton-Stubbs correction is valid, even after this purification. A small amount of non-linear irrelevant absorption may remain, which would cause over-correction in the calculation.

4. A.O.A.C. Procedure for Fortified Feeds. Chromatography is a key step in the A.O.A.C. procedure (11) for determining vitamin A in feeds which have been fortified with vitamin A ester in a form extractable with hexane. The extraction is discussed in Section IV.4. A 23 mm. diameter chromatograph tube is packed with a 1:1 (w./w.) mixture of diatomaceous earth (Johns-Manville Hyflo Super-Cel) and magnesia (Micron brand No. 2641, Westvaco Chlorine Products Corp.) to a depth of 10 cm. A 1 cm. layer of anhydrous sodium sulfate is placed on top of the adsorbent. Fifty milliliters of hexane containing the extract of 5 grams of feed are added to the column, followed by 35–40 ml. of 10% acetone in hexane (v./v.). If the feed does not contain β-carotene, some is added to act as a tracer for the vitamin A band. The vitamin A band moves down the column just ahead of the β-carotene band, so a slight amount of the latter is eluted with the vitamin A fraction to insure complete elution of the vitamin A. The vitamin A fraction is assayed by the antimony trichloride blue color determination (Section III.2.A). Some feeds contain vitamin A in a "stabilized" form that is not extractable with hexane. Proposed (27,63a) procedures for this situation have used saponification, so that the extract contains vitamin A alcohol instead of ester. In this case the vitamin A band follows the carotene, and the two are eluted together. A correction is then made for carotene interference as described by Bickoff (14) and in Section IV.5 of this chapter. The adsorptivity of the magnesia must be tested using a feed of known vitamin A content. If recovery of vitamin A is incomplete, it is necessary to deactivate the magnesia by exposing it in a thin layer to air for 1 to 3 days.

C. SOLVENT PARTITION

Distribution of the sample between two immiscible solvents can sometimes be used to separate vitamin A from interfering materials. Paper chromatography is a form of solvent partition that may be useful in purifying samples for assay. One procedure (20) separates vitamin A from vitamin E in pharmaceutical mixtures. Another (28) is designed to separate vitamin A from the irrelevant materials in cod liver oil. Distribution between petroleum ether and 83% aqueous ethanol has been used (49) to separate free vitamin A alcohol from the high molecular weight esters in fish liver oil. In this system, vitamin A alcohol distributes 50:50 between the alcohol and petroleum ether, while vitamin A palmitate distributes 1.2:98.8.

D. MOLECULAR DISTILLATION

Molecular distillation (36) has not been widely used for purification of samples for assay, but it does a remarkably good job of removing irrelevant absorption from fish liver oils. Morton and Stubbs (60) showed that distilled vitamin A concentrates were practically free from irrelevant absorption by their geometric criteria. (The 5% correction actually observed was probably caused by neovitamin A.) Clean separations of vitamin A alcohol from high molecular weight esters have been obtained (49) by molecular distillation. This step was a key one in concentrating vitamin A naturally present in lard (3).

IV. DETAILED PROCEDURES FOR SPECIFIC MATERIALS

1. Bulk Vitamin A and Pharmaceutical Products

Many commercial vitamin A products clearly come under official assay procedures. Complications arise when business is transacted between parties in different countries that are likely to have somewhat different official assay procedures. The U.S.P. assay tends to give results slightly higher than the British Pharmacopeia procedure (see "Comments" in Section III.B and C). Chromatographic procedures can sometimes lead to low results through loss of vitamin A. Procedures which depend on chromatography to remove irrelevant absorption, and do not employ a Morton-Stubbs correction, will fail to penalize neovitamin A to the proper extent (Section III.1.A.4). The Swedish Pharmacopeia (21) uses an excellent combination of procedures that should be quite accurate for relatively impure preparations. The sample is saponified (Section III.1.B), chromatographed using Hjarde's procedure (Section III.3.B.2), then assayed by *corrected* spectrophotometric measurement. To guard against serious bias in either the handling or the spectrophotometry, the vitamin A reference standard is treated in the same way; and the Morton-Stubbs calculation, as well as the conversion factor, is derived from measurements on this treated standard.

Another difficulty is often encountered when "non-official" products are assumed to come under an official assay procedure. Multivitamin preparations that contain high levels of vitamin E with the vitamin A should properly be treated to allow for the over-correction of the Morton-Stubbs calculation due to non-linearity of the irrelevant absorption. Other low potency pharmaceuticals, such as "elixirs" and "tonics," often exhibit non-linear irrelevant absorption and should not come under the U.S.P. procedure without an extra purification step.

2. Margarine

The official assay procedure for vitamin A under the Federal Definition and Standard of Identity for Oleomargarine is the rat growth bioassay. The vitamin sub-committee of the National Association of Margarine Manufacturers in 1948 (66) proposed saponification of the sample and assay using antimony trichloride. Details of these procedures are given in Sections III.3.A and III.2.A. The chromatographic procedure of Boldingh and Drost (16) has recently been studied by Morgareidge (58) and by Rosner (70). Details are given in Section III.3.B.3.

Again, neovitamin A can be a complication to official assays that do not employ a Morton-Stubbs correction. The antimony trichloride determination gives a response for neovitamin A equal to that for all-*trans*. Thus, it overestimates neovitamin A by about 33%;

and fish liver oils that have one-third their vitamin A in the neo form are overestimated by about 10%. Uncorrected spectrophotometric procedures overestimate fish oils by about 7%, because of the neo-vitamin A.

3. Milk

Any assay procedure suitable for margarine can be applied to the unsaponifiable fraction of milk fat. The saponification procedure for margarine given in Section IV.2 above can be used for milk fat. The Rose-Gottlieb procedure, which is the official A.O.A.C. method (11) for determining fat in milk, can be adapted to vitamin A assay by taking precautions against excessive heating of the extracted fat. Another potentially useful procedure has been proposed by Sager, Sanders, Norman, and Middleton (71). Sodium tetraphosphate and a detergent, such as Triton X-100 or Tergitol NPX, are used to separate milk fat from milk. See also the procedure using GDH described by Bickoff (14) and in Section IV.5.

4. Feeds

For determining vitamin A in feeds the official A.O.A.C. procedure (11) can be applied as long as the vitamin A is in such a form as to be extractable with hexane. A 10-g. sample of feed is refluxed for 30 minutes with exactly 100 ml. of hexane. Precautions are taken against loss of solvent. The mixture is cooled and allowed to settle, and a 50 ml. aliquot is taken for chromatography (see Section III.3.B.4) and assay by the antimony trichloride procedure (see Section III.2.-A.1).

A number of stabilized vitamin A preparations are now being used which are not extractable with hexane. Various saponification procedures have been proposed but none of these has yet been made official. A procedure recently reported by Gade and Kadlec (34) has been used successfully in our laboratories. The feed is mixed with water, methanol, and emulsifier, and extracted only once with ethyl ether containing 10% petroleum ether. By this procedure the vitamin A is completely extracted, troubles with emulsions are avoided, and the extract is readily chromatographed by the A.O.A.C. procedure.

A serious problem is likely to be encountered in assaying feeds fortified with "dry vitamin A" consisting of discrete particles. Some preparations contain as much as 8 units of vitamin A per particle on the average. A 10-g. sample of feed fortified at the level of 2000 units per lb. would be expected to contain 44 units of vitamin A. In some cases, these 44 units would be contained in only about 6 particles. The sampling error alone thus would give rise to a coefficient of variation of $(100 \times \sqrt{6})/6$ or about $\pm40\%$. To reduce the coefficient of variation to $\pm4\%$, a 1000-g. sample would be required.

5. Blood

The vitamin A-protein complex in blood is easily ruptured by adding alcohol or by saponifying the plasma or serum. Vitamin A may then be extracted with petroleum ether and measured colorimetrically using either the $SbCl_3$ (see Section III.2.A) or GDH (see Section III.2.B) procedure. A correction for blood carotenoids must be made since they are extracted along with vitamin A and contribute to the total $SbCl_3$-blue color or GDH-red color.

An alternative method, the micro-modification of which is most often used, is based on the measurement of absorbance at 328 mμ of blood lipid before and after controlled ultraviolet irradiation. Vitamin A is the only substance in blood lipid with absorption at 328 mμ which is destroyed by ultraviolet irradiation under the conditions of the procedure. Therefore, the decrease in absorbance at 328 mμ after destructive irradiation is a measure of vitamin A content.

Detailed descriptions of the procedures currently used for the determination of vitamin A in blood are as follows:

SbCl_3 Procedure (50). Five milliliters of plasma or serum is put into a centrifuge tube fitted with a ground glass stopper. An equal volume of 95% ethanol is added and the contents mixed. Fifteen milliliters of petroleum ether (40–60°) is added, the stopper firmly inserted, and the tube shaken vigorously for 5 minutes. The petroleum ether layer containing all of the vitamin A and carotene is separated by centrifuging. Twelve milliliters of this extract is pipetted into an Evelyn photoelectric colorimeter tube and the intensity of the yellow color determined using a 440 mμ filter. Reference to a standard curve gives the concentration of carotene in the petroleum ether extract (14).

The petroleum ether is evaporated directly from the colorimeter tube using a hot water bath and a fine jet of nitrogen directed into the tube. The residue is dissolved in 1 ml. of $CHCl_3$ and then the $SbCl_3$ blue color determined (see Section III.2.A). The total blue color intensity is corrected by subtracting the amount due to the carotene present [reference to a standard curve relating the yellow color of carotene in petroleum ether (440 mμ) to the blue color reaction product of carotene and SbCl$_3$ in CHCl$_3$ (620 mμ)] (14,86). The vitamin A in the aliquot is obtained from the corrected blue color by reference to a standard curve (see Section III.2.A.1). The following calculation is then made:

$$\mu\text{g. vit. A in tube} \times \frac{\text{ml. pet. ether added intially}}{\text{ml. pet. ether in aliquot}} \times$$

$$\frac{100}{\text{ml. of plasma used}} = \mu\text{g. vit. A per 100 ml. blood plasma}$$

GDH Procedure. Glycerol dichlorohydrin (1,3-dichloro-2-propanol) can be used instead of SbCl$_3$ (75). Its use presents the advantages (more stable color, less affected by moisture) and disadvantages (less sensitive, more color inhibition trouble) as enumerated in Section III.2.B. Saponification of the blood plasma or serum prior to extraction is an essential step in the procedure. It destroys an inhibitor present in the plasma which would otherwise be extracted and cause low values for both vitamin A and carotene (1).

The serum lipid extract is dissolved in CHCl$_3$ and the GDH reagent added. Absorbance measurements are made at 555 mμ and 830 mμ. The former is a measure of both vitamin A and carotene, while the latter measures only carotene. The absorbance at 555 mμ is corrected for carotene by reference to standard curves (14,75).

Microprocedure Based on Selective Ultraviolet Destruction of Vitamin A. A method for the determination of vitamin A (also carotene) in blood, developed by Bessey and co-workers (13), has been widely used because only 0.035 to 0.100 ml. of serum is needed for analysis. This quantity is easily obtained from a finger-tip sample of blood in contrast to the 2.5–10.0 ml. samples obtained by venipuncture for macro-methods. Its use makes possible nutritional surveys of infants and children and permits the repeated use of small experimental animals without having to kill animals for each analysis. Sera may be kept at 4° for several weeks or at −20° for several months before microanalysis without loss of either vitamin A or carotene.

Blood is collected in capillary tubes, one end is sealed cautiously with a small flame to prevent overheating the blood, and the top end is closed with sealing cement. The tubes are centrifuged to obtain serum and any with evidence of hemolyzed serum are discarded. An exact volume, about 0.06 ml., of serum is transferred to a long tube (100 x 3 mm.) and 0.06 ml. of 1 N alcoholic KOH (freshly prepared) is added and mixed thoroughly using a mechanical vibrator. The tubes are heated in a water bath at 60° for 20 minutes, cooled, and 0.06 ml. of kerosene-xylene (1:1 mixture) reagent added. Extraction is accomplished by agitation using the vibrator for 10–15 seconds. The tubes are then centrifuged for 10 minutes at 3000 RPM. The kerosene-xylene layer is removed as completely as possible by means of a fine-tipped, constricted pipette of about 0.05–0.06 ml. volume into a special narrow Beckman cuvette. Absorbance measurements are made at 460 and 328 mμ.

The sample is then removed to a short, soft glass tube (40 x 2.5 mm.) and irradiated (General Electric B-H 4 mercury discharge lamp with purple envelope) 30–60 minutes. The period of irradiation is 6–8 times as long as found necessary to destroy 50% of vitamin A in pure solutions. After irradiation, a second absorbance measurement at 328 mμ is made.

Calculation: $E_{460} \times 480 = \mu g.$ % of carotene; $(E_{328} - E_{\text{irradiated } 328}) \times 637 = \mu g.$ of vitamin A per 100 ml. of blood serum.

Critical evaluation of the Bessey micromethod has been made by several groups of investigators (15,23,24). The absorbance of the kerosene-xylene reagent should be checked frequently since absorbance in the region 310–400 mμ gradually increases as this reagent ages. Once started, it is greatly accelerated by exposure to the ultraviolet irradiation used in the analytical procedure. Refluxing the reagent over metallic sodium for several hours, then distilling xylene at 138–139° and kerosene at 180–195° eliminates interfering impurities (48). Serum samples showing hemolysis lead to falsely high values for both vitamin A and carotene, and should not be used.

Procedure for Determining Relative Proportion of Vitamin A Alcohol and Esters. Vitamin A occurs in blood and other tissues in both the free alcohol and ester form and it is sometimes necessary to determine the alcohol-ester ratio. Solvent partition between 83% aqueous ethanol and petroleum ether (see Section III.3.C), fluorescence measurement (see Section I.2.D), or chromatographic separation on bone meal (35) are quite suitable. A micromodification of the chromatography technique is described by Eden (29). The Glover, Goodwin, and Morton procedure is as follows (35):

Five grams of defatted bone meal (Soxhlet extracted with acetone 6 hrs. and dried at 60°C.) is sieved (through 120 on 200 mesh) and packed in a 150 x 15 mm. column (see Section III.3.B.1). Five milliliters of the vitamin A sample in petroleum ether (5 to 15 mg./100 ml.) is added and the ester fraction eluted with approximately 100 ml. of 2.5% chloroform in petroleum ether (v./v.). The receiver is changed and the adsorbed vitamin A alcohol is eluted with 50–60 ml. acetone. The two extracts are carefully evaporated to dryness under nitrogen, dissolved in $CHCl_3$, and analyzed for vitamin A by the antimony trichloride procedure (see Section II.2.A).

The vitamin A alcohol, while adsorbed on the bone meal, is very unstable and should be eluted as quickly as possible to minimize oxidative loss.

6. Liver, Kidney, and Other Organs

Practically all of the vitamin A (approx. 95%) in the animal body is stored in the liver. Analysis of this organ is usually of great interest because its vitamin A content is considered the best estimate of vitamin A nutriture. However, under circumstances in which liver storage of vitamin A may be reduced to zero, the vitamin A present in the kidneys, lungs, and other organs becomes of interest. Ames *et al.* (5) have described a procedure designed for the analysis of rat livers (liver-storage bioassay) but which can be used for the determination of vitamin A in any other organ. This procedure is simple, rapid, and precise when applied to organs containing more than 5–10 μg. vitamin A per gram tissue (approx. 200 μg./g. lipid). For analysis of organs possessing low concentrations of vitamin A (less than 200 μg./g. lipid), a saponification step such as described in Section III.-3.A must be incorporated as the initial step of the method.

Procedure. A 3 to 5 g. portion of tissue (preferably a whole organ) is ground in a mortar with 3–5 times its weight of anhydrous Na_2SO_4 until completely dry. The dry powdered sample is transferred quantitatively to a 250 ml. Perma-red glass-stoppered Erlenmeyer flask. Exactly 100 ml. of freshly redistilled anhydrous ethyl ether is added and the flask shaken for 2 minutes. After the suspended material has completely settled, an aliquot of the ether layer is transferred to an Evelyn photoelectric colorimeter tube and the solvent removed by evaporation under nitrogen. The residue is dissolved in 1 ml. of $CHCl_3$, and analyzed by the $SbCl_3$ reaction (see

Section III.2.A). The amount of vitamin A in the ether aliquot is obtained from a reference curve. Knowing the portion of the original 100 ml. of ether extract represented by the aliquot, and the weight of tissue taken, the vitamin A content, μg. vitamin A per 100 g. of tissue or per organ, is calculated. Excellent recoveries of added vitamin A, to liver tissue for example, and a precision of $\pm 2.4\%$ (SD of 19 values) indicate the utility of this simplified procedure.

An alternative technique for rapid and complete extraction of vitamin A from liver and other tissues is that described by Gade and Kadlec (34). Fresh tissue is used in this procedure, thus eliminating the time-consuming Na_2SO_4 drying step.

The relative distribution of vitamin A alcohol to vitamin A ester, if this is of interest in the problem under study, is carried out by solvent partition or chromatographic procedures (see Section III.3.C) on a separate aliquot of the organ or tissue extract. In the liver, stored vitamin A ester and vitamin A alcohol are associated with different proteins as shown by differential centrifugation studies (51,52).

7. Eggs

Thompson *et al.* (79) have described a method for determining vitamin A and carotenoids in dried eggs by saponification and chromatography on $Ca(OH)_2$, followed by colorimetric measurement of the individual eluates (14). Kyrning (53) has analyzed fresh eggs by a similar procedure, saponification and chromatography on $CaCO_3$. The chromatogram is developed with petroleum ether containing 5% acetone. When the strong yellow band of lutein moves to the bottom of the column, all of the vitamin A is in the eluate. The yellow pigments are then eluted separately with ethyl ether.

8. Adipose Tissue, Lard, and Low-Potency Tissues

Occasional references have been made in the literature to animal tissue which shows no vitamin A or provitamin A content by routine physicochemical analyses, yet has vitamin A activity. The existence of new factors, such as the "lard-factor," has been proposed to account for this phenomenon. Usually, however, more careful and critical analysis of the lard has shown that the sample is not devoid of vitamin A, as reported, but that it has enough to account for the slight biological potency observed. Careful analytical technique is required to detect and measure the minute amounts of vitamin A involved.   Critical examination of low-potency samples, of lard for example, may be made as follows:

Procedure.   Herb *et al.* (41) used saponification and chromatography on alumina to give fractions which were examined for spectrally pure vitamin A.   Quantities of vitamin A as low as 0.1 μg./g. of original sample can be determined if the ratio of unsaponifiable matter to vitamin A is low.

Ames and Harris (3) also showed that quantities of vitamin A as low as 0.15 μg./g. original lard could be measured if extreme care were taken to prevent destruction or loss of the vitamin during the manipulations involved in concentration and isolation.   For example, following molecular distillation and saponification, a relatively large amount of refined cottonseed oil is added to the ethyl ether extract of the unsaponifiable material.   The ether is removed under vacuum and thus a solution of unsaponifiable matter in cottonseed oil is achieved without loss of vitamin A.   One aliquot is bioassayed.   A second aliquot is analyzed by the increment blue-color test as described in Section III.2.A.2.   A third aliquot is treated with alcoholic HCl and the resulting anhydrovitamin A determined as discussed in Section III.1.D.   All of the vitamin A bioactivity of the sample was accounted for by the chemically and physically measured vitamin A.

9. Urine and Feces

Vitamin A occurs normally in the urine of dogs but its presence in the urine of other species of animals is abnormal, indicating disease or kidney injury due to the action of certain drugs.

Procedure (54).   Urine (100 ml.) is shaken with successive additions of 5 ml. of saturated KOH, 10 ml. ethanol, and 100 ml. ethyl ether.   The ether layer is washed with water, the ether evaporated, and the residue dissolved in 1 ml. of $CHCl_3$.   The vitamin A is measured by the $SbCl_3$ colorimetric procedure (see Section III.2.A).

Patients with pneumonia have been reported to excrete as much as 3200 units of vitamin A in one 24-hour period.   Concentrations of 23 units/mg. urine lipid are not uncommon in some patients with nephritis or with respiratory diseases.   This concentration of vitamin A, per unit of lipid in the urine, is at least 100 times greater than in blood (approx. 0.17 unit/mg. blood lipid).

The determination of the vitamin A in feces is of importance in balance studies in animals and sometimes in certain clinical studies. Kaiser and Kagan (47) developed a method which is precise, permits excellent recoveries of added vitamin A, and is superior to those proposed by earlier investigators. Vitamin A is stable at least 3 days in stool samples kept at refrigerator temperature.

Procedure. The entire stool sample is weighed and transferred to an Erlenmeyer flask. An equal quantity of 6% alcoholic KOH is added and a magnetic stirring bar is placed in the flask. The contents are stirred to a uniform suspension. Several 2–3 g. aliquots of this suspension are weighed into 20 ml. test tubes and saponified with 6% alcoholic KOH at 70° for 6–8 hours. The digested mixture is filtered and made up to 10 ml. with alcoholic KOH. Aliquots (2 ml.) are transferred to 50 ml. Erlenmeyer flasks and extracted with 2 ml. of a kerosene-xylene (1:1) mixture by vigorous stirring for 10 minutes. An 0.08 ml. portion of the kerosene-xylene extract is drawn off and its absorbance at 328 mμ is read. It is then irradiated with ultraviolet radiation to destroy the vitamin A. The absorbance at 328 mμ is again read, and the vitamin A content is calculated as in the Bessey micromethod for determining vitamin A in blood (see Section IV.5.).

References

1. Allen, R. S., Homeyer, P. G., and Jacobson, N. L., *Iowa State Coll. J. Sci.*, *29*, 721–734 (1954); through *Chem. Abstracts*, *49*, 10406 (1955).
2. Almquist, H. J., *Arch. Biochem. and Biophys.*, *39*, 243 (1952).
3. Ames, S. R., and Harris, P. L., *Science*, *120*, 391 (1954).
4. Ames, S. R., and Harris, P. L., *Anal. Chem.*, *28*, 874 (1956).
5. Ames, S. R., Risley, H. A., and Harris, P. L., *Anal. Chem.*, *26*, 1378 (1954).
6. Ames, S. R., Swanson, W. J., and Harris, P. L., *J. Am. Chem. Soc.*, *77*, 4134 (1955).
7. Ames, S. R., Swanson, W. J., and Harris, P. L., *J. Am. Chem. Soc.*, *77*, 4136 (1955).
8. Ames, S. R., Swanson, W. J., Risley, H. A., and Harris, P. L., *Federation Proc.*, *11*, 181 (1952).
9. Ames, S. R., Swanson, W. J., Risley, H. A., and Harris, P. L., *Federation Proc.*, *13*, 174 (1954).
10. Association of Official Agricultural Chemists, *Official and Tentative Methods of Analysis*, 6th ed., Association of Official Agricultural Chemists, Washington, 1945.

11. Association of Official Agricultural Chemists, *Official Methods of Analysis*, 8th ed., Association of Official Agricultural Chemists, Washington, 1955.
12. Awapara, J., Mattson, F. W., Mehl, J. W., and Deuel, H. J., Jr., *Science*, *104*, 602 (1946).
13. Bessey, O. A., Lowry, O. H., Brock, M. J., and Lopez, J. A., *J. Biol. Chem.*, *166*, 177 (1946).
14. Bickoff, E. M., "Determination of Carotene," in D. Glick, ed., *Methods of Biochemical Analysis*, Vol. IV, Interscience, New York, 1956.
15. Bieri, J. G., and Schultze, M. O., *Arch. Biochem. and Biophys.*, *34*, 273 (1951).
16. Boldingh, J., and Drost, J. R., *J. Am. Oil Chemists' Soc.*, *28*, 480 (1951).
17. *British Pharmacopoeia 1948*.
18. *British Pharmacopoeia 1953*.
19. Bro-Rasmussen, F., Hjarde, W., and Porotnikoff, O., *Analyst*, *80*, 418 (1955).
20. Brown, J. A., *Anal. Chem.*, *25*, 774 (1953).
21. Brunius, E., personal communication.
22. Cama, H. R., Collins, F. D., and Morton, R. A., *Biochem. J.*, *50*, 48 (1951).
23. Caster, W. O., and Michelsen, O., *Am. J. Clin. Nutrition*, *3*, 409 (1955).
24. Clayton, M. M., Babcock, M. J., Foster, W. D., Stregevsky, S., Tucker, R. E., Werts, A. W., and Williams, H. H., *J. Nutrition*, *52*, 383 (1954).
25. Clough, F. B., Kascher, H. M., Robeson, C. D., and Baxter, J. G., *Science*, *105*, 436 (1947).
26. Coetzee, W. H. K., *Biochem. J.*, *45*, 628 (1949).
27. Cooley, M. L., *J. Assoc. Offic. Agr. Chemists*, *36*, 812 (1953).
28. Dunckley, G. G., and Macfarlane, Y. J., *J. Sci. Food Agr.*, *6*, 559 (1955).
29. Eden, E., *Biochem. J.*, *46*, 259 (1950).
30. Embree, N. D., and Shantz, E. M., *J. Biol. Chem.*, *132*, 619 (1940).
31. Embree, N. D., and Shantz, E. M., *J. Am. Chem. Soc.*, *65*, 910 (1943).
32. Evans, H. M., and Bishop, K. S., *Anat. Record*, *23*, 17 (1922).
33. Fox, S. H., and Mueller, A., *J. Am. Pharm. Assoc.*, *Sci. Ed.*, *39*, 621 (1950).
34. Gade, E. T., and Kadlec, J. D., *J. Agr. Food Chem.*, *4*, 426 (1956).
35. Glover, J., Goodwin, T. W., and Morton, R. A., *Biochem. J.*, *41*, 94 (1947).
36. Gray, E. L., Hickman, K. C. D., and Brown, E. F., *J. Nutrition*, *19*, 39 (1940).
37. Greenberg, R., and Popper, H., *Am. J. Physiol.*, *134*, 114 (1941).
38. Guggenheim, K., and Koch, W., *Biochem. J.*, *38*, 256 (1948).
39. György, P., ed., *Vitamin Methods*, Vol. II, Academic Press, New York, 1951, pp. 41–275, 445–610.
40. Harris, P. L., Ames, S. R., and Brinkman, J. H., *J. Am. Chem. Soc.*, *73*, 1252 (1951).

41. Herb, S. F., Riemenschneider, R. W., Kaunitz, H., and Slanetz, C. A., *J. Nutrition, 51*, 393 (1953).
42. Hjarde, W., *Acta Chem. Scand., 4*, 628 (1950).
43. Hubbard, R., Gregerman, R. I., and Wald, G., *J. Gen. Physiol., 36*, 415 (1953).
44. Hubbard, R., and Wald, G., *J. Gen. Physiol., 36*, 269 (1952).
45. Hubbard, R., and Wald, G., *Science, 115*, 60 (1952).
46. Irving, J. T., and Richards, M. B., *Biochem. J., 34*, 198 (1940).
47. Kaiser, E., and Kagan, B. M., *Proc. Soc. Exptl. Biol. Med., 80*, 300 (1952).
48. Karmarkar, G., and Rajagopal, K., *Current Sci. (India), 21*, 193 (1952); through *Chem. Abstracts, 47*, 9389 (1953).
49. Kascher, H. M., and Baxter, J. G., *Ind. Eng. Chem., Anal. Ed., 17*, 499 (1945).
50. Kimble, M. S., *J. Lab. Clin. Med., 24*, 1055 (1939).
51. Krause, R. F., and Sanders, P. L., *Am. J. Clin. Nutrition, 4*, 68 (1956).
52. Krinsky, N. I., and Ganguly, J., *J. Biol. Chem., 202*, 227 (1953).
53. Kyrning, S., *Intern. Z. Vitaminforsch., 24*, 263 (1952).
54. Lawrie, N. R., Moore, T., and Rajagopal, K. R., *Biochem. J., 35*, 825 (1941).
55. Little, R. W., *Ind. Eng. Chem., 16*, 288 (1944).
56. Luckmann, F. H., Melnick, D., and Vahlteich, H. W., *J. Am. Oil Chemists' Soc., 29*, 121 (1952).
57. Moore, L. A., *Ind. Eng. Chem., Anal. Ed., 14*, 707 (1942).
58. Morgareidge, K., *J. Assoc. Offic. Agr. Chemists, 37*, 748 (1954).
59. Morton, R. A., and Stubbs, A. L., *Analyst, 71*, 348 (1946).
60. Morton, R. A., and Stubbs, A. L., *Biochem. J., 42*, 195 (1948).
61. Murray, T. K., and Campbell, J. A., *J. Pharm. and Pharmacol., 5*, 596 (1953).
62. Murray, T. K., and Campbell, J. A., personal communication.
62a. Oroshnik, W., *J. Am. Chem. Soc., 78*, 2651 (1956).
63. Oser, B. L., Melnick, D., and Pader, M., *Ind. Eng. Chem., Anal. Ed., 15*, 724 (1943).
63a. Parrish, D. B., and Smith, H. A., *J. Assoc. Offic. Agr. Chemists, 39*, 126 (1956).
64. Popper, H., *Proc. Soc. Exptl. Biol. Med., 43*, 133, 234 (1940).
65. Pugsley, L. I., Wills, G., and Crandall, W. A., *J. Nutrition, 28*, 365 (1944).
66. Rice, E. E., Primm, E., and Coombes, A. I., *J. Assoc. Offic. Agr. Chemists, 31*, 621 (1948).
67. Robeson, C. D., and Baxter, J. G., *J. Am. Chem. Soc., 69*, 136 (1947).
68. Robeson, C. D., Blum, W. P., Dieterle, J. M., Cawley, J. D., and Baxter, J. G., *J. Am. Chem. Soc., 77*, 4120 (1955).
69. Robeson, C. D., Cawley, J. D., Weisler, L., Stern, M. H., Eddinger, C. C., and Chechak, A. J., *J. Am. Chem. Soc., 77*, 4111 (1955).

70. Rosner, L., and Kan, H., *J. Assoc. Offic. Agr. Chemists, 37*, 887 (1954).
71. Sager, O. S., Sanders, G. P., Norman, G. H., and Middleton, M. B., *J. Assoc. Offic. Agr. Chemists, 38*, 931 (1955).
72. Shantz, E. M., *Science, 108*, 417 (1948).
73. Shantz, E. M., Cawley, J. D., and Embree, N. D., *J. Am. Chem. Soc., 65*, 901 (1943).
74. Sherman, H. C., and Todhunter, E. N., *J. Nutrition, 8*, 347 (1934).
75. Sobel, A. E., and Snow, S. D., *J. Biol. Chem., 171*, 617 (1947).
76. Sobel, A. E., and Werbin, H., *Anal. Chem., 19*, 107 (1947).
77. Sobotka, H., Kann, S., and Loewenstein, E., *J. Am. Chem. Soc., 65*, 1959 (1943).
78. Suggested Revision of the U.S.P. Biological Assays for Vitamins A and D Submitted by the Animal Nutrition Research Council through Dr. C. I. Bliss, Nov. 15, 1948.
79. Thompson, C. R., Ewan, M. A., Hauge, S. M.,, Bohren, B. B., and Quackenbush, F. W., *Ind. Eng. Chem., Anal. Ed., 18*, 113 (1946).
80. *U. S. Pharmacopeia* XIII (1947).
81. *U. S. Pharmacopeia* XIV (1950).
82. *U. S. Phormacopeia* XV (1955).
83. Wald, G., Brown, P. K., Hubbard, R., and Oroshnik, W., *Proc. Natl. Acad. Sci. U. S., 41*, 438 (1955).   Brown, P. K., and Wald, G., *J. Biol. Chem., 222*, 865 (1956).
84. *World Health Organization Tech. Rept. Ser. No. 3*, 3 (1950).
85. *World Health Organization Tech. Rept. Ser. No. 68*, 14 (1953).
86. Yudkin, S., *Biochem. J., 35*, 551 (1941).

Measurement of
POLYUNSATURATED FATTY ACIDS

RALPH T. HOLMAN, *University of Minnesota*

CONTENTS (*Continued*)

I. INTRODUCTION

The polyunsaturated fatty acids are currently assuming increasing importance in biochemistry because members of this group are dietary essential substances and because the polyunsaturated acids as a group appear to be involved in tissue lipid. These acids have physiological activities distinct from the more abundant saturated and mono-unsaturated acids with which they are associated in nature.

The family of polyunsaturated acids includes several known and many poorly described members. The well-characterized acids have normal aliphatic chains, but differ in chain length and number and position of double bonds. The best known members of the family have been shown to have all *cis* methylene-interrupted (skipped) unsaturation. It is presumed that all the polyunsaturated acids have this pattern of methylene-interrupted polyunsaturation, but a few reports suggest that some acids possess ethylene-interrupted polyunsaturated systems. Only the methylene-interrupted polyunsaturated acids will be discussed here.

The natural acids possessing skipped polyunsaturation may be divided into two groups according to structure and biological activity. Counting from the terminal methyl group of the chain, members of the *linoleic acid family* have double bonds at the 6 and 9 positions. Acids of this type which have been tested show essential fatty acid activity, curing dermal symptoms and maintaining growth. Members of the *linolenic acid family* have double bonds at the 3, 6, and 9 positions. These do not cure dermal symptoms of essential fatty acid deficiency but do maintain growth. The structures of possible members of these two families of acids are shown in Figure 1. Many of the acids shown in this speculative diagram of possible metabolic pathways have actually been isolated from animal tissues. For detailed discussion of essential fatty acid deficiency and the polyunsaturated acids, the reader is referred to a recent review (15).

The analysis of tissue lipids containing a variety of these acids presents a complex problem.   The usual methods of detection and measurement of the various types of polyenes do not distinguish between homologs having the same numbers of double bonds. Moreover, separation of acids by chain length cannot be achieved with the small samples available in biochemical studies without the

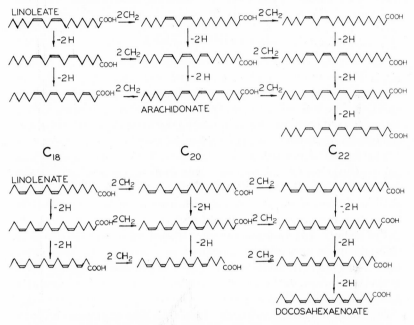

Fig. 1. Formula and relationships between possible members of the linoleic and linolenic acid families of polyunsaturated fatty acids.   In this speculative presentation it is assumed that the terminal portion of the fatty acids remains the same, and that dehydrogenation and acetylation occur only at the carboxyl end of the molecules.

use of specialized and expensive equipment, and the distillation method applicable to larger samples induces some destruction of the long chain polyenes.   No single method permits the analyst to determine individual acids in small samples.

Linoleic and linolenic acids occur in plant oils, and thus far no report has been made of more highly unsaturated non-conjugated acids in vegetable oils.   Therefore, the analysis of vegetable oils for polyunsaturated acids involves only the measurements of the non-conjugated diene and triene acids. For these measurements, several adequate methods of analysis are available.

Animal products contain a far more complex mixture of poly-unsaturated acids. Dienoic, trienoic, tetraenoic, pentaenoic, and hexaenoic acids are found, and for some of these the chain length may vary widely. The complete description of animal fats and fish oils is thus a very large task. Fractional distillation of fatty acid esters followed by analysis of the fractions is the best method available at present (27) but such an analysis assumes the proportion of a research problem and requires large samples. Ester fractionation requires highly specialized and expensive equipment. The experimenter must usually compromise and be satisfied with an analysis that will tell him the relative proportions of diene, triene, tetraene, pentaene, and hexaene acids present in his sample of a few milligrams or grams. Methods which will accomplish this are now available, and have found extensive use in biochemical problems. The methods are not specific, they are empirical, the errors are signifi-cant and the results must be interpreted cautiously. Nevertheless, with a proper understanding of the limitations of the methods, much useful information can be gained.

Preliminary detection and measurement of total unsaturation may be made by determining the iodine number or the hydrogen value of a fatty substance. Determination of iodine number contributes only gross information, and often is not worth the expenditure of sample that it requires. This is particularly true in measurements upon highly unsaturated acids, in which empirical iodine values appear to be lower than the theoretical values. Hydrogenation is often a better measure of total unsaturation. It approaches the theoretical value for unsaturation, and the reaction product is a more useful substance for further investigation than is the halogenated product one ob-tains after determining the iodine value.

It is not within the scope of this chapter to discuss all the methods of separation which are adjuncts to the determination of polyunsat-urated acids. However, it should be pointed out that if separation according to chain length can be made prior to measurements of the polyunsaturated acids, the results are much more precise and mean-ingful. This can be accomplished by fractional or amplified dis-tillation (27). Low temperature crystallization or column chroma-tography may be used to enrich the polyunsaturated fatty acids.

II. CHEMICAL METHODS

1. Thiocyanogen Value

Measurement of the thiocyanogen value provides an estimation of the amounts of oleic, linoleic, and linolenic acids in a mixture if the iodine value is also determined. Presumably, thiocyanogen adds to the double bond of oleic acid, one of the double bonds of linoleic acid, and two of the double bonds of linolenic acid. The halogen in the iodine-value reagent adds to all double bonds. Proper correction for the saturated acids present then allows calculation of the three unsaturated acids. The method has been adopted by the American Oil Chemists' Society (28) and can be applied to oils having no acids more unsaturated than linolenic acid. The method is not often used because the preparation of the reagent is tedious and often unsuccessful. Moreover, pure acids do not have stoichiometric thiocyanogen values. It cannot be applied to animal fats because these contain tetraene, pentaene, and hexaene acids for which the method makes no provision. Samples of 0.15 to 1.25 g. are required for the analysis.

2. Polybromide Methods

These methods have the common disadvantage that they determine only the most unsaturated component of a mixture. Solvents are chosen such that the polybromo derivative of the most unsaturated acid or ester is precipitated. Acids with less unsaturation cannot be determined by this method. All the polybromide determinations require 1 gram samples.

A. TETRABROMIDE METHOD

When bromine adds to the double bonds of polyunsaturated acids, polybromides are formed. If advantage is taken of their different solubilities in organic solvents, an assay of the individual acids from which they were formed can be performed. The amount of insoluble tetrabromides precipitated when linoleic acid is brominated in cold petroleum ether can be related to the linoleic acid content of the sample (32). The presence of other acids and the sample size both affect the apparent tetrabromide number. Strict adherence to the empirical conditions allows the measurement of linoleic acid in samples containing no more highly unsaturated acids. The chief value of the method is the demonstration that a diene acid is or is not natural linoleic acid.

B. HEXABROMIDE METHOD

The weight of insoluble bromides precipitated when mixed acids are brominated in cold ether is related to the linolenic acid content of the sample provided more highly unsaturated acids are not present (31). The yield is affected by sample size and presence of other fatty acids. The method is not applicable to fats or oils containing more highly unsaturated acids than linolenic acid because they would be calculated as linolenic acid. It is not applicable to animal fats.

C. POLYBROMIDE METHOD FOR ARACHIDONATE

A method has been proposed for estimation of arachidonate based upon bromination of methyl esters in cold ether (33). By comparison of yield with a standard curve obtained over a wide range of arachidonate concentrations, the arachidonate content can be estimated. The method suffers from being empirical, and the prescribed conditions must be followed scrupulously. It was proposed for use in ester mixtures which do not contain linolenate or excessive amounts of linoleate. No mention was made of interference by pentaene or hexaene acids, but these would be determined as arachidonate by this method.

III. SPECTROPHOTOMETRIC METHODS INVOLVING ALKALINE ISOMERIZATION

In recent years the spectrophotometric method has been widely used for determinations of polyunsaturated fatty acids because it is more specific than any other commonly used method. It allows the detection and measurement of dienoic, trienoic, tetraenoic, pentaenoic, and hexaenoic fatty acids *as classes*. The method has great potential and is rapidly performed. Discussion of this general method and its several modifications constitutes the bulk of this chapter.

1. Historical Development

The earliest reports of changes in spectra of oils upon prolonged saponification were made by Edisbury *et al.* (10) and by Moore (25). Edisbury concluded that the induced strong ultraviolet absorption was due to cyclization. However, Moore showed that new acids resembling eleostearic acid were formed from linseed oil, and he postulated that the absorption developed by prolonged saponification was due to the conjugation of double bonds. This was later proved by Moore (26) and by Kass and Burr (19) who isolated pseudoeleostearic acid from saponified linseed oil. The positions of the absorption maxima were found to be dependent upon the number of double bonds present in the acids, and their intensities were found to be proportional to the amounts of the various acids present.

Kass, Miller, Hendrickson, and Burr (20) introduced ethylene glycol as a solvent in which isomerization could be hastened by virtue of its higher boiling point. They used one part KOH to 4 parts ethylene glycol and a heating time of 30 minutes at the boiling point to isomerize the unsaturated acids. With this method they were able to determine the linoleic acid contents of several commercial oils (9).

Shortly thereafter Mitchell, Kraybill, and Zscheile (24) refined the method and standardized conditions to yield more reproducible results. They used 0.1 g. fat sample, 10 ml. of ethylene glycol containing 7.5% KOH, and a 25 minute reaction time. Standardized against linoleic and linolenic acids prepared by bromination-debromination, this method was applicable to analysis of vegetable oils. Later Beadle and Kraybill (4) extended its application to fats containing arachidonic acid by providing constants for this substance and used the method for distinguishing animal fat from vegetable products. From these beginnings, numerous modifications and improvements have been added to the method, and the method has been adapted to very specific analytical needs.

2. Isomerization Reaction

In the polyunsaturated system, the hydrogen atoms on the methylene groups between two double bonds are much more labile or reactive than are other hydrogen atoms in the molecule. Reaction with the labile hydrogens usually causes a shift of the double bond system to the conjugated condition. The isomerization of linoleate under alkaline conditions can be written as follows:

$$-CH=CH-CH_2-CH=CH- \xrightarrow[+H\cdot]{-H\cdot} \begin{cases} -CH=CH-CH-CH=CH- \\ -CH-CH=CH-CH=CH- \\ -CH=CH-CH=CH-CH- \end{cases}$$

$$-CH_2-CH=CH-CH=CH-$$
or
$$-CH=CH-CH=CHCH_2-$$

resonance hybrid

This shift in double bonds takes place, for instance, under catalysis of alkalis at high temperatures and by alkali amides even at very low temperature (2). It is accompanied by side reactions which lead to

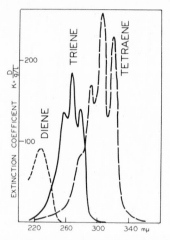

Fig. 2. Spectra of pure conjugated fatty acids. Diene = 10,12 linoleic acid, triene = pseudoeleostearic acid (10,12,14-octadecatrienoic acid), tetraene = parinaric acid.

destruction of the conjugated polyenes, probably through polymerization. Therefore, the unsaturated acids must be subjected to the reaction for a precise period of time if the maximum amount of conjugated acids are to be formed and measured.

As pointed out previously, the reason for isomerizing the polyunsaturates to conjugated forms is that the latter have specific absorption bands in the ultraviolet region, whereas the non-conjugated forms do not. The absorption spectra of some conjugated polyunsaturated fatty acids are shown together in Figure 2. In a mixture of such conjugated acids, each can be independently measured in a spectrophotometer.

When non-conjugated polyunsaturated fatty acids are isomerized by alkali catalysis, all possible types of conjugation are produced. Thus, from a non-conjugated hexaene, several hexaene isomers are formed in which 2, 3, 4, 5, or 6 of the double bonds are conjugated. This is illustrated in Figure 3, where spectra of isomerized diene, triene, tetraene, pentaene, and hexaene acids are collected.

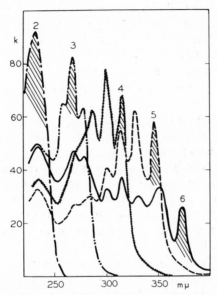

Fig. 3. Spectra of isomerized polyunsaturated fatty acids: 2 linoleic acid, 3 linolenic acid, 4 arachidonic acid, 5 eicosapentaenoic acid, 6 docosahexaenoic acid. Method of Herb and Riemenschneider. Cross-hatched maxima are those which are characteristic of the various polyenes and which are used in the calculations. (Holman and Hayes.)

As the number of double bonds in the molecule increases, the molecular absorption of the conjugated polyenoic acid increases (see Fig. 2). On the other hand, as the number of double bonds of a non-conjugated polyenoic acid increases, the yield of its characteristic conjugated polyenoic acid decreases (see Fig. 3). Thus the sensitivity of the isomerization methods for the polyunsaturated acids decreases considerably with increasing unsaturation. Unnatural isomers (*trans*) of the polyunsaturated acids isomerize at a lower rate and cannot be determined by the methods presented here.

In a mixture containing isomerized diene, triene, tetraene, pentaene, and hexaene acids, the total observed conjugated diene (measurable at 233 mμ) consists of contributions from diene, triene, tetraene, pentaene, and hexaene acid isomers in which two double bonds are conjugated. The triene absorption is equal to the sum of the absorptions of triene, tetraene, pentaene, and hexaene acid isomers in which only three double bonds are conjugated. The tetraene, pentaene, and hexaenes all form conjugated tetraene isomers, and the pentaene and hexaene contribute to the apparent pentaene absorption. The hexaene absorption is due largely to hexaene, but pentaene contributes enough absorption at the hexaene position so that a correction must be made for it. And calculation of the conjugated diene absorption due to linoleic acid in the mixture requires four such corrections!

If such calculations are to be meaningful, it is necessary that the proportions of the various conjugated polyene isomers derived from a single acid *be constant* and *be known*. Therefore it is necessary that the reaction be strictly reproducible and that the spectrum of isomerized pure acids be measured. It is these two requirements that have stimulated most of the work on the spectrophotometric measurement of polyenes, for most of the improvements in methodology propose better control of the conditions or advance new constants derived from purer fatty acids.

The yield of conjugated polyene from the non-conjugated polyene depends mainly upon the following factors. The temperature of the reaction, the concentration of alkali, and the time of reaction all influence the amounts of reaction products. To elevate the reaction temperature, a search for higher-boiling solvents was made and ultimately ethylene glycol became generally used for the reaction. The reaction temperature of 180°C., now commonly used, is safely below the boiling point of ethylene glycol, 197°.

The reaction of dienoic and trienoic acids is relatively insensitive to changes in alkali concentration but the isomerization of the more highly unsaturated acids is greatly affected by this variable. In contrast to this, Holman and Burr (16) found that the proportions of conjugated diene, triene, and tetraene from arachidonate varied greatly depending upon KOH concentration. They found that the formation of conjugated tetraene from arachidonate was favored by higher levels of KOH than had been used prior to that time. This is demonstrated in Figure 4.

Herb and Riemenschneider made a careful study of the isomerization of arachidonate and concluded that the optimum KOH concentration is 21% by weight in ethylene glycol at 180°C.   Under

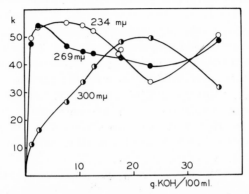

Fig. 4. The effect of KOH concentration upon the degree of isomerization of arachidonic acid. O-O-O = diene conjugation, 235 mμ; ●-●-● = triene conjugation 269 mμ; ◑-◑-◑ = tetraene conjugation 300 mμ.   (Holman and Burr, 16.)

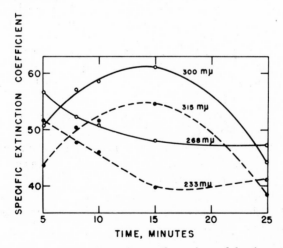

Fig. 5. The effect of time upon the products formed by isomerization of arachidonate under the conditions of Herb and Riemenschneider (13).

these conditions they then learned that the optimum reaction time is about 15 minutes.   Figure 5 shows the effect of time upon the isomerization of arachidonate. The work of Herb and Riemen-schneider led to a basically sound and generally used method for poly-unsaturated acid analysis of animal fats.

From studies of the rate of isomerization of several polyunsaturated acids, it has been learned that the dienoic, trienoic, tetraenoic, pentaenoic, and hexaenoic acids develop their maximum yields of conjugated isomers at different reaction times. Therefore a compro-mise must be made in selecting a reaction time. The methods first developed, using 6.6 or 11% KOH, favored long reaction times be-cause the methods were "tuned" to linoleic and linolenic acid isom-erization. More recent studies of the isomerization of the more highly unsaturated acids have shown that shorter reaction times are advisable for tetraene, pentaene, and hexaene acids.

3. Miscellaneous Modifications

A. MITCHELL, KRAYBILL, AND ZSCHEILE (24)

This method was the first spectrophotometric method for fat analysis to be published in detail. A 100 mg. sample of fat was isom-erized in 6.5–6.6% KOH in ethylene glycol (7.5 g. 85% KOH/100 ml.) at 180° for 25 minutes. The absorption of the blanks due to glycol and to KOH are low enough to permit ultraviolet measure-ments. However, the absorption due to glycol varies considerably causing error in measurement. In its original form it was useful only for determination of linoleic and linolenic acids. Later, refer-ence constants were determined for arachidonic acid to extend its usefulness to animal fats (4). A chief disadvantage is that the sensi-tivity of the method for arachidonic acid is low because low KOH concentration is used in the reagent. The method is really not appli-cable to analysis of animal fats because no provision has yet been made for measurement of (or correction for) the pentaene and hexaene acids found in animal fats. The method is suitable for analysis of vege-table oils, and in its more highly refined modification is described in detail under Section III.4.C.

B. HILDITCH, MORTON, AND RILEY (14)

These authors preferred to determine linoleic and linolenic acids by a method involving two isomerizations with 6.5–6.6% KOH in ethylene glycol. The amount of linolenic acid is determined after isomerization at 170° for 15 minutes, which induces a good yield of triene conjugation from linolenic acid but a low yield of diene conjugation from linoleate. The amount of linoleic acid is determined from the diene conjugation induced at 180° for 60 minutes.

The disadvantages of this method are that two isomerizations are required without any apparent increase in accuracy, and two hot baths (170° and 180°) must be maintained for the single analysis.

C. BERK, KRETCHMER, HOLMAN, AND BURR (5)

In an effort to devise a micromethod suitable for 0.1 mg. samples of lipid, isomerization was carried out for 15 min. in 6% aqueous alkali at 180°C. in a bomb autoclave heated by superheated steam. The samples were isomerized in nickel crucibles, the samples diluted to 10 ml. with water, and the spectral absorption measured.

The advantage is that with water as solvent, the absorption of the blank is low and rather constant, thereby making measurements on 0.1 mg. samples possible. The disadvantages of the method are that it requires a source of superheated steam, that the yield of specific conjugated isomers from the non-conjugated precursors is relatively low. No constants have been determined for pentaenoic and hexaenoic acids. This modification should not be used for animal lipids now that better ones are available.

D. VANDENHEUVEL AND RICHARDSON (30)

These investigators modified the mechanics of the isomerization procedure to allow simultaneous application of identical treatment to samples and blanks, to eliminate time lag resulting from delayed solution of the sample, and to increase reproducibility. They performed the reaction in a calibrated bottle to eliminate the transfer of the syrupy reaction mixture, and devised new apparatus for dispensing and storing the reagent, for nitrogen purification, and for the isomerization reaction itself. A reaction temperature of 159°C. was suggested, using 6 g. of reagent containing 6.5–6.6% KOH in ethylene glycol.

It seems that in an effort to make the method more precise the authors adopted unnecessarily elaborate equipment and cumbersome procedure. In light of the greater inherent limitation of the isomerization reaction, it appears to the writer that minor improvements in procedure which give better reproducibility at the loss of time and simplicity, are of little value when the reagent used is not adapted to analysis of all the polyunsaturated acids.

E. HOLMAN AND BURR (16)

These authors studied the effect of KOH concentration and time of reaction upon the yield of conjugated polyenes from the more common polyunsaturated acids. They suggested that high KOH and short reaction time would increase the sensitivity of the measurement of the unsaturated acids. The authors recommended 8 min. heating at 178°C. in 5 ml. of 23% KOH-ethylene glycol. It was not the intent to establish a new method, but this procedure was used for several years by the writer for estimation of relative changes in polyunsaturated fatty acid composition of animals. The macromethod of Herb and Riemenschneider has superseded that of Holman and Burr in the author's laboratory. However, while samples were available, constants were recently determined on a series of polyunsaturated acids in order that older data may be re-evaluated. The spectral constants are given in Table I.

TABLE I

k Values Developed in the Method of Holman and Burr

	Acid				
	Linoleic	Linolenic	Arachidonic	Eicosapenta-enoic	Docosa-hexaenoic
3725 A.	—	—	—	5.2	30.8
3450	—	—	—	66.8	38.1
3000	—	—	61.9	57.5	47.6
2700	—	77.8	62.8	54.6	65.8
2325	73.0	57.0	52.1	47.5	63.6

4. Recommended Methods

A. EQUIPMENT AND SUPPLIES REQUIRED BY RECOMMENDED METHODS

1. Beckman DU spectrophotometer equipped with ultraviolet source and fused silica 1 cm. matched cells.

2. Source of oxygen-free nitrogen and nitrogen manifold.

3. Isomerization bath held at 180° ± 0.5°C. This may be a liquid bath with adequate stirring or an electrically heated metal block (Lips and Tessier, 22).

4. Ethylene glycol.

5. Potassium hydroxide, C.P. or A.R.

6. Absolute methanol (or absolute ethanol).   The alcohol should be tested for transparency at 230 mμ prior to use for diluting samples.

B. METHOD OF BRICE AND SWAIN FOR VEGETABLE OILS (7,8)

This modification of the spectrophotometric method was proposed after very careful study of many conditions that affect sensitivity and reproducibility of the analysis.   Correction for pre-existing conjugated substances was introduced.   Correction for ester or acid absorption at 232 mμ was made.   An attempt was made to avoid the strong and variable absorption of the blank by substituting glycerol for ethylene glycol in the reagent.   This substitution greatly improved sensitivity and accuracy.   The effect of heating conjugated constituents with the isomerizing reagent was studied in order that appropriate correction be made for their effect upon the analysis.

The original standardization of this method was made with linoleic, linolenic, and arachidonic acids, prepared by debromination of polybromides (6), and containing isomers which do not isomerize at the same rate.   More recently, restandardization of the method has been made with these acids prepared by physical methods and which therefore do not contain unnatural isomers (7).   The authors also concluded from more recent data that 45 min. reaction time was better than the original 30 min. reaction time.   They have also incorporated about 0.1% pure stearic acid in the reagent to hasten saponification.

(1) Special Apparatus and Reagents.

(a) *Glycerol,* U.S.P. XII.

(b) *Stearic acid,* free of unsaturated acids.

(c) *Iso-octane* (2,2,4-trimethyl pentane) or other suitable hydrocarbon as solvent for spectral measurements.

(d) *Glass cups* of 1 ml. volume.   These may be cut from glass vials, preferably pyrex.

(2) Procedure.   A sample of oil, fat, ester, acid, or soap is weighed (approx. 200 mg.) and dissolved in 75 ml. of 95% ethanol, transferred quantitatively to a 100 ml. volumetric flask, and made up to volume. Optical densities are then measured with a Beckman spectrophotometer at 2 mμ intervals from 324 to 306 mμ, 282 to 260 mμ, and 240 to 226 mμ, using cells or dilutions such that densities range between 0.2

and 0.8. Extinction coefficients are calculated for use in computing the content of conjugated fatty acids.

Two other 100 mg. samples are weighed accurately into pyrex glass cups of 1 ml. capacity. The isomerizing reagent is prepared by dissolving 17.5 g. KOH (A.C.S.) and 0.1 g. pure stearic acid in 100 ml. glycerol (U.S.P. XII) and heating to 200° to dissolve the alkali and drive off the water. The resulting reagent should contain 10.9 to 11.0% KOH by weight, determined by titration. Into each of three 150 x 25 mm. pyrex test tubes 11.0 g. of reagent is weighed, and these are then hung to a depth of 11.5 cm. in a bath held at 180 ± 0.5°C. When the contents of the tubes reach 180°, the glass cups containing the samples are dropped into two of the tubes, the tubes are removed from the bath and swirled vigorously for 1 minute, and returned to the bath and covered. After 1 more minute, the tubes are removed and inspected. If they are not clear, they are swirled again. An empty cup is dropped into the third tube which serves as a blank. Exactly 45 minutes after a cup is dropped into a tube, the tube is removed from the bath and cooled under tap water. Absolute ethanol, 20 ml., is added and the mixture is stirred, using gentle heat to aid solution. The contents of the tube are then transferred quantitatively to a 100 ml. volumetric flask, and made up to volume with absolute ethanol. If absolute ethanol is used, settling does not occur, and filtering is unnecessary. Optical density measurements are made upon the solution, or appropriate dilutions of it, at the same wave lengths as given above. The blank for these measurements is the heated reagent which has been diluted the same as the sample. The extinction coefficients are calculated.

(3) Calculations. The reference constants obtained with pure

TABLE II

Reference Constants (k) for Natural Acids to Be Used in the Method Requiring 11% KOH in Glycerol (7)

Acid	Wave length, mμ	k	
		30 min.	45 min.
Linoleic	233	91.1	93.9
Linolenic	233	60.2	58.6
	268	49.3	48.6
Arachidonic	233	56.8	55.0
	268	53.4	46.8
	315	19.1	20.3

natural acids are given in Table II. Values are given both for the original 30 minute time and for the recommended 45 minute time. The following calculations are somewhat simpler than those originally prepared (6) but retain useful background corrections where small proportions of polyunsaturated acids are present, delete measurement of trace conjugated constituents and delete determination of arachidonic acid in vegetable oils. In this calculation, k'_{233}, k'_{268}, and k'_{315} are observed specific extinction coefficients after isomerization and k_{233} the coefficient before isomerization. k'_2, k'_3, k'_4, and k_2 are the foregoing coefficients after correction for extraneous absorption. The subscripts refer to the number of double bonds involved. x, y, z, and C_2 are the percentages of linoleic, linolenic, arachidonic and conjugated dienoic acids in the sample.

To calculate linoleic acid if it occurs in small proportions: If k'_{233} is less than 20, preformed conjugated dienoic acid may not be negligible. C_2 should be calculated as follows:

$$C_2 = 100k_2/119 = 0.84k_2$$

In this expression $k_2 = k_{233} - k_0$ where k_0 is 0.07 for fats and esters and 0.03 for soaps or acids. Then

$$k'_2 = k'_{233} - k_2 - 0.03 \text{ in the latter instance}$$

To calculate linoleic acid if it occurs in large proportions: If k'_{233} is greater than 20, C_2 need not be determined and k'_{233} need not be corrected. This is not true in such special cases where large amounts of conjugated diene are known to exist, i.e., dehydrated castor oil, tall oil, crude cottonseed oil, etc.

To calculate linolenic acid occurring in small proportions: If k'_{268} is less than 1, the following equation is used:

$$k'_3 = 4.08 \left(k'_{268} - \frac{k'_{262} + k'_{274}}{2} \right)$$

To calculate linolenic acid occurring in large proportions: If k'_{268} is more than 1, background absorption may be ignored and $k'_3 = k'_{268}$. Oils known to contain conjugated trienoic acids will nevertheless require the corrections mentioned in the previous paragraph. Such oils as tung, oiticica, and cucurbit fall in this class.

To calculate arachidonic acid present in small proportions: If k'_{315} is less than 1, correction for extraneous background must be made by the following equation:

$$k_4' = 2.06 \left(k_{315}' - \frac{k_{308} + k_{322}}{2} \right)$$

This calculation is not applicable to vegetable oils because arachidonic acid is assumed to be absent.

To calculate arachidonic acid present in large proportions: If k_{315}' is greater than 1, background absorption may be ignored and $k_4' = k_{315}'$.

Using the above k' values, the per cent of linoleic, linolenic, and arachidonic acids may be calculated using the following equations which apply only to data gained in 11% KOH-glycerol, heated for 45 minutes:

$$\% \text{ linoleic acid } = x = 1.065k_2' - 1.284k_3' + 0.08k_4'$$
$$\% \text{ linolenic acid } = y = 2.058k_3' - 4.74k_4'$$
$$\% \text{ arachidonic acid } = z = 4.93k_4'$$

Equations for 30 minute heating may be found in the original reference (7).

(4) Comment. This method has proved very satisfactory for the determination of linoleic and linolenic acids in vegetable oils. It has also been used for determination of "arachidonic acid" in animal fats. The method is very reproducible, but in the author's opinion it should no longer be applied to the analysis of animal fats because it makes no provision for measurement of, or correction for pentaenoic and hexaenoic acids which are known to be present in animal fats. For the macroanalysis of animal fats the method of Herb and Riemenschneider is more suitable.

C. METHOD OF AMERICAN OIL CHEMISTS' SOCIETY FOR VEGETABLE OILS (29)

This method is essentially the same as that of Mitchell, Kraybill, and Zscheile (24). It has been modified and improved and is now the official method of the American Oil Chemists' Society for analysis of polyunsaturated acids. Its very detailed description is found in the Official and Tentative Methods of that Society (29). It is the method of choice for analysis of vegetable oils.

(1) Apparatus and Reagents.

(a) *Pyrex test tubes* 25 x 250 mm.

(b) *Pyrex glass cups,* 1 ml. volume.

(c) *Nitrogen inlet caps for test tubes.*

(2) Reagents. Isomerization reagent is prepared by dissolving

60 g. of KOH (ACS grade) in 750 ml. ethylene glycol which has been previously heated to 190°C. to drive off water.   The KOH is added cautiously when the glycol is 150°C., and the solution is protected with nitrogen.   The reagent is reheated to 190°C. for 10 minutes. The glycol solution is titrated with 1 N HCl and should be 1.3 N (6.5 to 6.6% KOH).   Appropriate adjustment should be made if the strength is not between these limits.   The reagent should be stored under nitrogen in a refrigerator.

Methanol for dilution of isomerized samples should be distilled over zinc and KOH to insure maximum transparency in the ultraviolet range.

(3) Procedure for Conjugated Constituents.   About 200 mg. of sample is weighed accurately into a 1 ml. pyrex cup and is dissolved in iso-octane, hexane, or cyclohexane and made up to 100 ml.   Optical density is measured on this, or dilutions of it, at 322, 315, 308, 274, 268, 262, and 233 mμ, using a cell of solvent as blank.

(4) Procedure for Non-conjugated Polyunsaturated Acids.   100 mg. of sample is weighed into a 1 ml. pyrex glass cup.   11.0 ± 0.1 g. of the KOH glycol reagent is weighed into a 25 x 250 mm. test tube. Two blanks are prepared at the same time for each group of samples. The test tubes containing KOH glycol are immersed to a depth of 11.5 cm. in the bath held at 180.0° ± 0.5°C.   The test tubes are covered with the distributing heads which are connected to the nitrogen manifold.   Nitrogen is passed over the contents of the test tubes at a total flow rate of 50–100 ml./min.   After 20 minutes of preheating, the glass cups containing samples are dropped into the test tubes. A clean glass cup is dropped into each blank.   Keeping the distributing head in place, each test tube is removed from the bath and swirled vigorously for a few seconds and returned.   At the end of 1 minute the tubes are removed and inspected.   If they are not clear, they should be swirled again two or three times and returned.   At intervals of 1 minute the swirling is repeated until the saponification is complete and the solution is clear.   Individual tubes should be started at staggered times for convenience.   Exactly 25 minutes after the sample is dropped into the tube, that tube should be removed from the bath, wiped clean, and placed in a container of cold water. When the tube is cool, remove the distributor head and wash it with methanol, collecting the solvent in the test tube.   Using a 12 inch stirring rod, the contents of the tube are mixed and transferred quantitatively to a 100 ml. glass-stoppered volumetric flask.   Optical densities are measured on this solution, or dilutions of it, at 322, 315, 308, 274, 268, 262, and 233 mμ, with the blank solution in the reference cell, choosing dilutions such that density values lie between 0.2 and 0.8.

(5) Calculation of Conjugated Constituents (background absorption measured on fresh sample in hydrocarbon solvent). Calculate the specific extinction coefficient k, for each wave length. $k = D/Cl$ where D = observed optical density, c is concentration in grams per liter in the dilution used for measurement of D, and l is the length of cell in cm. In the following equations the subscripts 2, 3, and 4 refer to diene, triene, and tetraene. The extinction coefficient at 233 mμ is corrected for absorption by acid and ester groups:

$$k_2 = k_{233} - k_0$$

$k_0 = 0.07$ for esters, 0.03 for soaps and fatty acids.

The extinction coefficient at 268 mμ is corrected for background absorption:

$$k_3 = 2.8 \left(k_{268} - \frac{k_{262} + k_{274}}{2} \right)$$

The extinction coefficient at 315 mμ is corrected for background absorption:

$$k_4 = 2.5 \left(k_{315} - \frac{k_{308} + k_{322}}{2} \right)$$

If any of these calculated values is zero or negative, no characteristic polyene absorption maxima are present and the corresponding constituent is reported as absent.

$$C_2 = \%\text{ conjugated linoleic acid} = 0.84k_2$$
$$C_3 = \%\text{ conjugated trienoic acid} = 0.47k_3$$
$$C_4 = \%\text{ conjugated tetraenoic acid} = 0.45k_4$$

(6) Calculation of Non-conjugated Polyunsaturated Acids. The extinction coefficient k' is calculated for each wave length from the data gathered on the isomerized sample. The extinction coefficient at 233 mμ is corrected for conjugated diene acids originally present.

$$k'_2 = k'_{233} - k_2 - 0.03$$

The extinction coefficient at 268 mμ is corrected for background absorption and for undestroyed conjugated triene:

$$k_3' = 4.03 \left(k_{268}' - \frac{k_{262}' + k_{274}'}{2} \right) - k_3$$

When k_{268}' is greater than 1, no correction for background is made and

$$k_3' = k_{268}' - k_3$$

The extinction coefficient at 315 mμ is corrected for background and undestroyed conjugated tetraene:

$$k_4' = 2.06 \left(k_{315}' - \frac{k_{308}' + k_{322}'}{2} \right) - k_4$$

when k_{315}' is greater than 1, correction for background is unnecessary and

$$k_4' = k_{315}' - k_4$$

Using these corrected values the non-conjugated fatty acids may be calculated:

$$x = \% \text{ linoleic acid} = 1.086k_2' - 1.324k_3' + 0.40k_4'$$
$$y = \% \text{ linolenic acid} = 1.980k_3' - 4.92k_4'$$
$$z = \% \text{ arachidonic acid} = 4.69k_4'$$

Oleic acid content may be calculated if the iodine value (I.V.) of the sample is measured:

$\%$ oleic acid $=$

$$\frac{\text{I.V.} - 1.811(C_2 + x) + 2.737(C_3 + y) + 3.337(C_4 + z)}{0.899}$$

Saturated acids may also be calculated by difference. The total fatty acid content of most oils is about 95.6%.

(7) Comment. This highly developed and elaborate method is designed for use on vegetable oils. The formulas are based upon constants determined upon pure natural acids. Provision is made for calculation of arachidonic acid content of fats. The reader should be reminded that thus far arachidonic acid or non-conjugated tetraenoic acids have been found only in animal fats, and that these fats usually contain pentaenoic and hexaenoic acids. The method makes no provision for their analysis, and therefore "arachidonic acid" determined by this method includes the pentaenoic and hexaenoic acids, and the linoleic and linolenic acid values will also be in error. The analyst will be well advised to use this method only for vegetable oils, and to apply a different method to animal fats. This method is recommended for analysis of vegetable oils.

D. MICROMETHOD FOR POLYUNSATURATED ACIDS—HERB AND RIEMENSCHNEIDER (12)

This is the method of choice for analysis of weighable samples of animal fats. Reference standard extinction coefficients have been determined for a complete series of polyunsaturated acids, thus making this method useful for determination of families of fatty acids containing from 2 to 6 double bonds. The conditions of isomerization have been chosen to increase the yield of characteristic conjugated isomers of the more common polyunsaturated fatty acids. The method has been adopted for animal fats by the American Oil Chemists' Society.

(1) Equipment. The reaction tubes have been modified. Standard 25 x 250 mm. test tubes are cut off 14 cm. from the bottom, and 14 cm. length of 16 mm. test tube is sealed on. Weighing cups are made from pyrex glass tubing 8 mm. in diameter and 6 mm. high.

(2) Reagent. Ethylene glycol is heated to 190° for 10 minutes and allowed to cool to 150°C. The calculated amount of potassium hydroxide is added to give a solution of 21.0% KOH. This is approximately 28 g. of 85% KOH per 100 g. of glycol. The solution is reheated to 190° for 10 minutes and cooled to room temperature. All these manipulations are made under a protective blanket of nitrogen. The strength of the solution is determined titrimetrically, and adjusted, if necessary, to 21.0 ± 0.1% KOH. The reagent is stored under nitrogen at or below 5°C.

(3) Procedure. The reaction tube containing 5.0 g. of 21% KOH glycol reagent is blanketed with oxygen-free nitrogen and heated in the bath at 180° for 15 minutes. An accurately weighed sample, about 1 to 10 mg., in a weighing cup is added to the reaction tube. The tube is removed from the bath and shaken vigorously for 5 seconds and is then replaced. Shaking is repeated twice at 30 second intervals. A reaction tube containing reagent but no sample is treated in the same way for use as a blank. Exactly 15 minutes after the cup is dropped into the reagent, the tube is removed from the bath and cooled rapidly in water. The isomerized sample is diluted with absolute methanol to a volume of 25 ml. Appropriate dilutions are made for determination of optical densities at the prescribed wave lengths, 375, 346, 315, 268, and 233 mμ.

If a microbalance is not available, and samples of 10–30 mg. are at hand, these can be weighed with an error of about 1% on a good analytical balance and dissolved in ten times its weight of pure lauryl alcohol.   Weighed aliquots can then be used as replicates.

Background absorption can be measured in hexane or ethanol prior to isomerization, and the extinction coefficients calculated.   The extinction coefficient of the nonisomerized sample is subtracted from that after isomerization to yield the corrected k which is used in the final calculations.

(4) Calculations.   The reference standard values have been determined on natural isomers of representative fatty acids.   Herb and Riemenschneider (12) determined the constants for linoleic, linolenic, arachidonic, eicosapentaenoic, and docosapentaenoic acids. Hammond and Lundberg (11) isolated methyl docosahexaenoate from hog brain and determined the spectral constants upon it by this method.   Holman and Hayes determined the constants upon a similar sample which they found to be uniform by paper chromatographic analysis.   The constants were very close to, but higher than those of Hammond and Lundberg.   They also determined the constants of eicosapentaenoic acid supplied to them by Prof. Klenk of Cologne and found constants lower than those of Herb and Riemenschneider, although the sample was found uniform by the paper chromatography

TABLE III

Extinction Coefficients Determined upon Natural Polyunsaturated Acids Using the Method of Herb and Riemenschneider

Acid	k_{374}	k_{346}	k_{315}	k_{268}	k_{233}
Linoleic[a]	—	—	—	—	91.6
Linolenic[a]	—	—	—	90.5	47.5
Arachidonic[a]	—	—	60.6	48.2	39.7
Eicosapentaenoic[a]	—	87.5	82.4	41.2	39.4
Docosapentaenoic[a]	—	50.4	56.9	46.0	43.5
50% C_{20}–50% C_{22} pentaene[a]	—	69.0	69.7	43.6	41.5
Docosahexaenoic[b]	28.1	26.2	27.8	49.4	40.0
Eicosapentaenoic[c]	4.37	74.1	71.1	32.9	37.0
Docosahexaenoic[c]	28.6	29.4	32.8	54.0	43.9

[a] Data of Herb and Riemenschneider.
[b] Data of Hammond and Lundberg.
[c] Data of Holman and Hayes.

of Mangold, Lamp, and Schlenk (23).   These constants are collected in Table III.

Hammond and Lundberg pointed out that an error occurs in the calculation of hexaene and pentaene acids because correction is not made for the absorption of conjugated pentaene at 374 mμ.   Herb and Riemenschneider did not publish a constant for the pentaene absorption at this wave length.   Nevertheless, Hammond and Lundberg proposed the following equations based upon constants of their hexaene acid and the published constants of Herb and Riemenschneider:

If pentaene is C_{22},

% docosahexaenoic acid $= 3.41k_{374}$
% docosapentaenoic acid $= 1.98k_{346} - 1.84k_{374}$
% arachidonic acid $= 1.65k_{315} - 1.86k_{346} + 0.10k_{374}$
% linolenic acid $= 1.10k_{268} - 0.88k_{315} - 0.02k_{346} - 0.88k_{374}$
% linoleic acid $= 1.09k_{233} - 0.57k_{268} - 0.26k_{315} - 0.12k_{346} - 0.18k_{374}$

If pentaene is C_{20},

% docosahexaenoic acid $= 3.41k_{374}$
% eicosapentaenoic acid $= 1.14k_{346} - 1.06k_{374}$
% arachidonic acid $= 1.65k_{315} - 1.55k_{346} - 0.19k_{374}$
% linolenic acid $= 1.10k_{268} - 0.88k_{315} + 0.31k_{346} - 1.35k_{374}$
% linoleic acid $= 1.09k_{233} - 0.57k_{268} - 0.26k_{315} + 0.02k_{346} - 0.27k_{374}$

The writer prepared a set of equations based upon the constants of Herb and Riemenschneider for linoleic, linolenic, and arachidonic acids, and upon constants determined in his own laboratory for eicosapentaenoic acid and docosahexaenoic acid which were demonstrated to be uniform by paper chromatography (*vide infra*).   The calculations also incorporate correction for the pentaene absorption at 375 mμ.   All measurements were made with the hydrogen arc lamp as light source, using slit widths as follows: 0.2 mm at 375 and 346 mμ, 0.3 mm. at 315 mμ, 0.4 mm. at 268 mμ, and 0.8 mm. at 233 mμ.

% docosahexaenoic acid $= 3.722k_{374} - 0.219k_{346}$
% eicosapentaenoic acid $= 1.437\ k_{346} - 1.477k_{374}$
% arachidonic acid $= 1.65k_{315} - 1.567k_{346} - 0.2816k_{374}$
% linolenic acid $= 1.105k_{268} - 0.8787k_{315} + 0.4429k_{346} - 1.534k_{374}$
% linoleic acid $= 1.092\ k_{233} - 0.5729k_{268} - 0.2595k_{315} - 0.0261k_{346} -$
$$0.2696k_{374}$$

(5) Comment. Any analysis for all the polyunsaturated acid types will involve compromises. One must compromise on isomerization time because the optimum conditions for one polyene acid will be different from that of another acid. One cannot know beforehand in most cases whether he deals with a mixture in which the pentaene acid is C_{20} or C_{22}. The results of such spectrophotometric analyses must be interpreted with understanding. The data are not to be taken as absolute, but the data will be most useful in comparative studies in which one is not so much interested in the quantity of a component as in how much that component changed. The analyst must also be aware that in reporting his data, the value calculated *as* linoleic acid is not necessarily linoleic acid, but represents all dienoic acids. This is true also for values reported as linolenic acid, arachidonic acid, and eicosapentaenoic acid. The complex arrays of dienes, trienes, tetraenes, and pentaenes occurring in animal preparations are conveniently boiled down by the calculation to single values and are reported as the single substances which happened to be used to standardize the method.

Handling of the instrument may be important in this analysis. Hammond and Lundberg point out how slit width can affect extinction coefficients. They specified a slit width of 0.15 mm. for the measurements at 374 mμ. They also found variations in extinction coefficient when the sample size was varied, apparently related to the rapidity with which the sample is dissolved in the reagent. Fortunately, these effects can be minimized or held constant by standardized technique.

E. MACROMETHOD FOR POLYUNSATURATED ACIDS—HERB AND
RIEMENSCHNEIDER (13)

This method is essentially the same as the foregoing micromethod except for sample size. The macromodification employs a sample of 70–100 mg. in a 1 ml. glass cup and a 1 x 10 in. pyrex test tube as reaction vessel. The constants and calculations are the same as those given under D.

F. MICROMETHOD FOR BLOOD SERUM—WIESE AND HANSEN (34)

(1) Equipment.
(a) *Capillary-tipped pipette* with 2 ml. rubber bulb for transferring petroleum ether extracts.

(b) *Centrifuge tubes*, 50 ml. round bottom lipless.

(c) *Erlenmeyer flasks*, 125 ml.

(2) Reagents.

(a) *Aldehyde-free ethanol*, 95%, prepared by distilling from KOH.

(b) *Peroxide-free ethyl ether.*

(c) *KOH solution*, 50 g./100 ml. solution.

(d) *5% HCl.*   11 ml. conc. HCl per 100 ml.

(e) *Petroleum ether*, b.p. 20–40°.   30 ml. should not leave a weighable residue.

(f) *11% KOH in ethylene glycol.*   Heat 280 g. ethylene glycol with 35 g. KOH (85%) in a 1-liter stainless steel beaker.   Continue stirring until water is driven off and temperature is 180°.   Standardize by titrating 1–2 g. with 0.5 N HCl.   Cooling and reheating are avoided during standardization.   KOH content should be 11.0 ± 0.1%. Store under nitrogen in a refrigerator.

(3) Preparation of Sample.   3 ml. of serum is extracted with 15 ml. of boiling 3 : 1 alcohol-ether and the precipitated protein is filtered off. The protein residue is extracted twice more with boiling solvent in a 125 ml. flask.   To the combined filtrates 0.2 ml. of 0.1% hydroquinone (antioxidant) in ethanol and 0.1 ml. 50% aqueous KOH are added and saponified.   The solution is evaporated nearly to dryness. 5 ml. of distilled water is added to the residue to dissolve the soaps, and the fatty acids are liberated by HCl.   The fatty acids are extracted four times with 10 ml. and successive 4 ml. portions of petroleum ether in a 125 ml. Erlenmeyer flask, and transferred by a pipette to a centrifuge tube.   Hydroquinone is again added to the extract to prevent autoxidation and the extract is evaporated to about 3 ml. under an electric fan.   The fatty acids are dissolved with 3 ml. of 0.1 N fresh alcoholic KOH and 3 ml. water.   After standing one hour the tube is centrifuged and the petroleum ether layer containing the unsaponifiables is discarded.   This is repeated twice.   The soap solution is evaporated to dryness in $2^1/_2$ hours and the free acids are liberated by HCl.   The free fatty acids are extracted with 4 portions of petroleum ether, the combined extract is transferred to a tared flask and hydroquinone solution is added again.   Solvent is removed and the fatty acids are weighed using a semi-micro balance.   Correction is made for the weight of hydroquinone added the last time.   The fatty acids are transferred in petroleum ether to a 15 ml. test tube and the solvent is removed prior to addition of isomerization reagent.

(4) Isomerization.   A stock portion of 11.0 ± 0.1% KOH in ethyl-

TABLE IV

Spectral Constants for Polyunsaturated Acids Using the Method of Wiese and Hansen (34)

	Linoleic	Linolenic	Arachidonic	Eicosa-pentaenoic	Docosa-hexaenoic
3750 A.	—	—	—	1.47	15.3
3475	—	—	—	47.8	24.9
3000	—	—	43.9	62.4	28.9
2700	—	51.8[a]	48.1	50.2	43.8
2350	77.9[a]	52.4[a]	62.1	62.9	53.7

[a] Data of Wiese and Hansen. Remainder of constants determined by Holman and Hayes (17).

ene glycol is preheated for 12 minutes at 180° in the constant temperature oil bath. Two milliliters of the hot reagent are added from a 5 ml. Mohr pipette to each sample tube, the tubes are covered with marbles. The tubes are shaken 10 seconds and immediately replaced in the bath. One blank tube is prepared for each batch of determinations. The tubes are heated at 180° for 25 minutes and are then chilled in ice water. The soap solutions are diluted with absolute methanol and transferred to 25 ml. volumetric flasks. Density measurements are made at 375, 347.5, 300, 270, and 235 mu with an ultraviolet spectrophotometer in a cell of 1 cm. light path. Tenfold dilution may be necessary for measurement at the shorter wave lengths. The extinction coefficients, $k = D/g/\mathrm{L}$, are calculated.

(5) Calculations. Wiese and Hansen determined analytical constants for only linoleic, linolenic, and arachidonic acids. Thus calculations made by their method have the inherent error that correction for pentaenoic and hexaenoic acids cannot be made. Recently Holman and Hayes have determined spectral constants for the more highly unsaturated acids using this method, which now can be extended to measurement of all the polyene types. In Table IV the best available constants are listed. The calculation of the percentage of each type of polyene acid in the fatty acid mixture may be made using the following equations:

$\%$ docosahexaenoic acid $= 6.88k_{3750} - 0.2116k_{3475}$

$\%$ eicosapentaenoic acid $= 2.2203k_{3475} - 3.584k_{3750}$

$\%$ arachidonic acid $= 2.2279k_{3000} - 2.991k_{3475} + 0.5647k_{3750}$

$\%$ linolenic acid $= 1.930k_{2700} - 2.115k_{3000} + 0.8220k_{3475} - 2.869k_{3750}$

$\%$ linoleic acid $= 1.284k_{2350} - 1.297k_{2700} - 0.3932k_{3000} + 0.1991k_{3475} - 0.3694k_{3750}$

Data from this method of analysis can possibly be gathered without weighing the fatty acids, and results could be expressed as mg./100 ml. serum. If this is desired, see the method of Holman and Hayes (Section III.4.G) for the modification to be made in the calculations.

(6) Comments. The method of Wiese and Hansen employs the 11% KOH reagent and consequently lower yields of conjugated polyenes are obtained than with the methods using 21% KOH reagent. Consequently the method is less sensitive for the detection of higher polyenes than it might have been if it employed the 21% KOH reagent. The method of extraction involves many manipulations and is time-consuming. The influence of the hydroquinone is undetermined. Its major disadvantage is that it requires the weighing of very small samples and therefore requires the use of a semi-micro balance. In Wiese's hands, this method has given good reproducibility and has yielded some very valuable data.

G. SIMPLIFIED MICROMETHOD FOR BLOOD AND TISSUE—HOLMAN AND HAYES (17)

This micromethod was originally designed to determine poly-unsaturated acids in chromatographic fractions in which about 1 mg. of polyunsaturated acid was present per milliliter of ethanol. The good results suggested adaptation to blood and tissue analysis in which the total lipid content need not be determined, but in which the content of unsaturated acids per milliliter per gram is sought.

(1) Equipment.

(a) *A bath held at 180° ± 0.5°C.* must be provided. This may be a container of hot liquid or it may be a heated block such as used by Lips and Tessier (22). We found oil baths undesirable because the usual mineral oil or bath wax becomes progressively thicker with use and the stirring and heat transfer must become less effective.

(b) *Dow Corning silicone No. 710* has been used in baths in our laboratory with good results. The writer, however, still prefers the electrically heated block to maintain constant temperature (see Fig. 6). The holes for the test tubes contain DC 710 silicone to improve heat transfer.

(c) *Pear-shaped flasks*, 200 ml. in volume, are used in reducing volume of extracts. The reaction vessels used in this analysis are 5 ml. pyrex volumetric flasks sealed to the bottoms of 16 x 150 mm. pyrex test tubes. A supply of oxygen-free nitrogen is required.

(2) Reagents.

(a) *A solution of 21% KOH in ethylene glycol* is prepared as described in section III.4.D (2). The reagent is stored under nitrogen at −15°C. in glass-stoppered bottles. If stored in this manner it remains good for many months. The reagent (1.1 g.) is weighed into the reaction tubes on a pharmaceutical balance from a syringe fixed

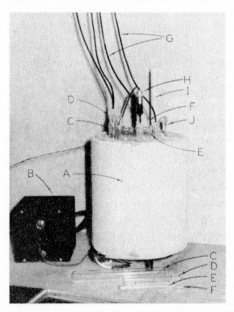

Fig. 6. Constant temperature bath for isomerization. Aluminum block, type of Lips and Tessier. A. Aluminum block covered with asbestos. B. Electronic relay control. C. Tubes for macroisomerizations. D. Nitrogen distributor caps. E. Tubes for microisomerization. F. Nitrogen distributor caps for E. G. Nitrogen lines. H. Mercury to mercury thermoregulator. I. Thermometer. J. Overshoot alarm thermoregulator.

directly above the tube which stands supported in a cork ring on the balance. Reaction tubes with weighed reagent may be filled with nitrogen, stoppered, and stored at −15° for several days prior to use.

(b) *Absolute methanol*. Test for transparency at 230 mμ.

(c) *Petroleum ether*. Test for transparency at 230 mμ.

(d) *Ethanol-ether*, 3:1. Must be made fresh each day from peroxide-free ether and absolute ethanol.

(e) *Acidic ethanol-ether.*   Add 5 ml. concentrated HCl to 95 ml. fresh ethanol-ether.

(f) *Anhydrous sodium sulfate.*

(3) Preparation of Extract.   Lipids may be extracted from serum, blood, or tissue by any standard means which does not involve acetone or a halogenated solvent.   Traces of these in the sample may later confuse the ultraviolet spectral measurements.   The lipid content of the extract need not be determined unless the polyunsaturated acid content is to be expressed in terms of per cent of lipid.

The procedure used in the writer's laboratory is as follows: Five to 10 ml. of serum or plasma is added with swirling to 20 volumes of ethanol-ether in an Erlenmeyer.   If tissue is to be extracted, it is macerated in acidic ethanol-ether, 30 ml./g.   The flasks are stoppered, left overnight, and the contents are filtered. The precipitates are extracted twice with 30 ml. portions ethanol-ether and given a final wash with petroleum ether.   The pooled extracts are transferred to separatory funnels, and 50 ml. of 0.5% NaCl solution is added.   The mixture is extracted with 100 ml. petroleum ether and twice with 50 ml. portions of petroleum ether.   A few drops of alcohol may be used to break emulsions.   The petroleum ether extracts are washed three times with 250 ml. distilled water or until neutral to litmus.   NaCl may be used to break emulsions.   The extract is dried with anhydrous sodium sulfate and filtered.   Reduce the volume of extract under vacuum in a pear-shaped flask to 1 to 2 ml., using an inverted capillary tube as anti-bumping device.   Transfer the lipid under nitrogen to a 10 ml. volumetric flask using several rinses of petroleum ether, and make to volume.   The optical density of this solution is measured at 375, 346, 315, 268, and 233 mμ against a solvent blank.

It may be advisable to conduct the analysis upon free fatty acids rather than upon total lipids in some cases.   If this is desired, saponification and removal of unsaponifiable matter can be performed as described under the method of Wiese and Hansen (see above).

(4) Isomerization Procedure.   One milliliter of ethanol solution of the sample is added to the reaction tube to which had previously been added 1.1 g. of reagent and the flow of nitrogen is begun in the tube. If the sample is not prepared in ethanol solution, 1 ml. of the solution is transferred to the reaction tube and the solvent is evaporated by a stream of nitrogen and 1 ml. of ethanol is added.   The ethanol and

KOH-glycol reagent are then thoroughly mixed and placed in the 180° bath. The boiling of the ethanol insures thorough mixing and complete solution of the sample. Exactly 20 minutes later the tube is removed from the bath and placed directly in ice water. A tube with reagent and ethanol but no sample is prepared as a blank and is treated similarly. The isomerized samples and blank are diluted bit by bit with methanol and mixed by vigorous shaking at each step. The volume is then made up to 5 ml. Optical density measurements are made upon this solution or appropriate dilutions at 375, 346, 315, 268, and 233 mμ, using appropriately diluted blank as reference and the slit widths listed in Table V. The hydrogen arc lamp is used for all measurements.

(5) **Calculations.** The specific extinction coefficients, k_b, are calculated for the background (non-isomerized) sample if the weight of lipid in the sample is known. The specific extinction coefficients, k_i, are calculated for the isomerized sample. The latter is corrected for background absorption to give the absorption due to the isomerized constituents.

$$k = k_i - k_b$$

If the weight of lipid in the extract is not known, the relative densities are calculated. These are the densities derived from 1 g. of tissue or 1 ml. of serum, etc. The relative densities are calculated by multiplying the observed densities by the dilution factor. The dilution factor is equal to the volume of final solution which represents or was derived from 1 ml. serum or 1 g. tissue. Thus, if 2.5 ml. serum was extracted and made up to 10 ml. and 1 ml. of the extract is isomerized, then 0.25 ml. "serum" was isomerized and made up to 5 ml. in the reaction vessel. If this was diluted ten times before an optical density of 0.300 was measured upon it, the final solution represents a 200 x dilution of serum. The relative density is then

$$D = (0.300)(200) = 60$$

Corrected k values may be substituted directly into the equations below to calculate the per cent of each of the polyunsaturated acid types present in a lipid. Relative optical density values, corrected for background, may also be substituted for the respective k values in the equations. When this is done the calculations yield results expressed in terms of mg./100 ml., or mg./100 g. as the case may be.

The spectral constants for this method were determined on natural linoleic, arachidonic, eicosapentaenoic, and docosahexaenoic acids. The linolenic acid was prepared by bromination-debromination. Constants are given in Table V. The equations derived from

TABLE V

Spectral Constants for Polyunsaturated Acids Using Simplified Micromethod with Ethanol.

Acid	k for free acid				
	375 mμ	346 mμ	315 mμ	268 mμ	233 mμ
Linoleic	—	—	—	—	92.0
Linolenic	—	—	—	79.0	44.7
Eicosatrienoic[a,b]	—	—	—	87.0	56.7
Arachidonic[a,b]	—	—	58.7	44.1	33.2
Eicosapentaenoic[a,b]	2.85	67.1	62.8	27.5	30.8
Docosahexaenoic[b]	25.0	26.1	31.2	48.6	43.3
Slit width, mm.	0.2	0.2	0.3	0.5	1.0

[a] Preparations supplied by Prof. E. Klenk of Cologne.
[b] Homogeneous by paper chromatography (23).

the constants of linoleic, linolenic, arachidonic, eicosapentaenoic, and docosahexaenoic acids are the following:

% docosahexaenoic acid $= 4.186k_{375} - 0.1778k_{.46}$
% eicosapentaenoic acid $= 1.559k_{346} - 1.628k_{375}$
% arachidonic acid $= 1.456k_{315} - 1.344k_{346} - 0.4128k_{375}$
% linolenic acid $= 1.266k_{268} - 0.8028k_{315} + 0.3172k_{346} - 1.778k_{375}$
% linoleic acid $= 1.087k_{233} - 0.615k_{268} - 0.1354k_{315} - 0.1072k_{346} - 0.412k_{375}$

The following equations are used for calculation of the content of polyunsaturated acids per 100 ml. of blood, serum, etc.

mg. docosahexaenoic acid/100 ml. serum $= 4.186D_{375} - 0.1778D_{346}$

mg. eicosapentaenoic acid/100 ml. serum $= 1.559D_{346} - 1.628D_{375}$

mg. arachidonic acid/100 ml. serum $= 1.456D_{315} - 1.344D_{346} - 0.4128D_{375}$

mg. linolenic acid/100 ml. serum $= 1.266D_{268} - 0.8028D_{315} + 0.3172D_{346} - 1.778D_{375}$

mg. linoleic acid/100 ml. serum $= 1.087D_{233} - 0.615D_{268} - 0.1354D_{315} - 0.1072D_{346} - 0.412D_{375}$

IV. PAPER CHROMATOGRAPHY

Paper chromatography is currently being applied to numerous analytical problems, and in some cases the success is striking. Asselineau has published a review on applications of paper chromatography in the lipid field (3).

Thus far, only a few investigators have made separations of polyunsaturated acids. Kaufmann and Nitsch (21) have succeeded in separating oleic and linoleic acids by reverse phase paper chromatography. They impregnated the paper with a hydrocarbon and used aqueous acetic acid as developing solvent. The spots of fatty acids were located by the fluorescent dye, Rhodamine B. An alternative method of locating the spots was to dip the papers in a copper acetate solution, wash out the excess copper salt, and stain with potassium ferrocyanide, to yield brown copper ferrocyanide. Osmium tetroxide was used with unsaturated substances.

A different method of separating polyunsaturated acids on paper has been published by Inouye, Noda, and Hiroyama (18). They were able to separate the methyl esters of oleic, linoleic, and linolenic acids as mercury acetate complexes. These mercurated compounds were prepared by warming the fatty esters to 80°C. for 30 minutes with a 20% excess of mercuric acetate in absolute methanol. The addition compounds are isolated, dissolved in ether, and spotted on the paper which had been pretreated with tetralin (or petroleum hydrocarbon). The papers were developed in methanol-acetic acid-tetralin (or in methanol-acetic acid-petroleum hydrocarbon). The papers were then dried and the spots were made visible by spraying with 0.2% ethanol solution of diphenyl carbazone which reacts with the mercury in the complexes to yield a purple color.

This method works well and warrants further study. The preparation of the mercury addition compounds requires more sample than is ordinarily available. In other words, although the paper separation is "micro," the initial preparation is not.

1. Recommended Method for Paper Chromatography—Mangold, Lamp, and Schlenk (23)

A. PRINCIPLE

Ascending reversed phase paper chromatography.

B. EQUIPMENT

(1) *Pyrex cylindrical jars* 15 x 45 cm. One is used for humidification, one for iodine vapor, and several for chromatography itself. Jars are provided with glass covers.

(2) *Modeling clay*, to be used to seal covers to jars.

(3) *Whatman No. 1 paper* for chromatography. Strips 11.5 x 43 cm. are cut, their length perpendicular to the milling direction of the paper.

(4) *Densitometer*, if quantitative measurements are to be made.

C. REAGENTS

(1) *Dow Corning silicone 200 fluid.*
(2) *Ether.*
(3) *Glacial acetic acid.*
(4) *88% formic acid.*
(5) *Iodine.*

D. PROCEDURE

The paper strips are impregnated with Dow Corning Silicon 200 fluid by dipping the paper through a 5% solution of silicone in ethyl ether and drying. Fatty acids or esters are spotted on the starting line about 2.5 cm. from one end of the papers. The papers are then suspended in the 15 x 45 cm. jars so that the lower end of the paper dips into the developing solvent. The solvent systems used are aqueous acetic acid or aqueous acetic-formic acid mixtures. An 85% solution of acetic acid is commonly used because it covers the broadest range of substances. R_f values are increased by increasing unsaturation; they are decreased by increasing chain length. They are increased by higher temperatures and less polar solvent system. For instance, equal portions of 88% formic acid and 85% acetic acid have proved very good for separation of acids of 1–5 double bonds and 18 or 20 carbon atoms chain length.

The papers are developed 12 to 18 hours and then hung up to dry in a hood. They are then humidified in a jar over warm water, or over a gentle flow of steam, and subsequently suspended in a covered jar of iodine vapor. The unsaturated substances become yellow-brown on a pale yellow background, but saturated substances yield no color and do not interfere.

An example of a separation is given in Figure 7.   In two chromato-grams the C_{18} unsaturated acids with 1 to 4 double bonds, and the C_{20} acids with 1 to 5 double bonds are separated.   Increase in the carbon chain by 2 carbon atoms is approximately offset by addition of 1 double bond.   Therefore, such acids as the C_{18} triene, the C_{20} tetraene, and the C_{22} pentaene will not separate clearly.

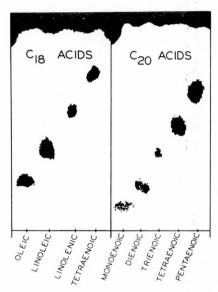

Fig. 7. Separation of unsaturated fatty acids 18 and 20 carbons in length using the method of Mangold, Lamp, and Schlenk.   The octadecatetraenoic acid was isolated from codliver oil and eicosaenoic and eicosadienoic acids from rapeseed oil by displacement chromatography by Holman and Hayes. Eicosatrienoic acid, eicosatetraenoic acid (arachidonic) and eicosapentaenoic acid were generously provided by Prof. Klenk of Cologne.   (Holman.)

The uniformity (or complexity) of chain length can easily be checked after hydrogenation in acetic acid with PtO_2 under 20 lb. pressure.   The resulting saturated acid(s) is chromatographed in 85% acetic and in the manner described above, except that α-cyclo-dextrin and iodine are used as indicators after separation (23).

The same group of workers have found that the method can be adapted to quantitative determination of oleic, linoleic, and linolenic acids, and esters and glycerides.   An example of their data is shown in Figure 8.   It is to be pointed out that this is the first direct deter-

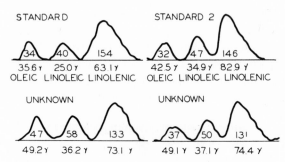

Fig. 8. Quantitative estimation of oleic, linoleic, and linolenic acids in an "unknown" mixture by comparison with model mixtures of known composition.

Visual observation of a preliminary chromatogram of the unknown permitted preparation of standard 1. This was chromatographed on the same sheet with the unknown. The areas under the densitometer curves were compared, and standard 2 was prepared as a closer approximation to the unknown. These were chromatographed as before and the densitometer curves are close enough for linear interpolation. The true amounts of acids in the "unknown" applied to the paper were 46.8 oleic acid, 38.2 linoleic acid, and 75.0 linolenic acid. (Schlenk and co-workers.)

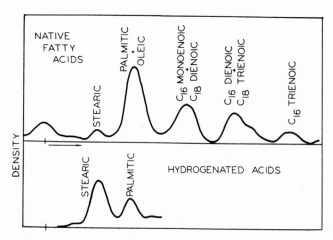

Fig. 9. Densitometer curves for native radioactive *Chlorella* fatty acids and hydrogenated *Chlorella* fatty acids demonstrating the use of paper chromatography for assessing complexity of a mixture. Densitometer measurements were made on radioautographs of the paper chromatograms. (Mangold *et al.*)

mination of oleic acid. All other determinations of oleic acid have been made by difference. Paper chromatography of a natural mixture is illustrated in Figure 9. Total chlorella fatty acids (radioactive) were chromatographed, and the radioautograph of the developed paper strip was made. The curves shown represent the densitometer data for the native mixture and the hydrogenated mixture.

The same authors have shown that autoxidation of polyunsaturated acids does not occur on the paper during their chromatography.

E. COMMENT

The recommended procedure for paper chromatography is being used routinely by the writer as a test for purity of preparations and as a monitor method for identifying desired chromatographic fractions. The simple technique is almost foolproof even in the hands of a novice.

At this early stage of development the method has been proved by several workers to be a very useful tool in the analysis of polyunsaturated fatty acids. It finds its usefulness as an adjunct to other separation procedures.

The identification of substances by this method requires the prior knowledge of the class to which the substance belongs. That is, it must be known that an acid *is* an acid, for esters and alcohols possessing unsaturation would migrate in the expected range and be accounted as acids. The R_f values of substances are influenced by size of spot, temperature, and slight variations in water content of developing solvent, and thus several chromatograms should be made in which spot size is varied, and in which known substances are run on the same paper as unknowns.

V. CONCLUSIONS

The complete analysis of a lipid for its content of polyunsaturated acids is a difficult procedure, and a task large enough to be a research problem in itself. The complete analysis requires first a separation of substances by chain length and then an analysis of the fractions for substances of equal chain length, but differing in unsaturation.

To accomplish this, investigators have used several combinations of procedures. The most effective means of separating by chain length is fractional distillation. Rough group separations can be achieved by low temperature crystallization, urea fractionation, and column chromatography. These methods do not yield sharp separations but provide segregation of saturated versus unsaturated acids, and are most useful as means of concentrating the unsaturated acids.

The most effective means of determining fatty acids of differing unsaturation is spectrophotometric analysis after alkaline isomerization. It finds its best use in the analysis of fractions of single chain lengths, but it can be used to determine the content of classes of polyenoic fatty acids, i.e., dienoic, trienoic, tetraenoic, pentaenoic, and hexaenoic acids in complex lipid mixtures. When it is used in this manner, the investigator should recognize the analysis for what it is, and be cautious in his interpretations. Nevertheless, alkaline isomerization is the best method we now have for this kind of analysis, and it can be used to gain very useful information. It is advisable that data gathered by different modifications of the method be not compared too closely, for each method has its inherent errors, and all are empirical. Therefore data gathered by different methods and in different laboratories may differ.

Very few data are available which permit evaluation of the reproducibility and accuracy of the methods of alkaline isomerization. Those modifications developed for use on vegetable oils give very reproducible results, probably within 1%. Those methods which attempt measurement of the entire gamut of polyunsaturated acids in animal lipids are subject to greater errors. The writer feels that a reproducibility of $\pm 5\%$ in such analyses is good. He regards data gained by these methods as most useful in making comparisons, but places little emphasis on the absolute values calculated.

The method of alkaline isomerization seems to have matured to the point now where no great improvements may be expected along its present line of development. To be sure, minor modifications in procedure, and new constants on more fatty acids may improve the accuracy of the analysis. It seems more likely that a search for better catalyst, or even for a new principle, may be more yielding. If the isomerization could be made a stoichiometric reaction rather than an empirically controlled one, this would be a significant improvement. Very recently some attempts have been made along this line. Davenport et al. (9a) and Sreenivasan and Brown (28a) have found that 5% potassium tertiary butoxide is a more active catalyst than is KOH in glycol. The isomerization takes place within a few hours at the boiling point of t-butanol, 90°C., thereby eliminating the need for a thermostatically controlled hot oil bath. Under these conditions there is much less side reaction. It appears that this catalyst holds some promise, and it may be anticipated that more investigations on homogenous catalysis at relatively low temperatures will be forthcoming.

Paper chromatography offers considerable hope that a more definitive analysis may be developed. If a micromethod for separation of native mixtures according to chain length can be developed, paper chromatography may supersede the currently used methods.

References

1. Abu-Nasr, A. M., and Holman, R. T., *J. Am. Oil Chemists' Soc.*, *31*, 41 (1954).
2. Abu-Nasr, A. M., and Holman, R. T., *J. Am. Oil Chemists' Soc.*, *32*, 414 (1955).
3. Asselineau, J., *Bull. soc. chim. France, 1952*, 884.
4. Beadle, B. W., and Kraybill, H. R., *J. Am. Chem. Soc.*, *66*, 1232 (1944).
5. Berk, L. C., Kretchmer, N., Holman, R. T., and Burr, G. O., *Anal. Chem.*, *22*, 718 (1950).
6. Brice, B. A., and Swain, M. L., *J. Opt. Soc. Amer.*, *35*, 532 (1945).
7. Brice, B. A., Swain, M. L., Herb, S. F., Nichols, P. L., and Riemenschneider, R. W., *J. Am. Oil Chemists' Soc.*, *29*, 279 (1952).
8. Brice, B. A., Swain, M. L., Schaeffer, B. B., and Ault, W. C., *J. Am. Oil Chemists' Soc.*, *22*, 219 (1945).
9. Burr, G. O., and Miller, E. S., *Chem. Revs.*, *29*, 419 (1941).
9a. Davenport, J. B., Birch, A. J., and Ryan, A. J., *Chem. Week*, No. 7, 136 (1956).
10. Edisbury, J. R., Morton, R. A., and Lovern, J. A., *Biochem. J.*, *29*, 899 (1935).
11. Hammond, E. G., and Lundberg, W. O., *J. Am. Oil Chemists' Soc.*, *30*, 433 (1953).
12. Herb, S. F., and Riemenschneider, R. W., *Anal. Chem.*, *25*, 953 (1953).
13. Herb, S. F., and Riemenschneider, R. W., *J. Am. Oil Chemists' Soc.*, *29*, 456 (1952).
14. Hilditch, T. P., Morton, R. A., and Riley, J. P., *Analyst*, *70*, 67 (1945).
15. Holman, R. T., in *The Vitamins*, Vol. 2, Chap. 7, Sebrell and Harris, Eds., Academic Press, New York, 1954, pp. 268–300.
16. Holman, R. T., and Burr, G. O., *Arch. Biochem.*, *19*, 474 (1948).
17. Holman, R. T., and Hayes, H., manuscript in preparation.
18. Inouye, I., Noda, M., and Hiroyama, O., *J. Am. Oil Chemists' Soc.*, *32*, 132 (1955).
19. Kass, P., and Burr, G. O., *J. Am. Chem. Soc.*, *61*, 3292 (1941).

20. Kass, P., Miller, E. S., Hendrickson, M., and Burr, G. O., Abstracts of meeting of the American Chemical Society, Cincinnati, 1940, p. 11.
21. Kaufmann, H. P., and Nitsch, W. H., *Fette Seifen Anstrichmittel, 57*, 473 (1955).
22. Lips, H. J., and Tessier, H., *J. Am. Oil Chemists' Soc., 26*, 659 (1949).
23. Mangold, H. K., Lamp, B., and Schlenk, H., *J. Am. Chem. Soc., 77*, 6070 (1955).
24. Mitchell, J. H., Kraybill, H. R., and Zscheile, F. P., *Ind. Eng. Chem., Anal. Ed., 15*, 1 (1943).
25. Moore, T., *Biochem. J., 31*, 138 (1937).
26. Moore, T., *Biochem. J., 33*, 1635 (1939).
27. Murray, K. E., *Progress in the Chemistry of Fats and Other Lipids*, Vol. III Pergamon Press, London, 1955, pp. 243–274.
28. *Official and Tentative Methods, American Oil Chemists' Society*, Cd 2–38, 1946.
28a. Sreenivasan, B., and Brown, J. B., *J. Am. Oil Chemists' Soc., 33*, 521 (1956).
29. *Tentative Methods of the American Oil Chemists' Society*, Cd 7–48, May, 1953.
30. Vandenheuvel, F. A., and Richardson, G. H., *J. Am. Oil Chemists' Soc., 30*, 104 (1953).
31. White, M. F., and Brown, J. B., *J. Am. Oil Chemists' Soc., 26*, 133 (1949).
32. White, M. F., and Brown, J. B., *J. Am. Oil Chemists, Soc., 26*, 385 (1949).
33. White, M. F., Orians, B. M., and Brown, J. B., *J. Am. Oil Chemists' Soc., 26*, 85 (1949).
34. Wiese, H. F., and Hansen, A. E., *J. Biol. Chem., 202*, 417 (1953).

Determination of
17,21-DIHYDROXY-20-KETOSTEROIDS
in Urine and Plasma

ROBERT H. SILBER AND CURT C. PORTER, *Merck Institute for Therapeutic Research, Rahway, N. J.*

I. INTRODUCTION

The chemical determination of 17,21-dihydroxy-20-ketosteroids (DKS) in plasma and urine is widely used to provide an index of adrenal cortical activity. It is being applied, not only in diagnosis, but also in studies dealing with the relationship between cortical function and various physiological and pathological states. Chemical methods of analysis, most of which have been developed since 1950, are also used to obtain information concerning absorption and excretion, distribution, rate of disappearance and metabolic degradation of DKS.

Although many chemical tests of varying specificity and sensitivity have been described (19,9,5,18,24,28,12,3) only a few have been successfully applied in more than one laboratory to the analysis of body fluids. The most widely used procedures utilize the reaction of the dihydroxy acetone side chain with phenylhydrazine in sulfuric acid and alcohol (19,23). In their application of this reaction, Nelson and Samuels (16) described a chromatographic procedure for the determination of hydrocortisone in human plasma. Reddy, Jenkins, and Thorn (20), who also used the phenylhydrazine reaction, devised a procedure for the analysis of total DKS in human urine, employing butanol for the extraction of both free and conjugated forms. Glenn and Nelson (8) reported a procedure for urinary analysis based upon the Nelson and Samuels procedure. Bovine β-glucuronidase was employed for hydrolysis of the glucuronide forms. Silber and Porter (23) described a procedure for the determination of free DKS in both plasma and urine, and conjugated steroid in urine after treatment with bacterial β-glucuronidase. The most recent versions of the procedures of Nelson and Samuels and of Silber and Porter are described in this chapter. The fluorometric procedure of Sweat (25,26) for hydrocortisone and corticosterone in plasma is also included.

Since the phenylhydrazine reaction is the one most widely used for these determinations, and is of course most familiar to the authors, it will be discussed in detail. Pertinent data, heretofore unpublished, will also be included.

II. EXTRACTION AND PURIFICATION OF STEROIDS

DKS, both free and those liberated by hydrolysis, can be extracted from aqueous solutions by any one of several solvents, including chloroform, methylene chloride, and ethyl acetate. Extracts contain variable amounts of both steroid and non-steroid impurities which may interfere in subsequent colorimetric reactions. These impurities can be partially or entirely removed either by chromatographic means (see 6 for references) or by judicious use of washes and extractions with solvents. The latter procedures appear to be relatively simple and suitable for routine use; hence, they are discussed in some detail below.

1. Extraction and Purification Solvents

A non-polar solvent such as petroleum ether can be safely used to wash aqueous samples containing cortical steroid (Table I). Such solvents extract not only lipides but also certain steroids which do not bear the dihydroxy acetone side chain. Carbon tetrachloride extracts very little DKS from aqueous solutions but is a fairly good solvent for the extraction of corticosterone, estrogens, and certain other steroids. Methylene chloride has solvent properties practically identical to those of chloroform; however, it has the advantage over chloroform in that it shows no tendency to decompose to yield phosgene and hydrochloric acid.

TABLE I

Partition of Steroids between Water and Solvents[a]

	Water and					
	Chloro-form	Ethyl acetate	Benzene	Carbon tetra-chloride	Petroleum ether	Methylene chloride
Cortisone	0.027	0.057	0.9	30	over 500	0.033
F	0.14	0.078	2.7	120	over 500	0.09
THE	0.12	0.048	3.3	75	over 500	0.065
THF	0.57	0.073	7.9	250	over 500	0.4
Δ¹E	0.048	0.072	1.3	60	over 500	0.042
9α-Fluoro F	0.23	0.042	3.7	265	over 500	0.21
Compound B	0.005	0.055	0.08	0.75	190	0.0065
Testosterone	<0.01	<0.01	<0.01	0.03	0.036	<0.01
Progesterone	<0.01	<0.01	<0.01	0.02	0.01	<0.01
Androstenedione	<0.01	<0.01	0.01	0.056	0.047	<0.01

[a] Merck reagents (not redistilled).

Certain 21-esters of DKS which have proved useful in therapeutics, e.g., the t-butyl acetates of cortisone (I) and hydrocortisone (II), can be extracted from aqueous solutions with carbon tetrachloride, whereas the parent free alcohols cannot. Thus, the esters and alcohols can be separated from one another and their concentrations independently estimated.

2. Alkali Washing of Extracts

Chloroform (or methylene chloride) extracts of urine contain variable amounts of materials that react with sulfuric acid-ethanol-water. Interference from this source is reduced about 50% by washing the extract with 0.1 volume of 0.1 N NaOH. Increasing the volume or concentration of alkaline wash 2-fold has little if any additional effect. Another wash of the original urine, with 3 volumes of carbon tetrachloride, removes about 25% more. Washing the solvent extract with 9% sodium carbonate or bicarbonate instead of 0.1 N sodium hydroxide is less satisfactory and an added wash with 2 N sulfuric acid offers no advantages.

III. HYDROLYSIS OF STEROID GLUCURONIDES

1. Urine

About 5% of the DKS found in human urine is in the free, i.e., unconjugated form. Most of the remaining 95% can be accounted for as compounds with reduced A rings (III, IV) which are con-

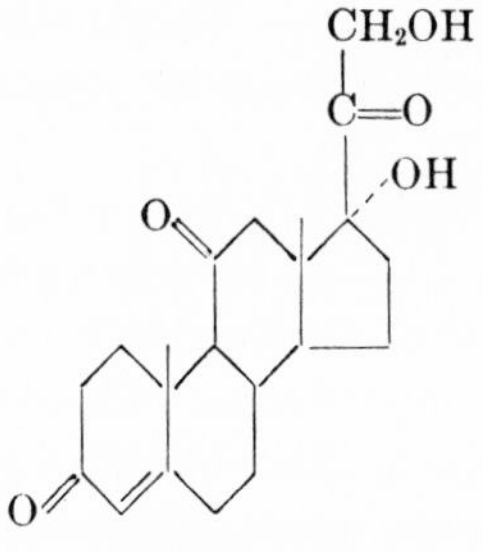

(I) Cortisone (E)
Δ⁴-Pregnene-17α,21-diol-
3,11,20-trione

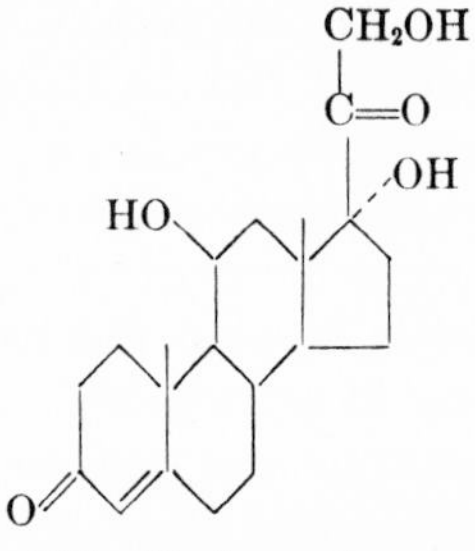

(II) Hydrocortisone (F)
Δ⁴-Pregnene-11β,17α,21-
triol-3,20-dione

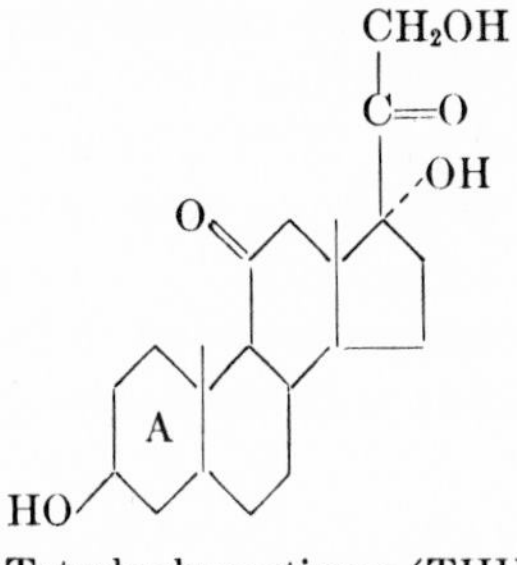

(III) Tetrahydrocortisone (THE)
Pregnane-3,17α,21-triol-11,20-
dione

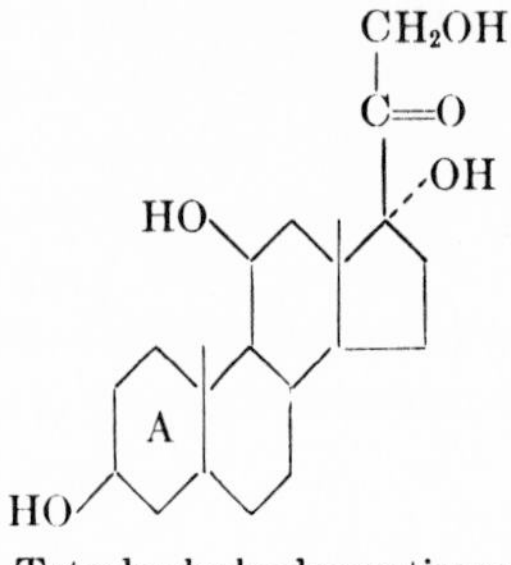

(IV) Tetrahydrohydrocortisone (THF)
Pregnane-3,11β,17α,21-tetrol-
20-one

CH$_2$OH
C=O
HO

CHO
C=O
HO

(V) Δ^{4,16}-Pregnadiene-11β,21-
diol-3,20-dione

(VI) Corticosterone-21-aldehyde
Δ^4-Pregnene-11β-ol-3,20-dione-21-al

jugated with glucuronic acid. The estimation of total DKS in urine after treatment with glucuronidase may be adequate for many purposes. However, independent estimation of both free and conjugated DKS has several advantages. First, smaller blanks are encountered in the estimation of glucuronide DKS than in the estimation of total DKS. Second, the DKS glucuronide fraction of human urine contains predominantly the conjugates of THE and THF. Total steroid can be estimated with greater precision when only these two are present (section V.2.B(1,2)). Third, alterations in the ratio of free to bound DKS excreted may be indicative of pathological changes, i.e., liver damage.

Maximum assay values for the glucuronide DKS in a number of human urines have been obtained with as little as 50–100 Sigma units of bacterial enzyme (Sigma Chemical, St. Louis, Mo.) at 37°C., pH 6.5, for 18 to 24 hours. Two-hundred fifty Sigma units of enzyme per ml. of urine liberated maximal amounts of DKS in only 4 hours at 37°C. However, since urines that require more enzyme may be encountered, it is recommended that at least 250 Sigma units per ml. of urine be used for routine purposes (18-hour incubation). It is obviously desirable to check the potency of any enzyme preparation under individual laboratory conditions, prior to use.

In the authors' laboratory, one Sigma unit (37°C., 24 hr., pH 6.5) has been found to be equivalent to 10–20 Fishman units of Ketodase (Warner-Chilcott, New York, 45°C., 24 hr., pH 5). Assay values obtained on urine samples treated with Ketodase tend to be 5–10% lower than those obtained after incubation with the bacterial preparation.

2. Plasma

Klein, Papadatos, Fortunato, and Byers (11) hydrolyzed the bound

DKS of plasma with acid. Bongiovanni and Eberlein (2) used Ketodase (Warner-Chilcott) for this purpose (Section V.1.B(1)), and report that acid hydrolysis is unsatisfactory.

Weichselbaum and Margraf (27) also employed enzymatic hydrolysis, but with bacterial glucuronidase (Sigma). Repeated additions of enzyme were made, to a total of 3000 units per 10 or 20 ml. plasma. They also added 0.5 ml. of an aqueous solution of disodium ethylenediaminetetraacetic acid prior to incubation at 37°C., pH 6.5–6.8, for 4 hours. The chelating agent is said to retard destruction of the enzyme.

IV. THE PHENYLHYDRAZINE-SULFURIC ACID REACTION

1. Reagent

Although satisfactory for the determination of cortisone, the reagent (phenylhydrazine-sulfuric acid-methanol) described in 1950 (19) produces inferior color intensity with hydrocortisone. The sulfuric acid–water–ethanol (100 ml. 310:190 (v/v) sulfuric acid-water + 50 ml. absolute ethanol) solution containing 43 mg. % phenylhydrazine hydrochloride which was recommended in 1954 (23) yields satisfactory color intensities with both cortisone and hydrocortisone (Table II). Alterations in composition of this reagent have failed to produce a significantly superior one for the determination of these two steroids.

TABLE II

Optical Density/mM/liter at 410 mμ

(Steroid treated with phenylhydrazine reagent at 25°C. for 18 hours)

Hydrocortisone	26
Cortisone	26.7
Tetrahydrohydrocortisone	18
Tetrahydrocortisone	24.7
Substance S	27.4
9α-Fluorohydrocortisone	28.5
Δ^1-Cortisone	27

However, with this reagent, tetrahydrohydrocortisone yields a less intense color, about 70% that obtained with cortisone or hydrocortisone (Table II), employing the 410 mμ peak only, or 85% using a 3 point calculation (see below).   Practically identical results can be obtained, on addition of reagent directly to the dry steroid, if one mixes 85 ml. of the 3.1 : 1.9 sulfuric acid with 65 ml. of alcohol instead of 100 ml. of acid with 50 ml. of alcohol, prior to addition of the phenylhydrazine.   One then calculates the results by subtracting the sum of the optical densities at 380 mμ and 440 mμ from twice the optical density at 410 mμ.   The values thus obtained with cortisone, hydrocortisone, and their tetrahydro forms are then comparable, although about 20% lower than the values obtained with the usual reagent.

Unfortunately, in the procedure as applied to aqueous samples or urines the use of this reagent does not appear to offer significant advantages.

2. Color Development

Maximum color is developed in DKS-reagent solutions by heating them at 60°C. for 30 min., or by allowing them to stand at 23°–25°C. overnight (18 hours).   Other temperatures can also be employed, with appropriate adjustment of time.   In general, higher temperatures tend to yield less reproducible results; consequently, incubation at 23°–25°C. for 18 hours is recommended.

3. Specificity

As noted elsewhere (13,21) the reaction is not in itself specific for DKS.   Many non-steroid substances also react to yield a yellow color with the reagent.   Therefore, the specificity of any procedure employing this reagent depends upon the purification steps carried out prior to application of the color reaction.   If appropriate solvent extraction or purification procedures are employed (Section II.1, II.2) the reaction then becomes specific for steroids with the 17,21-dihydroxy-20-keto configuration (Figure 1).   If the 17, 20, or 21 position has undergone reduction the reaction does not take place (Figure 1).   The 21-aldehydes of compounds A and B also give the reaction in spite of the absence of the OH group at the 17 position. The reason for this is discussed in Section IV.4.   One other compound, which has been synthesized but not found in nature, gives the reaction also (15).   This compound has a double bond between carbons 16 and 17 and no oxygen attached to carbon 17 (V).   Although of fundamental interest, compounds of this type have no bearing on the application of the reaction to the analysis of biological fluids.

The pregnane forms of cortisone and hydrocortisone, commonly
termed tetrahydrocortisone (THE, III) and tetrahydrohydrocortisone
(THF, IV) react typically, but yield slightly less intense colors than
the parent steroids (410 mµ peak only).

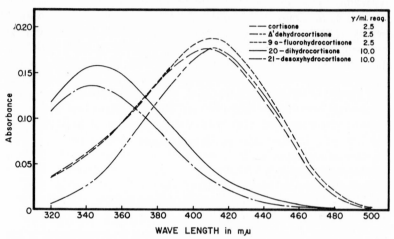

Fig. 1. Absorption curves after addition of reagent directly to steroid, 18
hours at 23°C.

4. Mechanism

As shown by Silber and Porter (23), steroids without the dihydroxyacetone side-chain but with the 3-keto-Δ⁴ A ring react with phenylhydrazine-sulfuric acid, but peak absorption of the resulting products
centers at a wave length of about 340 mµ. This class of compounds
includes corticosterone, desoxycorticosterone, progesterone, testos-
terone, and many others. THE and THF react to yield a practically
symmetrical curve with an absorption peak at 410 mµ, whereas cortisone and hydrocortisone show the typical 410 mµ peak, but, in addition, absorption is greater in the 320–380 mµ range. These findings
led to the conclusion that phenylhydrazine reacts not only with the
dihydroxy acetone side chain but also with the 3-ketone group.

Analyses of the isolated yellow reaction products of hydrocortisone
and of THF for nitrogen indicate that one phenylhydrazine molecule
is attached to the dihydroxy acetone side-chain and another to the
3-keto-group. The theoretical N content of the phenylhydrazone
of THF is 6.13%; found, 6.17%. The theoretical N content of hy-

drocortisone diphenylhydrazone is 10.32%; found, 9.94% (23). Thus, it is reasonable to conclude that under the conditions employed in the procedure, hydrocortisone and cortisone react to form 3,20- or 3,21-bisphenylhydrazones.

Similarly to cortisone and hydrocortisone, reaction of the 21-aldehydes of compounds A and B (VI) with phenylhydrazine in sulfuric acid yields products with peak absorption centered at 410 mμ. However, the reaction proceeds more rapidly with the aldehydes as it does also with cortisone which has been treated with sulfuric acid-alcohol-water overnight prior to the addition of phenylhydrazine. This has led us to the conclusion that, under the conditions employed, compounds bearing the dihydroxyacetone side chain first undergo a Mattox rearrangement (14) with the production of a 20,21-ketal. One phenylhydrazine molecule then reacts at the 21 position, and in the case of cortisone or hydrocortisone, a 3,21-bisphenylhydrazone results.

5. Standards and Calculations

It has been established (16,7,17,10,4) that hydrocortisone is the principal DKS in human plasma. Therefore, this steroid should be used as a standard in plasma analyses. Automatic correction for incomplete recovery of DKS from plasma can be made (23) by simultaneously analyzing chloroform or methylene chloride-washed plasma to which hydrocortisone has been added, or a calculated correction can be applied if aqueous standards are preferred.

The DKS concentration in plasma can be calculated by either of two methods. (*1*) An aliquot of a steroid-containing solution is treated with the reagent, and an equal aliquot is treated with a blank reagent, i.e., one which does not contain phenylhydrazine. The optical density of the latter (at 410 mμ) is subtracted from that of the former to yield a corrected optical density. This value is then compared with corrected optical densities of recovery standards. (*2*) Optical density measurements are made at 410 mμ, and at two other wave lengths, equidistant above and below 410 mμ, i.e., at 370 and 450 mμ, or at 380 and 440 mμ. The average of the two non-peak optical densities is subtracted from the peak (410 mu) value as a blank correction. This procedure, based upon a study by Allen (1), depends upon the assumption that interfering substances have a peak absorption distinctly different from that of hydrocortisone, and that their absorption curve in the range studied, 370–450 mu, is a straight line.

In performing *urinary* analyses, the analyst is confronted with the following problem in choosing a DKS standard.   Urine contains the chloroform-soluble free forms of cortisone, hydrocortisone, and possibly reduction products of these, and in addition the glucuronides of THE and THF.   A single steroid may not be satisfactory as a standard for all purposes, as will become evident in the following discussion.

The steroid used as a standard in the determination of free DKS can be either cortisone or hydrocortisone, since these are recovered similarly from urine, and yield equivalent color intensities.   However, the glucuronide fraction may contain a large proportion of THF, and this steroid is not recovered quantitatively in terms of cortisone or hydrocortisone.

Table III summarizes the analyses of the glucuronide fraction of five 8-hour human urine samples.   Four different steroids were used as standards, and results were calculated in two ways.   In both calculations, optical density readings of the blanks (no phenylhydrazine) were subtracted from optical densities of phenylhydrazine-treated aliquots.   Then, the tabulated data were calculated using the 410 mu readings only, or by subtracting the sum of the readings at 380 mu and 440 mu from twice the reading at 410 mu (a "modified" Allen calculation (1), carried out *after* subtracting the blank values).

TABLE III

Analysis of Glucuronide Fraction of 8-Hour Human Urines after Oral Ingestion of Steroids or Intramuscular Injection of ACTH (mg. excreted in 8 hours)

	E, F, or THE standard		THF standard	
Given	410 mu	Peak[a]	410 mu	Peak[a]
E 100 mg.	43.0–49.5	51.5–52.5	90 0	84.5
F 100 mg.	24.7 28.5	31.5–32.5	51.8	51.8
THF 100 mg.	21.6–25.7	27.0–27.7	45.5	44.5
ACTH 40 units	8.2–9.4	9.6–9.8	17.2	15.9
Control	2.5–2.9	2.9–3.0	5.2	4.8

[a] Peak calculation, using readings at 380, 410, and 440 mu after subtraction of blank readings.   Procedure of Silber and Porter (23).

The results obtained by comparison with cortisone, hydrocortisone, and THE standards were comparable, particularly after applying the "peak" calculation.   This appears to be the calculation of choice because assay results would not be influenced significantly by variations in the proportions of these three steroids in the urine.

However, if THF is used as the standard, assay values will be higher due to the fact that, in the procedure used, this steroid gives only 60–65% as intense color as the other three. Conversely, a urine sample containing this steroid exclusively would assay 35–40% too low, provided any one of the other three steroids was used as the standard. For practical purposes, unless one has reason to believe he is dealing with a variable proportion of THF, results can be expressed in terms of an arbitrary standard, say hydrocortisone, as is frequently done in biochemical analyses. If the chloroform or methylene chloride extracts of urine are taken to dryness before addition of the reagent, the recovery of THF is improved, to about 85%, with a hydrocortisone standard, but the blank readings are increased 50–100%.

Two alternative procedures are available if more nearly absolute analytical data are desired: An independent method for the determination of THF in the glucuronide fraction can be used; or standards of both THE and THF can be run, and a simple algebraic calculation made to determine the total THE and THF in a urine sample. These two procedures are described in section V.2.B(1,2).

V. ANALYTICAL PROCEDURES

1. Plasma

A. FREE 17,21-DIHYDROXY-20-KETOSTEROIDS

(1) **Procedure of Nelson and Samuels** (16), submitted by Nelson, 2/21/56.

(a) *Reagents*

Chloroform, USP, redistilled from K_2CO_3 immediately before use.

Florisil (60/100 mesh, obtained from Floridin Company, Warren, Pa.). Washed with ethanol. Dried and heated to 600°C. for 4 hours. Stored in a desiccator for not more than 4 days.

Methanol, redistilled from 2,4-dinitrophenylhydrazine.

Dilute sulfuric acid (190 ml. H_2O : 310 ml. conc. H_2SO_4).

Phenylhydrazine HCl, recrystallized from ethanol 2–4 times.

Phenylhydrazine–sulfuric acid solution (16 mg. of reagent 5, plus 10 ml. of reagent 4). This solution is prepared each day.

(b) Procedure

Blood samples are mixed with 1 mg. heparin per 10 ml. and immediately centrifuged. The plasma is removed and frozen until the determination is to be made. Ten milliliter samples of plasma are preferable and are extracted with 1.5 volumes of chloroform three times. This extract is poured directly on to the chromatographic column, described below.

A column of Florisil is prepared by tamping the adsorbent as it is added to a 10–11 mm. column to a height of 70 mm. The Florisil should be taken directly from the oven or desiccator. A column with a sintered glass bottom has been found most convenient.

The column is thoroughly wet with chloroform and as the solvent drains to the upper level of the absorbent the chloroform extract of approximately 45 ml. is poured onto the column. Elution is then carried out with 25 ml. $CHCl_3$, 25 ml. of 1% methanol in chloroform and 45 ml. of 25% methanol in chloroform. The last fraction contains the 17-hydroxycorticosteroids and is collected in a 50-ml. round bottom flask which has a 1-ml. well in the bottom. The eluate is evaporated to dryness in a 50° water bath with a stream of air. The sides of the flask are washed down into the well three times with a small amount of chloroform and each time evaporated to dryness. The steroid should now be entirely in the well and is dissolved in 0.25 ml. of methanol. A 0.2-ml. fraction is transferred to a small test tube and 0.3 ml. of the phenylhydrazine–sulfuric acid solution is added with gentle shaking. The tubes are incubated at 60°C. for one hour. After incubation they are cooled in tap water, centrifuged for five minutes, and poured into 0.5-ml. microcuvettes for reading in the spectrophotometer. Absorption is measured at 370, 410, and 450 mμ with a solvent sample run through the columns as a blank.

Two standards of 2 and 4 μg. cortisone are run through similar columns with each 12 unknown samples. Quantitation is by comparison of "absorption factor" of standards and unknown using the following simple formula:

$$\text{Absorption at 410 m}\mu - \frac{(\text{absorption at 370 m}\mu + \text{absorption at 450 m}u)}{2} = \text{"absorption factor"}$$

This correction assumes a uniform change in the background with change in wave length, a condition which is probably not quite true, but in practice works well.

Normal values by this procedure are 13 ± 6 ug./100 ml. plasma at 8 a.m.   The entire procedure is carried out in one working day.

(2) **Procedure of Silber and Busch** (22).

(a) *Reagents*

Methylene chloride (reagent, Merck).

Carbon tetrachloride (reagent, Merck).

Petroleum ether (reagent, Merck).

Phenylhydrazine hydrochloride, recrystallized from ethanol and dried over calcium chloride.

Dilute sulfuric acid, 190 ml. of water plus 310 ml. of concentrated acid (reagent, Merck).

Blank reagent, 100 ml. of dilute sulfuric acid mixed with 50 ml. of absolute ethanol.

Phenylhydrazine–sulfuric acid reagent with ethanol, 65 mg. phenyl-hydrazine hydrochloride dissolved in 150 ml. of blank reagent.

Hydrocortisone standard, 5–20 μg. per ml. Diluted before use to 0.5 ug.–3.0 μg. per ml.

(b) *Materials and Equipment.*

Centrifuge tubes, 45–50 ml. capacity, to which plastic caps can be fitted.

Test tubes, about 160–180 mm. long with 15 mm. inside diameter, to which plastic caps can be fitted, calibrated at 10 ml.   If extracts are taken to dryness, the test tubes do not need to be calibrated.

Small test tubes, about 100 mm. long with 10 mm. inside diameter (or 12–15 ml. centrifuge tubes).

Plastic caps, No. 590, Lumelite Corp., Pawling, N. Y.

Blunt tip needles, about 7 inches long, 16 or 18 gauge.

Microcuvettes for the Beckman Model DU spectrophotometer, silica cells, with 3 x 10 x 38 mm. inside dimensions, and diaphragm attachment (smaller cuvettes with a 10 mm. light path can be used).

(c) *Procedure*

Twelve milliliters or more plasma is washed with $2^{1}/_{2}$ volumes of carbon tetrachloride by shaking 15 seconds in a centrifuge tube equipped with plastic cap.   (If a 5-ml. sample is to be analyzed, 7 or 8 ml. should be used here.)   After centrifugation, the solvent layer is discarded and $2^{1}/_{2}$ volumes of petroleum ether are added.   Again, after the tube and contents are shaken 15 seconds and centrifuged, the solvent layer is discarded.

A 10-ml. sample of the plasma is now extracted in a second centri-fuge tube by shaking for 20–30 seconds with 25 ml. of methylene chloride. After centrifuging once, the aqueous phase is frozen, if necessary to break the emulsion, by means of a dry ice-solvent mixture, and centrifugation is repeated. The solvent layer is transferred, by means of a blunt tip needle and a 10-ml. syringe, to a 160–180-mm. test tube calibrated at 10 ml. Ten milliliters of methylene chloride is added to the tube containing the plasma.

The first extract (22–24 ml. of solvent) is evaporated to dryness in a stream of air in the test tube immersed in a 25–30°C. water bath. The second extraction (with 10 ml. solvent) is carried out like the first, and the extract is transferred with the same syringe to the tube containing the residue from the first extraction. The volume is carefully adjusted to 10 ml. by either evaporating in air or by adding a small amount of methylene chloride, as needed. An alternative procedure which eliminates the need for calibrated tubes is to take the total extract to dryness, and add 10 ml. of fresh methylene chloride. This also eliminates any acetone that may be present in the plasma.

One ml. of 0.1 N NaOH is added and after the tube is capped, it is shaken for 15 seconds. After centrifugation, the alkaline wash is discarded and two 4-ml. aliquots of the extract are placed in each of two small test tubes. To one is added 0.5 ml. of phenylhydrazine reagent and to the other 0.5 ml. of blank reagent. The tubes are then shaken vigorously for 15 seconds with the thumb over the top of the tube. A rubber finger (rinsed carefully with water and solvents) is worn to protect the thumb and prevent contamination of the sample. After centrifugation, the solvent is removed with a blunt needle connected to an aspirator.

After standing overnight, optical densities are measured at 410 mμ. Aqueous standards (0.5γ–5γ) are carried through the same procedure. Cuvettes are rinsed with ethanol and allowed to drain thoroughly between samples.

(d) *Notes*

All glassware, needles, and caps are washed with water, alcohol, and methylene chloride before use.

When centrifuging the 180-mm. test tubes the speed of the centrifuge must be increased slowly until the tubes reach a horizontal position.

It is desirable to take readings at 380 and 440 mμ to make certain that the sample gives a typical 410 mμ peak.

Ten milliliter replicates of a normal pooled plasma were found to contain 1.9 ± 0.03 (s.e.)γ.   Five milliliter replicates assayed $1.05 \pm$ 0.024 (s.e.)γ.   Recovery of 0.5 to 1.0γ of hydrocortisone from plasma was 91–92%.

The solvent washings of the plasma prior to hydrocortisone extraction serve to remove many steroids, fat, and certain medications. If samples are not lipemic and solvent-soluble medication has not been administered, a single wash, with carbon tetrachloride, is sufficient.   Even this wash can be omitted if desired.

(3) Fluorometric Procedure of Sweat (25,26) for both hydrocortisone and corticosterone, taken from procedure submitted by Sweat, 5/1/56.

(a) *Reagents*

Silica gel.   For preparation see Sweat (26).

Ethyl alcohol, absolute, redistilled.   Middle 80% of distillate used.

Chloroform, Mallinckrodt reagent grade, preserved with 0.75% alcohol.   Fractionated by a 2-theoretical plate column.   First 90% of distillate used.

Powdered glass, borosilicate, ground in a mortar under alcohol. Samples containing particles less than 30, greater than 40 mesh, and less than 40, greater than 50 mesh are used.

Concentrated sulfuric acid, reagent, duPont.   Some batches have been unsatisfactory.

Pentane, commercial grade (Phillips Petroleum Products Co.), redistilled and extracted with 70% redistilled ethanol.

Standard steroid solutions, 10 and 100 γ/μg. 17-hydroxycorticosterone or corticosterone (Merck) per ml. ethanol.   Solutions prepared and stored at 4°C.

(b) *Materials and Equipment.*

"Two sizes of chromatographic columns are employed: one having an overall length of 230 mm. is used for chromatographic analysis of 1 to 10γ of steroids; the other, 126 mm. in length, is used for 0.25 to 1γ.   Water jackets are necessary to keep the adsorbent cool. Stopcocks regulate the rate of "packing" in the column.   Too rapid packing or too high temperature causes small vapor bubbles to form in the silica gel."   For structure details of the columns, see Figure 2.

Fluorometer, Farrand photoelectric fluorometer (Farrand Optical Co.).

Primary filters, Corning 3389 and 5113.

Secondary filters, Wratten Gelatin Filters.   No. 74 and 16.

Two sets of secondary filters may be required to balance the instrument.

(c) *Procedure*

Two to 10 ml. of plasma is extracted with a volume of chloroform equal to 10 times that of the plasma; 0.1 to 4.0 ml. of adrenal venous

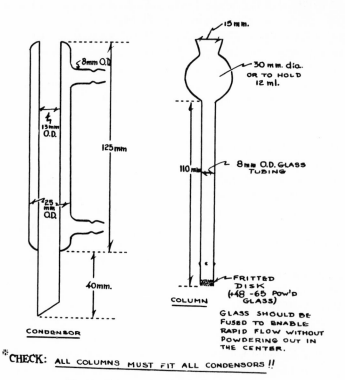

Fig. 2. Columns for Procedure of Sweat

blood is extracted with 10 to 20 ml. of chloroform.   The mixtures are centrifuged.   The chloroform layer is transferred to a round bottom flask where it is evaporated (below 50°C.) to dryness by means of a water aspirator.

To the dry residue is first added 20 ml. of petroleum ether, then 10 ml. of 70% ethanol. The flask is shaken and allowed to stand 30 minutes. The two liquids are again intermixed several times by shaking and transferred to a separatory funnel where they are allowed to separate. The ethanol layer is returned to the original flask and the petroleum ether layer discarded. Twenty milliliters of petroleum ether is added to the flask and the process of shaking and transferring to the separatory funnel repeated. Additions of 1 to 2 ml. of 70% ethanol are used to wash the sample from the flask to the separatory funnel during each transfer. After the separatory funnel has been shaken for 30 seconds, the ethanol layer is removed to a small round bottom flask where it is evaporated to dryness at a temperature not exceeding 50°C. To the residue is added 0.5 to 1.0 ml. of redistilled chloroform, which is allowed to stand in the stoppered flask at room temperature for 30 minutes in preparation for chromatography.

The liquid is transferred to a silica column (see below) by means of a fine capillary pipette attached to a rubber bulb. The flask is washed twice with 0.1 ml. chloroform and the washings are transferred to the column. When the surface of the liquid has reached the surface of the silica gel, 10 ml. of chloroform is added to the column. The combined effluents from these four additions are labeled "Fraction 1." Additional chloroform and alcohol-chloroform eluents are added to the column, collected as effluents in 50-ml. round bottom flasks, and labeled in the order shown in Table IV.

The solvents are removed under reduced pressure, care being taken to avoid contamination of the samples with organic matter. The residue in each flask is dissolved in 0.2 ml. redistilled ethanol, and 0.1 ml. of the solutions transferred to optically matched, 10 x 75 mm. Corning test tubes. (The tubes are first selected for uniform diameters by means of a drill gauge and then for optical uniformity by determining the fluorescence transmitted through them when they are filled with concentrated sulfuric acid.) One milliliter of concentrated sulfuric acid is then added to the tube and thoroughly mixed with the ethanol by means of a footed glass rod (movement up and down). After the mixture is allowed to stand 20 minutes the degree of fluorescence is determined in the fluorometer as follows:

With the dark current dials turned to the extreme right and the sensitivity dials turned to the extreme left the shutter is opened and

TABLE IV

Fraction No.	Solvent % EtOH in CHCl₃	Quantity	Remarks
			H-230 mm. column or modified column
1	0	10	Fraction No. 1 also contains chloroform of the
2	0	10	introduced sample.
3	0	5	
4	0.5	10	
5	1.0	10	Corticosterone region.
6	1.0	10	
7	1.0	5	
8	1.0	5	
9	4.0	5	17-Hydroxycorticosterone region.
10	4.0	5	
11	4.0	10	
12	10.0	10	(Reichstein's substance E 20-hydroxycortol
13	10.0	10	region.)
14	10.0	10	
			B-122 mm. column
1	0.0	4.0	
2	0.0	2.0	
3	1.0	2.0	Corticosterone region.
4	1.0	6.0	
5	1.0	2.0	
6	4.0	2.0	17-Hydroxycorticosterone region.
7	4.0	2.0	
8	4.0	2.0	

the sensitivity dials are adjusted to allow the blank (1.0 ml. sulfuric acid plus 0.1 ml. ethanol) to read 10.0. With the shutter still open the dark current dials are rotated counterclockwise until the galvanometer again reads zero. The 1 μg. standard (0.1 ml. ethanol containing 1 μg. steroid plus 1 ml. conc. H_2SO_4) is then adjusted to read 100 on the galvanometer scale. The unknown samples may then be placed in the fluorometer to determine their relative degrees of fluorescence. It is recommended that for precise work all tubes be read in the same compartment of the cuvette carrier. The ethanol in the standard cuvettes should be evaporated and replaced by ethanol from the same batch of ethanol employed for the chromatogram fractions.

(d) *Calculations.*

By setting the machine as described above, the galvanometer reading bears a rectilinear relation to the quantity of steroid. The quantities of steroid may be calculated from the following equation:

$$\frac{\text{Galvanometer reading} \times 100}{\% \text{ Recovery of blank}} \times \frac{2}{\text{quantity of plasma}} = \frac{\mu\text{g. of steroid per}}{100 \text{ ml. plasma}}$$

(e) *Preparation of Columns.*

230-mm. column. "With the stopcock of the column open and cold tap water running through the cooling jacket, enough powdered glass (-30, $+40$) is added to the column to form a layer 2 to 3 mm. above the fritted glass disk. The powdered glass is washed into place with a small quantity of chloroform. Two additional and approximately equal amounts of powdered glass (-30, $+40$ and -40, $+50$) are added in succession. The chloroform is allowed to drain and the stopcock is closed. A suspension of 0.5 gram of activated silica gel and 5 ml. of chloroform is poured into the column. Two additional 2-ml. quantities of chloroform are used to rinse the beaker and the sides of the column. The stopcock remains closed until the silica gel has settled completely; the chloroform is now run off until its upper level coincides with the upper level of the silica gel. Three 10-ml. quantities of ethyl alcohol in chloroform (1 to 10) and three 10-ml. quantities of chloroform are added to the column in succession and collected in 50-ml. round bottom flasks labeled A to F, respectively. Filter paper, glass wool, sand, or cotton should not be used in the preparation of the column, because they contain extractives which interfere with the phenylhydrazine and fluorescence tests."

122-mm. column. A quantity of -30, $+40$ powdered glass sufficient to form a 5-mm. layer is added to the column and washed into place with a small quantity of chloroform. 0.1 gram of silica gel is introduced into the column in a manner similar to that employed in the preparation of the 230-mm. column. It is then washed three times with 2-ml. portions of 1 to 10 ethanol in chloroform and three times with 2 ml. chloroform. The eluates from the washings, labeled

A to F as above, may be analyzed for background fluorescence contributed by the silica gel.   See Table IV.

B. CONJUGATED 17,21-DIHYDROXY-20-KETOSTEROIDS

(1) Procedure of Bongiovanni and Eberlein (2).

Within an hour of collection, 10 ml. or more heparinized plasma is mixed with 2.5 volumes of 95% ethanol.   The precipitate is removed by centrifugation or by filtration through Whatman No. 4 paper. After evaporation, almost to dryness, at 45°C. in a stream of air, a volume of water equal to the original volume of plasma is added and three extractions with $^2/_3$ volume of methylene chloride are performed. This extraction removes the free steroid.

The aqueous phase remaining after the methylene chloride extractions is incubated at 37°C. for 48 hours after addition of acetate buffer (0.1 M, pH 4.5) and 300–500 Fishman units of β-glucuronidase (Ketodase) per ml.   After methylene chloride extraction, as above, the steroid is chromatographed on Fluorisil, and the dried residue is finally treated with 0.25 ml. of absolute ethanol and 0.75 ml. of phenylhydrazine reagent (65 mg. phenylhydrazine hydrochloride in 100 ml. 62% v/v sulfuric acid).   After 16 hours in the dark at room temperature, optical density is measured at 370, 410, and 450 mμ and calculations are carried out as described by Nelson and Samuels (16).

Note: In a personal communication (4/30/56), Bongiovanni states that it is desirable to carry out two hexane washes of a 70% ethanol solution of the steroid, prior to methylene chloride extraction.

2. Urine

A. FREE 17,21-DIHYDROXY-20-KETOSTEROIDS

(1) Procedure of Silber and Porter (23).

(*a*) *Reagents and Materials.*

All are included under the procedure for analysis of plasma. Chloroform and methylene chloride are interchangeable.

(*b*) *Procedure.*

Six to 10 ml. of filtered urine is shaken for 15 seconds with 3 volumes of carbon tetrachloride.   After centrifugation, the solvent wash is discarded and a 5-ml. aliquot of the washed urine is shaken with 25 ml. of chloroform 20–30 seconds in a centrifuge tube equipped with a plastic cap.

After centrifugation, the aqueous phase is discarded and 2 ml. of 0.1 N NaOH is added. The tube and contents are shaken for 15 seconds, centrifuged, and the alkaline wash is discarded. A 10-ml. aliquot of the washed chloroform extract is placed in each of two test tubes (150–160 mm. long with 15-mm. inside diameter), with 1 ml. of phenylhydrazine reagent added to one and 1 ml. of blank reagent added to the other. After capping tightly and shaking vigorously for 15–20 seconds, with the thumb over the cap, the cap is carefully removed and the tube and contents are centrifuged.

The chloroform layer is carefully removed and discarded, by means of a long needle connected to an aspirator, and the 1-ml. portions of reagent and blank reagent are left at room temperature (about 25°C.) overnight (about 18 hours). Standards, 5–20γ hydrocortisone, diluted to 5 ml. with water, are carried through the same procedure.

(c) Calculations.

The optical density of the sample and its blank are measured at 380, 410, and 440 mμ. After subtracting the readings of the blank from those of the sample at each of these wave lengths, the sum of the 380 and 440 mμ values is subtracted from twice the 410 mμ value. This yields a "corrected optical density" value which is then compared with similarly obtained "corrected optical density" values for the standards.

B. CONJUGATED 17,21-DIHYDROXY-20-KETOSTEROIDS

(1) **Procedure of Silber and Porter** (23).

(a) Reagents and Materials.

All included in the plasma procedure except the bacterial β-glucuronidase (Sigma) solution, 250 Sigma units per ml. pH 6.5 buffer.

(b) Procedure.

Several milliliters of filtered urine at pH 6.5 is washed with 3 volumes of chloroform twice, by shaking 15–20 seconds in a centrifuge tube equipped with a plastic cap. 0.5 to 2.0 ml. of the washed urine is mixed with an equal volume of the enzyme solution and incubated at 37°C. overnight (about 18 hours).

The samples and hydrocortisone standards (5–20γ) are diluted to 5 ml. with water and shaken 20–30 seconds with 25 ml. of chloroform. From this point on, the procedure and calculations are identical to those just described for the determination of the free steroid in urine.

The procedure can be made more specific by treating a larger sample of urine with the enzyme and washing the incubated sample and standard solution with 3 volumes of carbon tetrachloride prior to taking aliquots of the enzyme-treated urine and the hydrocortisone standard for dilution to 5 ml. prior to chloroform extraction.

If the investigator wishes to obtain more nearly absolute assays of the glucuronide fraction, he can do so by using the above procedure with the carbon tetrachloride wash prior to chloroform extraction of the steroids and employing both THE and THF standards. Generally, one must have a prior assay to choose aliquots that will give optical density values close to those of the standards.

Readings are made at 380, 410, and 440 mμ as usual, and a "corrected optical density" value is calculated in such a way that THE and THF yield identical values, in spite of differences in optical density at 410 mμ. This is done by utilizing the fact that the optical density found with THE at 440 mμ is relatively greater than that found with THF.

The following calculations illustrate the principles of the procedure:

Urines	380 mμ	410 mμ
Control 1.5 ml.	$0.162 - 0.022 = 0.14$	$0.212 - 0.014 = 0.198$
ACTH treated 0.7 ml.	$0.155 - 0.009 = 0.146$	$0.213 - 0.005 = 0.208$
THF dosed 0.5 ml.	$0.170 - 0.110 = 0.160$	$0.238 - 0.007 = 0.231$
THF standard 24γ	$0.175 - 0.004 = 0.171$	$0.252 - 0.003 = 0.249$
THE standard 12γ	$0.152 + 0.003 = 0.155$	$0.224 + 0.002 = 0.226$

Urines	440 mμ
Control 1.5 ml.	$0.147 - 0.012 = 0.135$
ACTH treated 0.7 ml.	$0.149 - 0.006 = 0.143$
THF dosed 0.5 ml.	$0.163 - 0.011 = 0.152$
THF standard 24γ	$0.170 - 0.008 = 0.162$
THE standard 12γ	$0.160 + 0.001 = 0.161$

A "corrected" optical density is then calculated for THE and THF as follows.

$10 \times$ OD at 410 $- 5 \times$ OD at 380 $- a \times$ OD at 440 for THF $=$

$10 \times$ OD at 410 $- 5 \times$ OD at 380 $- a \times$ OD at 440 for THE

Substituting the standard readings, for 24γ standard, and solving for a:

$$2.49 - 0.855 - 0.162a = 2(2.26 - 0.775 - 0.161a)$$
$$a = 8.35$$

Then to obtain "corrected" OD value,

$$2.49 - 0.855 - 1.355 = 0.28 \text{ for } 24\gamma \text{ THF}$$
$$4.52 - 1.55\ \ - 2.69\ \ = 0.28 \text{ for } 24\gamma \text{ THE}$$
and $\dfrac{24\gamma}{0.28} = 85.7$ (factor)

Now to obtain total THF and THE in the samples:

Control urine $1.98 - 0.7\ \ - 8.35 \times 0.135 = 0.155$ so $0.155 \times 85.7 = 13.3\gamma/1.5$ ml.

"ACTH" urine $2.08 - 0.73 - 8.35 \times 0.143 = 0.155$ so $0.155 \times 85.7 = 13.3\gamma/0.7$ ml.

"THF" urine $2.31 - 0.8\ \ - 8.35 \times 0.152 = 0.21$ so $0.21\ \ \times 85.7 = 18\gamma/0.5$ ml.

If one used the THE standard only, which is essentially the same as using a hydrocortisone standard, the values obtained for the above three urine samples would be 10.7γ, 11.2γ, and 13.2γ, respectively.

Aqueous mixtures of THE and THF have been determined (from 5–15γ THE and 5–30γ THF) with a precision of $99.0\% \pm 3.65$ (SE), and from urine (from 5–20γ THE and 10–40γ THF) with a precision of $99.9\% \pm 2.1$ (SE).

It is also possible to determine the conjugated 17-hydroxycorticosteroids by the usual procedure, with F, E, or THE as the standard and to make a correction for the incomplete recovery of THF. This, of course, requires an independent procedure for THF, which can be carried out as follows:

(2) Determination of Tetrahydrohydrocortisone.

(a) *Reagents.*

Chloroform (reagent, Merck).

Carbon tetrachloride (reagent, Merck).

0.1 N NaOH.

β-Glucuronidase (Sigma), 250 units per ml. pH 6.5 buffer

Reagent A.

   192 ml. distilled water

   300 ml. sulfuric acid (conc.)

   318 ml. ethanol (absolute)

Reagent B.

   175 ml. distilled water

   133 ml. sulfuric acid (conc.)

   492 ml. glacial acetic acid

Standard. Tetrahydrohydrocortisone 20–40γ/ml. water.

(b) *Materials.*

Tubes and caps as described under Section V.1.A(2).

(c) *Procedure.*

Filtered urine at pH 6.5 is washed twice with 3 volumes of chloroform. After incubation at 37°C. for 18 hours with an equal volume of the enzyme solution, the urine is washed with 3 volumes of carbon tetrachloride.

The sample is diluted to 5 or 1ϕ ml. and shaken in a capped centrifuge tube for 20–30 seconds with 25 ml. of chloroform. The aqueous phase is discarded and the chloroform extract is washed with 2 ml. of 0.1 N NaOH. After centrifugation and discarding the alkaline wash, 20 ml. of the chloroform extract is shaken for 20–30 seconds with 1 ml. of reagent A in a capped test tube.

After centrifugation, 1 ml. of reagent B is added, mixed gently with the 1 ml. of reagent A with a clean stirring rod, and the chloroform is immediately discarded. The mixed A and B reagent is split into 2 portions in test tubes. One is warmed in a water bath to about 60°C., capped, and incubated at 50°C. overnight (18 hours) and the other is warmed to about 40°C., capped, and incubated at 35°C. to serve as a blank.

Optical density measurements are made at 440, 460, and 480 mu, either reading each sample against its blank or reading both against a reagent blank carried through the procedure. 20–150γ standards of THF are carried through the procedure starting with the carbon tetrachloride washing.

(d) *Calculations* (reading against a reagent blank).

	440 mµ	460 mµ
After THF dose	$0.093 - 0.013 = 0.08$	$0.114 - 0.015 = 0.099$
After F dose	$0.101 - 0.020 = 0.081$	$0.123 - 0.020 = 0.103$
After E dose	$0.119 - 0.037 = 0.082$	$0.136 - 0.035 = 0.101$
THF std. 60γ	$0.129 - 0.007 = 0.122$	$0.166 - 0.010 = 0.156$

	480 mµ
After THF dose	$0.089 - 0.012 = 0.077$
After F dose	$0.098 - 0.017 = 0.081$
After E dose	$0.109 - 0.03\ \ = 0.079$
THF std. 60γ	$0.129 - 0.008 = 0.121$

Standard 60γ: $2 \times 0.156 - 0.122 - 0.121 = 0.069$

$60γ/0.069 = 820$ (factor)

THF urine $0.198 - 0.157 = 0.041$; then $0.041 \times 820 = 33.6γ$
in the sample

F urine $0.206 - 0.162 = 0.044$; then $0.044 \times 820 = 36.0γ$
in the sample

E urine $0.202 - 0.161 = 0.041$; then $0.041 \times 820 = 33.6γ$
in the sample

Note: Reaction is not given by THE, tetrahydro B, or tetrahydro A.
Dihydro F and Δ^1-F react like THF.

Greater accuracy is obtained when the largest practical samples and standards are used (optical density at peak about 0.4 or 0.5). Recovery of THF added to urine (40γ–140γ) was 94.2% ± 2.7 (SE).

C. PRESERVATION OF URINE SAMPLES

A concentration of one gram of phenol per liter preserves urine satisfactorily until it can be refrigerated or frozen. DKS are stable in frozen urine for at least a month, but unfrozen, refrigerated samples should be assayed within a few days of collection.

D. APPLICATION OF THE PHENYLHYDRAZINE PROCEDURE TO URINES OF MAN, DOG, GUINEA PIG, AND RAT

Man. Absorption curves obtained with the free and the glucuronide fractions of human urine are shown in Figures 3 and 4. One urine was an 8-hour control sample, others were collected for 8 hours after oral doses of 100 mg. of cortisone, hydrocortisone, or THF. Another 8-hour urine was collected after intramuscular administration of 40 units of ACTH (ACTHAR). The free steroid of the control sample showed a small peak at 410 mµ; after administration of the steroids or ACTH, more typical curves were obtained. The conjugated fraction of all urines gave typical curves with the reagent.

Dog. Similar studies carried out with 24-hour urines of dogs showed that this animal excretes very little free or conjugated DKS normally, but after ACTH, cortisone, or hydrocortisone administration, he excretes both free and conjugated forms (Figures 5 and 6).

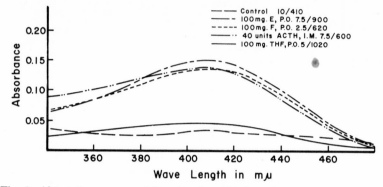

Fig. 3. Absorption curves of free fraction of 8-hour human urine samples. Aliquot analyzed indicated as fraction of total urine.

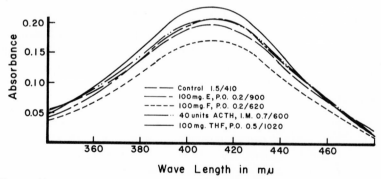

Fig. 4. Absorption curves of glucuronide fraction of the 8-hour human urine samples. Smaller aliquots analyzed as indicated.

An adrenalectomized dog given 40 units of ACTH excreted nothing that was detected by this procedure.

Guinea Pig. This animal excreted significant amounts of free steroid, with typical curves obtained on control urines as well as on urines collected after daily intraperitoneal administration of cortisone, hydrocortisone, or ACTH (Figures 7 and 8). On the other hand, only after cortisone administration was a 410-mμ peak observed with the glucuronide fraction and this represented only a very small portion of the dose administered.   Thus, the guinea pig excretes negligible amounts of DKS in the glucuronide form.

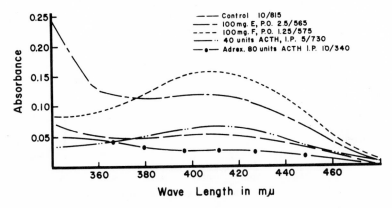

Fig. 5. Absorption curves of free fraction of 24-hour dog urines.

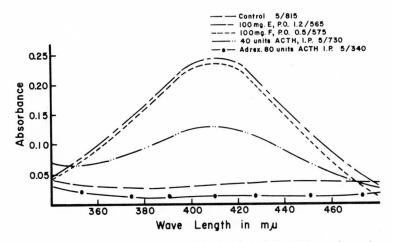

Fig. 6. Absorption curves of glucuronide fraction of the 24-hour dog urines.

Rat.   Even after daily intraperitoneal administration of 24 mg. of cortisone or hydrocortisone, the rat excreted very little steroid (Table V) and typical 410 mμ peaks were not observed with any of the urine samples examined (Figures 9 and 10).   Obviously, this procedure is not applicable to rat urine. Table VI summarizes the above data in terms of mg. steroid excreted per 8 or 24 hours before

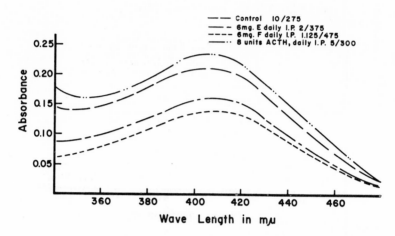

Fig. 7. Absorption curves of free fraction of 4-day guinea pig urines.

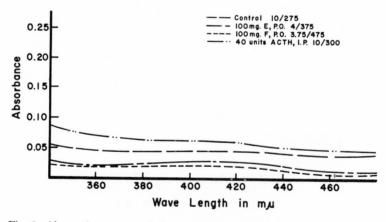

Fig. 8. Absorption curves of glucuronide fraction of the 4-day guinea pig urines.

and after administration of ACTH. In Table V, excretion is expressed as per cent of steroid dose.

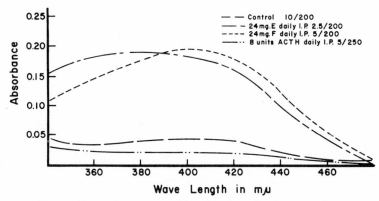

Fig. 9. Absorption curves of free fraction of 4-day rat urines.

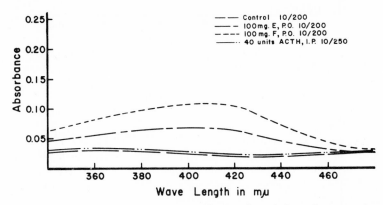

Fig. 10. Absorption curves of glucuronide fraction of the 4-day rat urines.

TABLE V

Per Cent of Administered Steroid Excreted in Urine as 17,21-Dihydroxy-20-keto-steroids

	Daily dose (mg.)	Cortisone		Hydrocortisone	
		Free	Conjugated	Free	Conjugated
Rat (24 hr.)	24	0.26?	0.10?	0.74?	0.21?
Guinea pig (24 hr.)	6	4.2	0.5	10.9	0.3
Dog (24 hr.)	100	0.74	6.3	3.0	25.3[a]
Man (24 hr.)	100	0.88	48.6	1.54	49.5[a]

[a] Corrected for incomplete recovery of THF. Other results calculated from 410 mμ readings only.

TABLE VI

Excretion of 17,21-Dihydroxy-20-ketosteroids (mg.) before and after ACTH Injection

	ACTH units	Control		ACTH Treated	
		Free	Conjugated	Free	Conjugated
Rat (24 hr.)	8 I.P.	0.005?	0	0.009?	0
Guinea pig (24 hr.)	8 I.P.	0.07	0.003?	0.19	0.005?
Dog (24 hr.)	40 I.P.	0.2	0.03	0.48	1.15
Man (8 hr.)	40 I.M.	0.05	2.9	0.5	9.6

References

1. Allen, W. M., *J. Clin. Endocrinol. and Metabolism, 10,* 71 (1950).
2. Bongiovanni, A. M., and Eberlein, W. R., *Proc. Soc. Exptl. Biol. Med., 89,* 281 (1955).
3. Brooks, C. J. W., and Norymberski, J. K., *Chemistry & Industry, 1952,* 804.
4. Bush, I. E., and Sandberg, A. A., *J. Biol. Chem., 205,* 783 (1953).
5. Clark, I., *Nature, 175,* 123 (1955).
6. Cook, E. R., Dell, B., and Wareham, D. J., *Analyst, 80,* 215 (1955).
7. Coste, F., and Delbarre, F., *Presse Med., 61,* 46 (1953).
8. Glenn, E. M., and Nelson, D. H., *J. Clin. Endocrinol. and Metabolism, 13,* 911 (1953).
9. Gornall, A. G., and MacDonald, M. P., *J. Biol. Chem., 201,* 279 (1953).
10. Hechter, O. M., in E. P. Ralli, ed., *Adrenal Cortex,* Josiah Macy, Jr., Foundation, New York, 115, 3rd Conference, Nov., 1951 (1952).
11. Klein, R., Papadatos, C., Fortunato, J., and Byers, C., *J. Clin. Endocrinol. and Metabolism, 15,* 215 (1955).
12. Mader, W. J., and Buck, R. R., *Anal. Chem., 24,* 666 (1952).
13. Marks, L. J., and Leftin, J. H., *J. Clin. Endocrinol. and Metabolism, 14,* 1263 (1954).
14. Mattox, V. R., *J. Am. Chem. Soc., 74,* 4340 (1952).
15. Mattox, V. R., Mason, H. L., and Albert, A., *Proc. Staff Meetings, Mayo Clin., 28,* 569 (1953).
16. Nelson, D. H., and Samuels, L. T., *J. Clin. Endocrinol. and Metabolism, 12,* 519 (1952).
17. Nelson, D. H., Samuels, L. T., Willardson, D. G., and Tyler, F. H., *J. Clin. Endocrinol. and Metabolism, 11,* 1021 (1951).
18. Nowaczynski, W. J., and Steyermark, P. R., *Arch. Biochem. and Biophys., 58,* 453 (1955).
19. Porter, C. C., and Silber, R. H., *J. Biol. Chem., 185,* 201 (1950).
20. Reddy, W. J., Jenkins, D., and Thorn, G. W., *Metab., 1,* 511 (1952).

21. Silber, R. H., and Busch, R. D., *J. Clin. Endocrinol. and Metabolism, 15,* 505 (1955).
22. Silber, R. H., and Busch, R. D., *J. Clin. Endocrinol. and Metab. 16,* 1333 (1956).
23. Silber, R. H., and Porter, C. C., *J. Biol. Chem., 210,* 923 (1954).
24. Steyermark, P. R., and Nowaczynski, W. J., *Arch. Biochem. and Biophys., 59,* 1 (1955).
25. Sweat, M. L., *Anal. Chem., 26,* 773 (1954).
26. Sweat, M. L., *Anal. Chem., 26,* 1964 (1954).
27. Weichselbaum, T. E., and Margraf, H. W., *J. Clin. Endocrinol. and Metabolism, 15,* 970 (1955).
28. Zaffaroni, A., *J. Am. Chem. Soc., 72,* 3829 (1950).

THE pH-STAT and Its Use in Biochemistry

C. F. Jacobsen, J. Léonis, K. Linderstrøm-Lang, and M.
Ottesen, *Carlsberg Laboratory, Copenhagen, Denmark*

I. INTRODUCTION

The problem of measuring the rate and extension of chemical reactions under constant and well defined conditions is a fundamental one. In liquid systems the distribution of electric charges on the reacting molecules is, besides the temperature, the most important general rate-controlling factor, and since the hydrogen ion plays a dominant role in determining this distribution, it is natural that in the past years much stress has been laid upon the maintenance of a constant hydrogen ion potential during chemical reactions. The rate at which proton equilibria are reached is generally so high in proportion to reaction rates measured in biochemistry that the charge distribution at any transient state of a reacting system is well reflected in the hydrogen ion potential μ_{H^+} or in pH. We shall not enter here into a discussion of the significance (or non-significance) of the potential of single ions (see e.g., Bates (2) but define pH by the electric potential, E, of a suitable cell consisting of a hydrogen ion electrode, immersed in the reaction system, a KCl-bridge, and a reference electrode, assuming that the diffusion potential is negligible or independent of any changes of the system, i.e.,

$$\text{pH} = \frac{(E_0 - E) \cdot F \cdot 0.4343}{RT} = -0.4343 \frac{\mu_{H^+}}{RT} + C$$

where E_0 and C are constants at constant temperature T (F = Faraday constant, R = gas constant).

Maintenance of a constant pH may be effected in two different ways, viz., by letting the reaction proceed in a buffered solution or by continuous addition of acid or base during the reaction. In the latter case buffering is unnecessary or even undesirable. The former method which was developed in detail by Sørensen (20) is especially suitable for the study of reactions in which there is no formation of acid or base (e.g., the splitting of sucrose) so that a relatively low concentration of buffer suffices to fix and maintain the pH of the reaction system. The latter method which, as regards biochemical application, originates in the work of Knaffl-Lenz (9) is advantageous in cases where the reaction studied causes strong drifts of pH due to changes in the acidic or basic properties of the reacting molecules (e.g., the splitting of carboxylic acid esters). The fact that the quantities of acid or base required to keep pH constant may be used as a measure of the extension of the reaction makes this method attractively simple and explains the extensive use to which it has been put. Its main disadvantage is that in its original and simplest form it requires the continuous presence of an observer who reads and adjusts the pH, while noting the time and quantity of acid or base added. It is therefore natural that a series of attempts have been made to automatize the method, and in this chapter we shall describe some of the latest developments in this regard.

Knaffl-Lenz in his esterase work adjusted pH colorimetrically, a procedure which may give excellent results in this case provided pH is outside the buffer range of the acid formed and lies in the neighborhood of the pH-optimum of the enzyme where the acitivity is but slightly dependent upon pH. However, the colorimetric method is not very well suited for automatization, a color registration requiring quite clear reaction systems.

The direct registration of an electrode potential, the variation of which directs the addition of acid or base from a burette, seems the most obvious principle to adopt but progress along this line was held up by the lack of suitable instruments for the registration of the potential and for the adjustment of pH (19). One of the first who took advantage of the technical development in this field of pH-meters was Whitnah (22) who in 1933 constructed an automatic burette which was electromagnetically operated from a potentiometer in connection with the cell containing the reaction system. Both glass and antimony electrodes where tried. Longsworth and MacInnes (13) in 1935, using a glass electrode cell in connection with a special compensation potentiometer, registered the pH change by means of a Compton electrometer, the reflected light-beam of which operated their electromagnetic burette photoelectrically. The authors discussed the more important sources of errors and emphasized the insufficient stability of the vacuum tube potentiometers available at that time.

This technical problem was solved in the following years but the interest in building fully automatic pH-stats for kinetic studies seems to have faded simultaneously. Instead, a series of automatic devices serving to titrate a given solution to a given endpoint or to record the titration curve of a given substance have been described, and several of these are commercially available. Only one of these devices shall be mentioned here, viz., that of Lingane (12), because some of its principles have been used in the instrument built at the Carlsberg Laboratory (8). In Lingane's apparatus the potential of the glass electrode cell is registered by a vacuum-tube pH-meter in connection with a recorder and controller. The acid or base is added by means of a burette syringe which is operated by a synchronous motor. The recorder draws the pH-time curve and since the curve for the relationship between the quantity of acid (or base) added and time is a straight line, the titration curve (with suitable change of abscissae) is actually drawn by the recorder.

The controller plays a role only in automatic titrations to a fixed endpoint where it serves to break the current of the burette motor when the endpoint is reached. The tricks used to prevent the burette motor from overshooting in this case are not advantageous in pH-stats and are hardly of interest for the present problem.

Before going into details of recent pH-stats it may be of value to emphasize the general usefulness of an instrument which is able to maintain the potential of a given reaction system against an electrode and record the quantity of a particular reagent necessary for this maintenance. There may be cases where it is of importance to keep the redox potential constant in a chemical reaction and where consequently the acid or base should be replaced by a suitable oxidizing or reducing agent. Actually most of Lingane's work was concerned with measurements of redox systems. In the following, however, we shall deal exclusively with hydrogen ion electrode potentials and pH.

II. PRINCIPLE AND CONSTRUCTIONAL DETAILS OF THE pH-STAT

1. Principle

As mentioned above, a pH-stat consists of an appropriate cell comprising a hydrogen ion electrode (in the following, a glass electrode) immersed in the reaction system, a KCl-bridge and a reference electrode. This cell is connected with a suitable pH-meter which in turn is connected with an adjustable controlling device. This device operates a motor-driven burette dipping into the reaction system and supplying the system with acid or base, in the following termed *reagent*, and it is so adjusted that when the potential of the cell differs from that corresponding to the desired pH-value, it will start and maintain addition of reagent until the potential is restored to its original value. If the instrument works properly, the deviations from the desired electrode potential or pH will be very small, and the reaction may be regarded as being performed at constant pH. The uptake of reagent as a function of time can be read directly from the burette or, as is more common, be recorded on a mechanical recorder.

This apparatus functions by having the burette drive operate a pen, the displacement of which is proportional to the amount of reagent delivered by the burette, while a synchronous motor moves the graph paper, on which the pen writes, along a time axis perpendicular to the displacement of the pen.

2. The pH-meter

According to our experience reasonably accurate kinetic work requires that pH be kept constant within less than 0.01 pH-unit for at least 24 hours. Hence the demands on the pH-meter are more exacting than on instruments used in accurate but discontinuous pH-work. A sensitivity better than 0.01 pH-unit is achieved with many pH-meters, but only few of them have a sufficiently small zero drift and a sufficiently constant sensitivity to permit keeping pH within this range for several hours without adjustment.

Since it is much more difficult to build a very stable D.C.-amplifier than a stable A.C.-amplifier, the above mentioned requirements seem to be best fulfilled by using a pH-meter with modulated input. In such instruments the D.C.-potential of the electrodes is converted into A.C. by means of a modulator of either the mechanical switch-type or the dynamic condenser-type. The A.C.-signal goes into an amplifier which is tuned to the modulating frequency to avoid the possibility of amplifying undesired voltages of other frequencies. If the amplifier furthermore has "negative feedback," the sensitivity will remain constant, regardless of small variations in the characteristics of the amplifier tubes and of the line voltage. In the Carlsberg Laboratory we have used pH-meters of this type (pH-M 22, Radiometer, Copenhagen) in pH-stat set-ups with satisfactory results. An instrument of the same type is described by S. O. Nielsen and T. Rosenberg (15). It is characterized by a still better stability, viz., a drift below 30 μV in 12 hours, and a higher sensitivity, i.e., about 10 μV. Theoretically it is possible to improve these amplifiers further, but imperfections of the present types of glass electrodes and variations of the liquid junction potential of the cell make the advantage of increased sensitivity questionable.

3. Controlling Device

The function of the controller is to start the motor-driven burette when the output potential of the pH-meter deviates from the fixed value, and stop it when the potential is restored to the original value. The difference between the starting and the stopping position has to be less than that corresponding to 0.01 pH-unit, and the rate of response should be suitably high (see Section III.3). We have mainly used the previously described milliammeter with movable contacts (8). This instrument gives full deflection for ±5 mA., and the internal resistance is 500 ohms. The moving coil carries a platinum pointer which is made as short as possible (2.5 cm.) in order to keep the inertia low, and friction is decreased by a loose fitting of the upper bearing. Contact is made between the pointer and an adjustable platinum needle. Since this controller is able to break only weak currents, it is connected with a simple electronic relay having a control current of a fraction of a milliampere. In spite of these precautions sticking of the needle contacts is a serious problem, and this difficulty can only be overcome by adjusting the moving coil part of the relay so that the small A.C.-component in the D.C.-output from the pH-meter will keep it vibrating continuously. The effect of this is that the contact during an experiment is never actually closed for more than $1/_{50}$ sec. The small current impulses from the closings of the contact are summed up by means of a 0.1 μF condenser, and a 125 ohm resister in series across the contacts, which arrangement facilitates the functioning of the electronic relay which starts or stops the burette motor.

We have also had some experience with a capacity-sensitive relay (Fielden Electronics Ltd., Manchester, England) which served excellently. The instrument consists of a moving coil-meter (connected as the one above), the pointer being fitted with a small light metal vane which acts as one plate of a variable condenser. Another similar vane, adjusted by a control handle on the front of the case, moves in the same arc as that operated by the meter, and an electronic capacity-senstive relay operates when the two vanes are a given distance apart.

The difference between the levels of energization and de-energization of the relay corresponds to less than 0.01 pH-unit. The stability is excellent. Sticking of the vanes (e.g., due to contact during setting) does not take place, since one of the vanes carries a small graphite guard-point.

Besides the contact-meter and the capacity-meter used at the Carlsberg Laboratory, a photocell-controlled unit is routinely used in certain other laboratories. The output is sent from the pH-meter to a sensitive galvanometer with a very short reaction time; the galvanometer's light-beam, transmitted through mirrors in order to achieve a compact unit, reaches an R.C.A. 920 twin photocell of which one component stops, and the other starts, the syringe motor (compare (13)). By means of this circuit, the light-beam is kept within narrow fluctuations in the space between the two components of the photocell. The amplification circuit between photocell and motor includes a 6SC7 double triode, a Siemens polarized relay (with permanent contact in either direction) sensitized to ± 0.3 ma., followed by a stronger relay of the usual type (input about 10 ma., output sufficient for the motor).

The advantages of this instrument are that there is no sticking of needles and that the adjustment of the galvanometer to the working position (by means of a suitable potentiometer in series with the pH-meter) is very fine. A possible drawback might be found in the relative sluggishness of the whole unit, the time-lag being of the order of $1/5$ to $1/2$ sec., but steps in the recorded curve are avoided by having a very mobile galvanometer and a well sensitized Siemens relay.

4. Automatic Titrators as pH-Stats

A more refined and at the same time robust and reliable pH-stat can be made by the use of elaborate electronic circuitry. Several "automatic titrators" incorporating adjustable proportional control are produced commercially. Our own experience is again limited to a single instrument of this type (Titrator TTTI, Radiometer, Copenhagen). It contains a stable amplifier similar to the one used in pH-M 22, and an adjustable potentiometer in connection with a thyratron circuit which determines the pH-value at which the relay will operate the burette motor. Proportional control offers the advantage that, within an adjustable pH-range near the set endpoint pH_p, the burette motor will run discontinuously with smaller and smaller current impulses the closer pH comes to pH_p, and the motor will stop completely when pH_p is reached. Outside this range the motor will run continuously at maximum speed. This behavior has its advantages especially in automatic titrations because it prevents "overshooting" the endpoint. It has the drawback in pH-stat work that pH_p will never be reached in practice, the working pH deviating the more from pH_p the faster the reaction studied (see Section III.3). In our attempt to reduce $pH - pH_p$ to the smallest possible value we have chosen the narrowest proportionality band of the instrument, *viz.*, 0.1 pH-unit, and, by proper selection of gear-train for the burette motor, the maximum rate of reagent addition, corresponding to continuous running of the motor, was made at least two or three times the maximal rate required for the reaction. In this way the pH-deviations due to the proportional control may be kept within the range 0.03–0.05 pH-units, which, as will be shown in Section III.4, example 1c, is sufficient in most cases.

5. Burette

In most automatic titrators addition of reagent is made with an ordinary burette operated by some type of magnetic valve. However, such a burette is not suitable for automatic registration, and we have therefore adopted the principle introduced by Lingane (12) of using a motor-driven burette-syringe. The problem of registration is then reduced to the simple problem of registering the number of revolutions of a screw, and besides small volumes can be handled with greater accuracy. The size of the syringe burette is naturally determined by the volume of reagent needed to follow a particular reaction, but for most purposes we have found the "AGLA"-micrometer syringe satisfactory (Burroughs Wellcome and Co., London). It is an all-glass syringe with a total capacity of 0.5 ml.; displacement of the plunger is effected by means of a micrometer screw, one revolution corresponding to 10 μl. The standard metal needle for the syringe is normally replaced by a bent tip made of glass capillary tubing (int. diam. 0.2–0.3 mm.) connected with the syringe by a small piece of rubber tubing.*

6. Recorder with Syringe Motor

The purpose of the recorder is to register the reagent-consumption, *viz.*, the number of revolutions of the micrometer screw of the burette as a function of time. We have adopted the simple principle of a mechanical recorder directly connected with the micrometer burette, and the burette motor has been built in as a part of the recorder. The first design (O. Dich, Copenhagen) is shown in Figure 1. The base is a plywood board or a metal plate A on which are screwed two

* Burroughs Wellcome and Co. now offers glass needles for the Agla syringe; they can be obtained bent at a right angle (about 6 cm. long) and with standard ground glass joint, so that rubber connections may be avoided.

steel rails B.   The Lucite carriage C rolls on the rails on two wheels
D; it is moved by the time axis lead screw E (1 mm. pitch) which is
turned by the synchronous motor M_1 via the gear train G_1.   The
lower half of the nut P at the extreme right of the carriage, connecting
the carriage with the lead screw, is cut away.   By lifting the right
end of the carriage this can be brought back to the starting position
after the completion of an experiment, without having to turn the
lead screw all the way back.   The graph paper is clamped to the
carriage by means of the bars F.

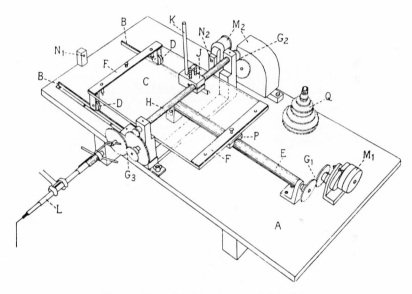

Fig. 1. Recorder (Jacobsen and Léonis).

Another lead screw H (1 mm. pitch) is placed perpendicular to the
time axis lead screw E.   H carries a nut J (sawed through, spring
loaded); J carries a pencil or pen K.   The direction of rotation of H
is such that the pencil is pressed slightly against the graph paper.
H is turned by the speed-reduced motor M_2 via the gear train G_2.
M_2 is controlled by the electronic relay.   The lead screw H turns the
burette L via the gear train G_3.

This recorder has served excellently for the registration of many
types of reactions, but it has certain limitations with regard to following fast reactions.   Since considerable power is required to drive

the recorder and syringe the motor must have an appreciable size, and the rotor will therefore have so much inertia that it will continue to rotate for a few seconds after the current has been interrupted. The result is an addition of excess reagent causing the pH to "overshoot." This difficulty is avoided in a new type of recorder shown in Figure 2 (O. Dich, Copenhagen). The drive motor for burette and recorder is placed inside the wooden box underneath the metal top plate and it runs continuously. Connection with the gear train for

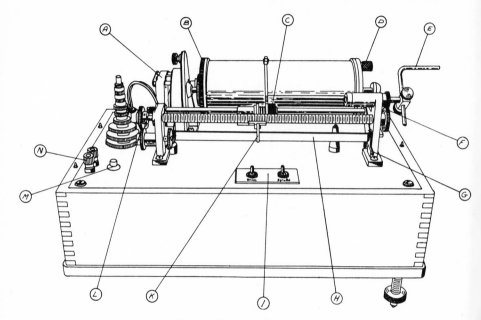

Fig. 2. Recorder (Ottesen).

the recorder spindle is made with an electromagnetic clutch operated from the relay in the pH-stat. In this way the addition of reagent may be stopped within a fraction of a second after the current has been interrupted. The selectable gear train L from the motor to the spindle carrying the pen corresponds to a pen movement of from 0.2 mm. per sec. to 1.0 mm. per sec. Gear train F at the other end of the spindle corresponds to either a 10 or a 5 mm. movement of the pen per turn of the burette screw. The pen can be disengaged from the spindle by pressing down the arm K. The graph paper is bent round a cylindrical drum driven by an exchangeable synchronous motor A. The ends of the paper are bent inside a slit in the drum and held in place by a spring operated by knob D.   By this arrangement, experiments lasting longer than the time for one revolution of the drum may be followed without interruption, a definite improvement over the first model where the paper carriage has to be brought back to a new starting point when it has come to the end of its travel.   The recorder unit is placed on three adjustable legs so that the axis for the pin E connecting recorder with burette can be adjusted to the same level as the axis of the burette screw.

7. Titration Vessels

The types of titration vessels are determined by the size of the electrodes used and the amounts of solution available.   Some typical reaction vessels are shown in Figure 3.   These reaction vessels fit a

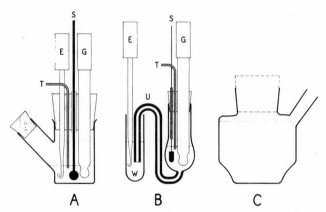

Fig. 3. Titration vessels.   G, glass electrode; E, calomel electrode; S, stirrer; T, burette tip; U, agar bridge; W, vessel with saturated KCl.   The lower part of the titration vessel in B is flattened perpendicular to the plane of the paper in order to reduce volume and still leave space for the stirrer.

standard shielded glass electrode, 9 cm. long, stem diameter 10 mm., and a calomel electrode with a 9 cm. long stem, 4 mm. in diameter, which is drawn out at the end to form a U-bend.   If the question of quantity of material is of minor importance, the type shown in Figure 3A is to be preferred.   It consists of a 30 ml. beaker provided with a side arm for introducing or withdrawing samples, and it takes about

10 ml. reaction mixture. It is normally closed with a rubber stopper through which the glass and calomel electrodes are introduced, and in which there are additional holes for the stirrer, the burette tip, and the inlet for inert gas when oxygen or carbon dioxide should be excluded. If the stopper fits tightly enough, no other support is required to hold the vessel in position, since both electrodes are solidly mounted on stands.

The vessel shown in Figure 3B is convenient for volumes of about 2 ml. The rubber stopper is furnished with holes for the glass electrode, the burette tip, and the stirrer, while an auxiliary hole serves for the introduction of samples or for gas. Also here, the glass electrode with the rubber stopper offers sufficient support for the vessel. The contact with the calomel electrode is made through an agar bridge in a capillary tube leading to the bottom of the reaction vessel.

For bigger volumes, up to 100 ml., we have used the type shown in Figure 3C, where the neck is so dimensioned that it fits the same stopper as vessel A.

The vessels described above are the simplest and most robust ones in use at the moment. It should, however, be mentioned that in rare cases, viz., in measurements of reactions in certain non-aqueous solvents it is advantageous to avoid the use of rubber stoppers and all-glass vessels would be preferred. Since, in the design of such complicated and rigid constructions, specific requirements have to be fulfilled with regard to fitting-in of electrodes, stirring device, burette tip, etc., their shape must necessarily be adjusted not only to the specific problem at hand, but also to the type of electrodes, etc. commercially available to the laboratory applying the method. For this reason we shall refrain from giving examples of all-glass vessels, although such have been devised and used at several places.

8. Stirring

Theoretically, the stirring ought to be so efficient that any small quantity of reagent added to the reaction mixture is evenly distributed in a much shorter time than that of the response of the instrument, i.e., in less than 0.6 second. It is our belief that for the quantities of solution dealt with here the old-fashioned mechanical stirrers, viz., rotating rods with blades, are the most effective ones. The necessity of avoiding splashing and foaming sets a limit to the rate of revolution of such mechanical stirrers, and slight defects in their mounting

may cause unsteadiness of movement which at high speed, in the
limited space available for the stirrer, may become a danger to the
glass electrode. The problem of completely adequate stirring is
therefore still an unsolved one.

For the reaction vessels used with volumes of 10 ml. or more, a
glass spatula with the head immersed in the liquid serves as a stirrer.
It is held in position in the rubber stopper by a low-friction bearing
made of a well-fitting sleeve of polythene tubing, neither too tight nor
too loose, in order not to create static electricity by friction, since this
would cause unsteadiness of the potentiometer. In the 2 ml. reaction vessels stirring is produced with a small platinum rod (0.8 mm.
in diameter) having a rectangular piece of platinum welded to the end.
For the bearing and support for the platinum wire, a loosely fitting
glass tube fixed in the rubber stopper and protruding down close to
the surface of the liquid is used.

The stirrers are driven by small electrical motors with adjustable
speed. Connection between motor axis and stirrer is made by a
short piece of rubber tubing. Motors giving so much electrical noise
that they disturb the potentiometer should naturally be avoided.

9. Electrodes (and Shielding)

Glass electrodes used in pH-stats have to be especially stable and
well shielded; low resistance, and practical size and shape (see Section
II.7) are other desirable properties. Equal stabilities are required
of the reference electrodes, and preference should be given to types
which can be brought into direct contact with the reaction mixture
without appreciable loss of salt, i.e., types which have narrow U-bends
at the tip (see Sections II.7 and II.12).

The outlet from the calomel electrode is normally the one that is
grounded in our setups while the glass electrode is effectively insulated. Naturally both the reaction mixture and the liquid in the
burette, which is in contact with it, should also be kept well insulated
from the surroundings.

10. Temperature Regulation

The electrode vessels shown in Figure 3 are all shaped and mounted
in a manner which facilitates their partial immersion in a water thermostat. The reaction system and the glass electrode may therefore

be kept at constant temperature ($\pm 0.01°C.$).   However, the calomel electrodes used by us contain the packing of mercury and calomel, i.e., the electrode proper, in the upper end of the tube (with KCl) which passes through the above named rubber stopper into the reaction vessel.   The electrode is therefore actually outside of the thermostat, and the full utilization of the temperature regulation of the water thermostat can only be obtained in this case by placing the pH-stat in a constant temperature room.   Whenever possible the temperature of this room should be within $1°C.$ of the temperature of the water thermostat.   In coarse experiments ordinary room temperature is constant enough, a change of $1°C.$ corresponding to 0.005 pH-unit.

The ideal calomel electrode would have its packing of mercury and calomel at the lower end of the electrode stem near the U-bend (Section II.7), where contact is made between KCl and reaction mixture. The glass electrode and the calomel electrode would then be under identical conditions, and the regulation of the air temperature would mainly serve to keep the electrical system of the pH-stat in a constant environment.*

11. Some Sources of Error

In general we have found that the pH-stat is a very reliable instrument, but from time to time erratic functioning has been observed, registered mostly as rapid, more or less violent, intermittent deflections of the potentiometer needle, indicating some fault in the electrical system (poor screening, contact trouble, etc.).   There are, however, also treacherous errors, inside or outside the electrical system, which, if registered at all, are observed only occasionally and therefore may go unnoticed.   We shall deal with these errors below.

1. Most of the glass electrodes used have had a drift of less than 0.01 pH-unit per day.   A few of them showed, however, though stable at constant room temperature, a considerable drift after having

---

* Several firms (Beckman, Radiometer) manufacture electrodes which in part fulfill these requirements, but the way in which the contact between reaction mixture and saturated KCl is made (e.g., through a film of KCl between two conical ground glass surfaces) excludes an ocular inspection of the junction and leads to rather uncontrolled leaking of the denser KCl into the reaction mixture from above. However, in experiments where changes in the ionic strength of the system are of little importance, such electrodes may still be useful.

been exposed to sudden temperature changes of only a few degrees centigrade.   Such electrodes should be picked out by testing for stability at two different temperatures, and discarded.*

2.   One of the problems in precise pH-stat work is the liquid junction or diffusion potential at the boundary between saturated KCl and reaction mixture.   This potential is insufficiently known except for very simple systems, and its variation, e.g., during a kinetic run with a biological reaction mixture, cannot be estimated.   It is generally accepted that the diffusion potential is better defined at fresh interfaces than at ones which have been established for some time, and since renewal of the interface is inadvisable or, in the case of a KCl-agar-bridge, impossible in the course of a kinetic run, the measurements are encumbered with errors due to such changes of the state of the interface that would also occur in a static system.   It is reasonable to believe, however, that the diffusion potential is small in dilute systems between pH 3 and 11 (in 0.001 N HCl in 0.1 N KCl it is of the order of 0.1 mv. $\sim$ 0.002 pH-unit) and that, consequently, its variations may be neglected.   In more concentrated solutions, e.g., studying an enzymatic reaction, the zero uptake of reagent before addition of enzyme may be used for a correction hoping that the change in diffusion potential with time is taken care of together with other unexplained effects.

It is advisable, when working on the 10-ml. scale, where the liquid junction is at the upward-bent tip of the calomel electrode, to inspect the boundary here from time to time during an experiment.   Sometimes the KCl solution is washed out all the way down to the bend, so that some less dense reaction mixture may be carried by convection currents into the electrode.

In vessels with an agar-bridge this should be renewed frequently.

3.   Since the tip of the burette is continuously under the surface of the reaction mixture, it should be as narrow as possible.   In practice,

---

* The well-known phenomenon of electrode poisoning by organic compounds should perhaps also be mentioned.   Several organic reagents like fluorodinitrobenzene or substituted phenylisothiocyanates may occasionally act in this way, and proteins may sometimes denature on the surface of the electrode thus causing drifts of potentials.   Electrodes used in a mixture of water and another solvent (ethanol, propanol, dioxane, pyridine) should, as far as possible, be reserved for measurements in the particular system studied, since shifts from one mixed solvent to another often disturb the balance of the electrode.

however, especially in the study of fast reactions, a limit is set by the necessity of adding a rapid stream of reagent without bringing the pressure inside the burette to the danger point where reagent will leak out, e.g., between the piston and the inner wall.

The use of a wider tip implies that an appreciable amount of reagent may be contained in the vertical part of the tip, and if the

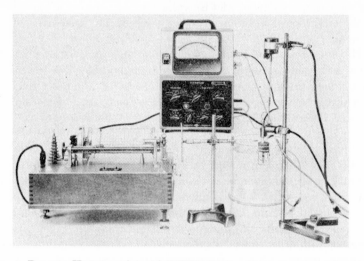

Fig. 4. Recent pH-stat model with TTTI titrator, Ottesen recorder, burette, titration vessel (10 ml., Fig. 3A), and thermostat.

reagent has but a slightly higher density than the reaction mixture, convection currents may carry reaction mixture into the tip and deliver unregistered reagent to the solution. This naturally occurs in the period when the syringe motor is not operating. The subsequent effect is that when the motor starts adding reagent, this will be contaminated with reaction mixture at the beginning before pure reagent is added. When the motor stops again, the leaking out of reagent will start and the sequence of events is repeated. The result of this defect is that the rate curve for the slow part of a reaction is not smooth but discontinuous, consisting of a series of big steps (see Section III.3). The defect can easily be adjusted by choosing reagent solutions of lower density than that of the reaction mixture, or if this is not possible, by giving the burette-tip a small U-bend.

4. In some cases another burette error may arise. The narrow space between burette wall and glass piston is normally filled with

reagent, and hence, at the end of the burette there is a small free liquid surface from which slow evaporation may take place, thus causing an error in the volume of reagent added to the reaction mixture. This effect is only of significance in prolonged experiments or with badly worn syringes, and may easily be prevented by a thin coating of silicone grease on the piston.

12. Operating Procedure for the pH-Stat

Before starting an experiment the electrodes are standardized with buffers at the temperature of the experiment. In enzymatic rate studies the reaction vessel is then filled with the substrate solution, assembled with the rubber stopper, electrodes, and stirrer, and placed in the water thermostat. If required inert gas is led through. The burette is next filled with reagent and placed in position, its tip being pushed down through the hole provided for it in the rubber stopper until it dips in the substrate solution. The controller device is finally adjusted to regulate at the proper pH, the recorder with the burette drive is started, and the pH-stat will function and record possible blank reactions. After a suitable time, without stopping the machine, enzyme is added to the substrate, and the reaction may then be followed for any time required. If the enzyme solution added deviates much from the substrate as regards pH, it is advisable to bring it to the correct pH in a separate experiment before mixing it with the substrate solution.

Figure 4 shows one of the pH-stats in use at Carlsberg Laboratory at present.

III. THEORETICAL OBSERVATIONS

1. Elementary Theory of Acid or Base Formation at Constant pH

The theory of acid-base equilibria is so well known that a very brief discussion of the problem pertaining to the formation ("creation") of acids or bases at constant pH may suffice for the present purpose.

As a basis for our consideration we may use the mass action equation

$$pH = pK + \log b/a \qquad (1)$$

where a and b are the concentrations of an acid, A, and its corresponding base, B, which are in equilibrium according to the scheme

$$A \rightleftharpoons B + H^+ \tag{2}$$

pH may be measured and calculated in any suitable way, provided
pK, the pH of a solution containing A and B in equal concentrations
($a = b$) is measured and calculated in the same way and under the
same conditions (same solvent, same temperature, same electric cell).
Furthermore the formulation of equation (1) implies that the activities of A and B are proportional to a and b. It should be emphasized
that in equation (2) A may be uncharged (like RCOOH), while B is
negatively charged (RCOO$^-$), or A may be positively charged (like
RNH$_3^+$) and B uncharged (RNH$_2$) (3). The above condition is
therefore satisfied with fair accuracy if pH (and pK) is measured in a
medium of constant ionic strength (e.g., 0.1 M KCl choosing a and b
$\ll 0.1$).

If the acid or base considered is the solvent itself, denoted SH,
equation (1) may be written

$$pH = pS - \log SH_2^+ \tag{1a}$$

where the basic properties of SH are taken into account, or

$$pH = pSH + \log S^- \tag{1b}$$

where the acidic properties of SH are considered. S^- and SH_2^+ are
the concentrations of S$^-$ and SH$_2^+$. SH is put equal to 1 in both ex-
pressions.   In the case of water SH$_2^+$ = H$_3^+$O, S$^-$ = OH$^-$, pS $\sim$ 0,
and pSH $\sim$ 14, the latter values depending upon the particular pH-
definition used.   According to Sørensen's original scale (20),

$$pS = 0.04 \qquad pSH = 14.07$$

$$pSH - pS = - \log (SH_2^+ \cdot S^-) = 14.03 \qquad (18°C.)$$

If other pH scales are used and especially if solvents other than water
are considered, pS or pSH may have quite different values (see (2)).

We shall later return to a brief discussion of the errors involved
in applying these simple considerations to actual measurements.

Assuming equation (1) to be valid, we have:

The quantity of hydrogen ions (n_{H^+}) which is required to keep pH
constant while a base is created in a given system is

$$n_{H^+} = B \cdot \frac{a}{a + b} = B \cdot \frac{1}{1 + 10^{pH - pB}} = B \cdot \beta \text{ moles} \tag{3}$$

B is the total quantity of base created, equal to $V(a + b)$ where V is the volume of the system, and pB is the pK-value of the base formed. V is assumed to be constant. β is given in Figure 5 as a function of pH − pB.

Similarly the quantity of hydrogen ions which must be removed in order to keep pH constant while an acid is created in a given system is

$$-n_{H^+} = A \cdot \frac{b}{a + b} = A \frac{10^{pH-pA}}{1 + 10^{pH-pA}} = A \cdot \alpha \text{ moles} \qquad (4)$$

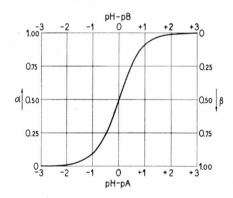

Fig. 5. Ionization curve for acids and bases.

A is the total quantity of acid formed $(= V(a + b))$ and pA the pK-value of the acid. α is given in Figure 5 as a function of pH − pA.

For the sake of simplicity the addition of acid or base has been expressed in terms of an addition or a removal of hydrogen ions, n_{H^+}. This leaves the character and strength of the reagent acid and base A_R and B_R undetermined. We have, however, from equations (3) and (4),

$$A_R \alpha_R = n_{H^+} = B\beta \qquad (5)$$

$$B_R \beta_R = -n_{H^+} = A\alpha \qquad (6)$$

which are the reactions between the quantities of acid or base, A_R or B_R, required to keep pH constant during the formation of B or A. If A_R is a strong acid, $\alpha_R = 1$, $A_R = n_{H^+}$ (e.g., HCl). If B_R is a strong base $\beta_R = 1$, $B_R = -n_{H^+}$ (e.g., NaOH).

In general we therefore get

$$\left.\begin{array}{c} A_R\alpha_R \\ -B_R\beta_R \end{array}\right\} N_{H^+} =$$

$$\left\{\sum_i B_i\beta_i - \sum_k A_k\alpha_k\right\}_{\text{final}} - \left\{\sum_l B_l\beta_l - \sum_m A_m\alpha_m\right\}_{\text{initial}} \quad (7)$$

for the quantity of hydrogen ions, N_{H^+}, required to keep pH constant, while k acids and i bases are formed at the expense of m acids and l bases. Correspondingly we get for the rate of uptake of hydrogen ions

$$\frac{dN_{H^+}}{dt} = \sum_r \beta_r \frac{dB_r}{dt} - \sum_s \alpha_s \frac{dA_s}{dt} \qquad (r \text{ bases, } s \text{ acids}) \quad (8)$$

If V is not constant but varies from V_i to V_f—and in actual experiments the system is naturally diluted by the solutions of acid or base added—a correction has to be applied for the adjustment of the volume $V_f - V_i$ of the solvent to the pH in question. The quantity of reagent acid or base required for this adjustment should be found by titrating the solvent with A_R or B_R. The correction is generally small and may be neglected except in regions of low and high pH-values, where the measurement is less accurate anyhow (see below). In water using HCl and NaOH for titration, the correction on N_{H^+} is

$$- (H_3^+O - OH^-)(V_f - V_i)$$

2. Buffer Capacity and pH-Regulation

The accuracy with which the formation of acids and bases can be followed is given by the buffer capacity of the system

$$BC = \frac{dN_{H^+}}{d\text{pH}} \quad (9)$$

The smaller the quantity BC, the smaller are the fluctuations of pH (see Section III.3). For a single acid or base we find by differentiation of equations (3) and (4) with respect to pH

$$\frac{dn_{H^+}}{d\text{pH}} = -2.303B \frac{10^{\text{pH}-\text{pB}}}{(1 + 10^{\text{pH}-\text{pB}})^2} = -2.303A \frac{10^{\text{pH}-\text{pA}}}{(1 + 10^{\text{pH}-\text{pA}})^2} \quad (10)$$

The buffer capacity of the solvent is found from equations (1a) and (1b), viz.,

$$\frac{dn_{H^+}}{d\text{pH}} = -2.303 \cdot V \cdot 10^{\text{pS}-\text{pH}} \qquad \text{pH approaching pS} \quad (11)$$

$$\frac{dn_{H^+}}{d\text{pH}} = -2.303 \cdot V \cdot 10^{\text{pH}-\text{pSH}} \qquad \text{pH approaching pSH} \quad (12)$$

In general we have at a given time when r bases and s acids are present in the system

$$BC = -2.303 \left\{ \sum_r B_r \gamma_r + \sum_s A_s \gamma_s + \right.$$

$$\left. V \cdot 10^{\text{pS}-\text{pH}} + V \cdot 10^{\text{pH}-\text{pSH}} \right\} \quad (13)$$

where

$$\gamma = \frac{10^{\text{pH}-\text{pK}}}{(1 + 10^{\text{pH}-\text{pK}})^2}, \ \text{pK} = \text{pA or pB}$$

γ is seen in Figure 6.

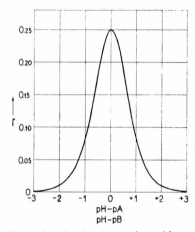

Fig. 6. Slope of ionization curve for acids and bases.

Naturally in more complex cases, e.g., titration in protein solutions, BC must be determined experimentally.

The buffer capacity is also of importance if the pH registered during a reaction like equation (7) or equation (8) changes for any reason other than a change of the system. Thus, if the asymmetrical potential of the glass electrode, the potential of the calomel electrode, the diffusion potential, or the zero point of the potentiometer undergoes variation, there will be an error of N_{H^+} of

$$\delta N_{H^+} = BC\delta\text{pH} \qquad (14)$$

where δpH is the variation of pH corresponding to the changes of potential mentioned.

3. Time-Relationships

As described in Sections I, II.1, and II.4, the pH-stat is based on the principle of adding a series of discrete quantities of acid or base to a system in which base or acid is formed, these additions being directed by the electrical and mechanical system to maintain pH within an interval of say ΔpH_c, e.g., between pH_c and $pH_c + \Delta pH_c$. If now

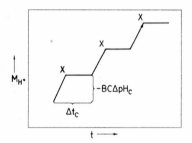

Fig. 7. M_{H^+}-time curve with ΔpH_c-control.

in a given undisturbed reaction system, pH changes at a rate $(dpH/dt)_0$, we may assign a time element Δt_c to ΔpH_c (or ΔpH_c may be assigned to Δt_c, see below) so that $\Delta pH_c/\Delta t_c = (dpH/dt)_0$. The rate curve drawn by the recorder will then, in the ideal case, take the shape of a staircase, the steps of which are $-BC\Delta pH_c$ high and Δt_c deep (Figure 7), M_{H^+} being the quantity of reagent (acid or base) added. It will be seen that

$$\left(\frac{dM_{H^+}}{dt}\right)_{\text{average}} = \frac{dN_{H^+}}{dt} = -BC\frac{\Delta pH_c}{\Delta t_c} = -BC\left(\frac{dpH}{dt}\right)_0 \quad (15)$$

(compare equation 9), the change of sign being due to the trivial fact that here dN_{H^+} does not *produce* the change dpH (equation 9) but *compensates* it. M_{H^+} is equal to N_{H^+}, the theoretical quantity of reagent, at the points X where $pH = pH_c$.

The conditions under which the picture in Figure 7 is true are:

(1) Within a time element, $\Delta t_a \ll \Delta t_c$, after pH has reached the value $pH_c + \Delta pH_c$, the motor should start and add the reagent during the time, $\Delta t_i < \Delta t_c$, at a rate, dM_{H^+}/dt, which is higher than $dN_{H^+}/$

$dt = -BC \, \Delta\mathrm{pH}_c/\Delta t_c$. Stirring should be effective so that mixing is complete at any moment during Δt_i.

(2) Within a time element, $\Delta t_s \ll \Delta t_c$, after pH has reached the value pH_c, the motor should stop.

When these conditions are fulfilled, the N_{H^+}-time curve may be determined with precision, pH_c being identical with pH_p, the value of pH set on the controller. However, the situation depicted in Figure 7 requires that the pH-stat be furnished with a contact, the opening and closing potentials of which differ in a well defined way and correspond to the difference $\Delta\mathrm{pH}_c$. The simplest, but not the most satisfactory, execution of this principle in practice is represented by a contact with a slight adherence between the pointer and needle (Section II.3), which is overcome when pH reaches $\mathrm{pH}_p + \Delta\mathrm{pH}_c$. If the proportional control is disconnected, the TTTI titrator also functions according to this principle, and with greater precision. The value for $\Delta\mathrm{pH}_c$ is, however, relatively large in this case, and the overshooting of the motor is a dominant source of error (see below), since rather pronounced staircase-formation is observed, even when BC is low (see Section IV.2).

When the proportional control operates, instruments of the type of TTTI have a contact system which functions quite differently, *viz.*, in the way that discrete amounts of reagent are added at regular intervals, but so that either the frequency of addition or the amount added decreases with decrease between pH and pH_p and becomes zero when $\mathrm{pH} = \mathrm{pH}_p$. This principle is actually also inherent in our original controlling device without adherence (Section II.3), the time intervals between the impulses from the vibrating pointer becoming shorter the more that pH approaches pH_p. It is therefore immediately apparent that, first, pH_c, the working pH, never actually reaches pH_p in this case and that, second, it is not $\Delta\mathrm{pH}_c$ which is set by the controller, but rather Δt_c to which we may then assign a value of $\Delta\mathrm{pH}_c$, so that $(d\mathrm{pH}/dt)_0 = \Delta\mathrm{pH}_c/\Delta t_c$. The maintenance of a stationary working pH, pH_c, on the basis of $\mathrm{pH} - \mathrm{pH}_p$ may be described as follows:

If we express any drift of pH observed as due to insufficient compensation of $(d\mathrm{pH}/dt)_0$ by $(dM_{\mathrm{H}^+}/dt)_{\text{average}}$ we get

$$\left(\frac{dM_{\mathrm{H}^+}}{dt}\right)_{\text{average}} + BC \left(\frac{d\mathrm{pH}}{dt}\right)_0 = BC \, \frac{d\mathrm{pH}}{dt} \qquad (16)$$

When the average rate of reagent addition is proportional to $\mathrm{pH} - \mathrm{pH}_p$ (proportional control), we obtain

$$\left(\frac{dM_{H^+}}{dt}\right)_{\text{average}} = P(\text{pH} - \text{pH}_p) \qquad (17)$$

P being a constant.   Combining equations (16) and (17) leads to a differential equation the solution of which is

$$\text{pH} = \text{pH}_p + e^{Pt/BC} \int_0^t \left(\frac{d\text{pH}}{dt}\right)_0 e^{-Pt/BC}\, dt \qquad (18)$$

If we consider the simple case of a zero order reaction $((d\text{pH}/dt)_0 = \text{constant})$, equation (18) becomes

$$\text{pH} = \text{pH}_p - \frac{BC}{P}\left(\frac{d\text{pH}}{dt}\right)_0 (1 - e^{Pt/BC}) \qquad (19)$$

which, when the system has reached a stationary state $((Pt/BC) << 0,\ BC$ being negative), is transformed into

$$\text{pH}_c = \text{pH}_p - \frac{BC}{P}\left(\frac{d\text{pH}}{dt}\right)_0 = \text{pH}_p + \frac{1}{P}\frac{dN_{H^+}}{dt} \qquad (20)$$

Considering now that when $\text{pH} - \text{pH}_p$ is equal to ΔpH_m, by which we shall denote the width of the proportionality band selected (see Section II.4), the impulses from the controller will merge and the motor will run continuously adding reagent at maximum speed, then we find from equation (17)

$$\left(\frac{dM_{H^+}}{dt}\right)_{\text{max}} = P\Delta\text{pH}_m \qquad (21)$$

which serves for the determination of P.   Introducing equation (21) into equation (20) leads to

$$\text{pH}_c - \text{pH}_p = \frac{\Delta\text{pH}_m}{x} \qquad (22)$$

where

$$x = \left(\frac{dM_{H^+}}{dt}\right)_{\text{max}} : \frac{dN_{H^+}}{dt} \qquad (23)$$

i.e., x is the ratio between the maximum rate of reagent addition and the theoretical rate of reagent uptake at constant pH.

According to equations (22) and (23) x and consequently pH_c will vary during any reaction in which dN_{H^+}/dt changes with time (reactions of higher order than zero) and it is therefore of importance to choose x as high as possible within the limits set by the practical difficulties discussed below.

The ideal M_{H^+}-time curve for a pH-stat with proportional control is shown in Figure 8.

A comparison between this figure and Figure 7 demonstrates the essential difference between what we may term the Δt_c-control (Figure 8) and the ΔpH_c-control (Figure 7). In the latter the size of the steps is proportional to BC, in the former it is largely independent of BC, because $(dpH/dt)_0$ is approximately inversely proportional to BC. This difference is clearly seen in the example described in Section IV.2, Figure 11.

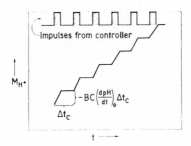

Fig. 8. M_{H^+}-time curve with Δt_c-control

While in the ideal case of ΔpH_c control the average rate curve drawn by the recorder is correct even for large values of BC (pH$_c$ being constant and identical with pH$_p$ at the points X along the curve in Figure 7), this is not so when the system is followed with Δt_c-control. In zero order reactions the average slope is correct after an initial non-stationary period which may be quite long, if BC is high (see equation 19 and Sections III.4 and IV.2), but in first order reactions the rate curve is incorrect outside of the non-stationary part too.

Combining the equation

$$\left(\frac{dpH}{dt}\right)_0 = -\frac{kN_f}{BC}e^{-kt} \qquad (24)$$

with equation (18) we get, assuming that the rate constant k and BC are independent of pH,

$$\frac{dpH}{dt} = -\frac{kN_f}{BC(k-\omega)}\{k\cdot e^{-kt} - \omega e^{-\omega t}\} \qquad (25)$$

for the drift of pH during the reaction, $pH = pH_p$ for $t = 0$. N_f is the final value of N_{H^+} in a first order reaction, and $\omega = -P/BC$.

The error of $(dM_{H^+}/dt)_{\text{average}}$ is therefore

$$\left(\frac{dM_{H^+}}{dt}\right)_{\text{average}} - \frac{dN_{H^+}}{dt} = kN_f \left\{ \frac{\omega}{k - \omega} e^{-\omega t} - \frac{k}{k - \omega} e^{-kt} \right\} \quad (26)$$

ω may be expressed in terms of x, ΔpH_m and N_f using equations (21) and (23), i.e.,

$$\omega = - \frac{x_0 k N_f}{BC \Delta pH_m} \quad (27)$$

where x_0 is the value of x for $t = 0$ (and $(dN_{H^+}/dt)_0 = kN_f$).

We therefore see from equation (26) that for

$$k - \omega = k \left(1 + \frac{x_0 N_f}{BC \Delta pH_m} \right) < 0$$

(e.g., $x_0 = 3$, $BC = -11.6$, $N_f = -20$, $\Delta pH_m = -0.1$, $\omega = 51.7 \cdot k$, see example 1c, Section III.4) the M_{H^+}-time curve will be S-shaped, starting with a zero slope but recording a higher and higher rate of reagent addition as the last term in equation (26) becomes more and more dominant. In the final "stationary" part of the curve, the slope exceeds that of the correct curve for N_{H^+} by $- 100/(1 - \omega/k)$ per cent.

If $k - \omega > 0$ (e.g., $x_0 = 3$, $BC = -1200$ corresponding to 0.21 M buffer, (pH = pK of buffer), $N_f = -20$, $\Delta pH_m = -0.1$, $\omega = 0.5 \cdot k$, see example 1c) the M_{H^+}-time curve will also be S-shaped and start with a zero slope, but the initial part will be governed more by the last term in equation (26), and pH will drop (or rise) steadily until toward the end of the reaction, where pH is restored to pH_p. In this last part of the curve the first term on the right side of equation (26) will be dominant. Although, in simple cases, the kinetics may be found by means of the curve and equation (26) if BC is known, Δt_c-control is certainly not an ideal method for the study of chemical reactions in this case, and systems with a high value of ω/k are therefore definitely to be chosen. It will appear from equation (27) that ω/k may be increased by increasing x_0 or N_f/BC and by decreasing ΔpH_m. It is especially important to emphasize that, in first order reactions at any rate, it is the ratio between the quantity of reacting substance and the buffer capacity which determines the error.

On the preceding pages the simple theory for the maintenance of a constant pH during a rate process has been given for two characteristic types of control, in their ideal forms. In practice results have been obtained, which essentially are in agreement with the theory, but unavoidable irregularities in the functioning of the electrical and mechanical system cause variations of Δt_a, Δt_i, and Δt_s, so that the steps of the "staircase" will vary in size and shape. The burette will "overshoot," partly due to insufficient stirring—an important source of error—and partly to the not insignificant response time of the controller and, especially in unbuffered solutions, of the glass electrode (Δt_a, Δt_s). In addition, in the original type of pH-stat (Section II.3), errors may arise from occasional adherence of the needles of the contact instrument and from inertia of the motor, which will continue to run for a short while, after the current has been broken. Slow fluctuations or drifts of potential in any part of the electric circuit should also be mentioned. They are the more important the higher the buffer capacity (see Section III.2). All of these errors are of course impossible to evaluate theoretically, but must be investigated experimentally.

It is our experience that with a well working instrument (sections II.3 and II.4) and a motor, which is effectively disengaged by a magnetic clutch (Section II.6), the pH-stat TTTI with ΔpH_c-control gives regular steps corresponding to $\Delta pH_c \sim 0.005$–0.01. The overshooting frequently observed at low buffer capacity is mainly due to the above mentioned fact that Δt_a and Δt_s are not negligible (Section IV.2, Figure 11, curve II). If by ΔpH_r we denote the actual variation of pH from its highest to its lowest value, we find from equations (15) and (23)

$$\Delta pH_r = \Delta pH_c - \frac{\Delta t_a}{BC} \cdot \frac{dN_{H^+}}{dt} - \frac{\Delta t_s}{BC} \left\{ \left(\frac{dM_{H^+}}{dt} \right)_{max} - \frac{dN_{H^+}}{dt} \right\} =$$

$$\Delta pH_c - \frac{\Delta t_a + (x-1)\Delta t_s}{BC} \cdot \frac{dN_{H^+}}{dt} \quad (28)$$

With Δt_c-control the steps are generally invisible, except in cases where stirring is ineffective, e.g., due to a high viscosity of the reaction mixture. The value of Δt_c is of the order of 1 second.

As mentioned before (Section II.2), the fluctuations of the potential due to instability of the pH-meter are below 0.01 pH-unit.

4. Examples

In the examples we shall treat the following system

Solvent: 0.1 N KCl in H_2O
$V:$ 10 ml. $= 10^4 \mu$l.
A or B: 20 μmoles
$a + b:$ 0.002 M
Concentration of reagent, acid or base: 0.1 N α_R or $\beta_R = 1$ (HCl or NaOH)
$\Delta V = V_f - V_t$: 200 μl (final volume of reagent added)
Δ pH$_c$: ± 0.005 (Figure 7)
Δ pH$_m$: ± 0.1 (equation 21)
x_0: 3 (equation 23)
$\omega/k:$ $-600/BC$ (equation 27)

Example 1. Splitting of an esterbond.

$$\beta_i = \beta_t = \alpha_m = 0 \qquad k = 1 \text{ (equation 7)}$$
$$\beta_r = 0 \qquad s = 1 \text{ (equation 8)}$$

Equations (7) and (8) give

$$N_{H^+} = -(A_1)_f \alpha_1; \quad dN_{H^+}/dt = -\alpha_1 dA_1/dt \text{ (titration with base)}$$
$$\Delta pH_c = -0.005$$

(a) $pSH \gg pH \gg pA_1$, $\alpha_1 = 1$, $BC \sim 0$

If $pA_1 = 5$, $pH = 8$ these conditions are fulfilled, and

$$\frac{dN_{H^+}}{dt} = -\frac{dA_?}{dt}$$

with negligible errors except that due to overshooting in unbuffered solutions (see Sections III.3 and IV.2).

(b) $pSH \gg pH = pA_1$, $\alpha_1 = 0.5$, $BC = -A_1 \cdot 0.58$ (equation 13)

$$\frac{dN_{H^+}}{dt} = -\frac{1}{2}\frac{dA_1}{dt}; \qquad -BC \cdot \Delta pH_c = -A_1 \cdot 0.003 \ \mu\text{mole}$$

Hence at any stage of the process in which A_1 is formed the height of the steps in Figure 7 is 0.6% of M_{H^+}, which goes from zero to $-10 \ \mu$moles (10 μmoles of base).

(•) As in (a) except that BC is assumed to be finite due to the presence of a stable buffer BF.

If $pA_1 = 5$, $pH = 8$, the quantity of buffer $BF = 20 \ \mu$moles, pK-value of BF $= 8$, we find

$$\frac{dN_{H^+}}{dt} = -\frac{dA_1}{dt}$$

$$BC = -20 \cdot 0.58 = -11.6; \quad -BC\Delta pH_c = -0.06 \;\mu mole.$$

The error due to the proportional control is judged on the basis of the consideration in Section III.3 ($\Delta pH_m = -0.1$).

If the reaction studied is first order and is started at pH_p, pH will first drop by approximately $\Delta pH_m/x_0$ in an initial non-stationary period. The quantity of reagent (base) added in this period is

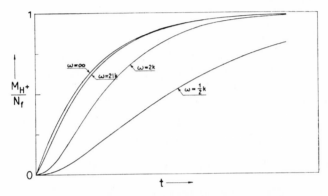

Fig. 9. Rate curves measured with Δt_c-control at different buffer capacities.

therefore in error by $BC\Delta pH_m/x_0$. Putting $x_0 = 3$, we find that the base consumption is 0.39 μmole too small. During the rest of the reaction, base is now used not only to keep pace with the reaction, but also to bring pH closer and closer to pH_p, which will be reached when t is high and $M_{H^+} = N_{H^+} = -A_1$; in other words a quantity of 0.39 μmole of base is added in excess of the quantity of about 20 μmoles required to follow the reaction to the end at constant pH. Since the initial period is generally badly recorded (e.g., due to a slight pH-change caused by the addition of enzyme), the zero-point is often found by extrapolation, which means that the apparent quantity of base recorded will be 0.39 μmole or 2% too high. Our kinetic calculation in Section III.3 also shows that the slope of the rate curve will be 2% too high everywhere outside the non-stationary period. The length of this period, expressed by its half-time, is determined by the same quantities which enter into the expression for the error of the slope, and is again 2% of the half-time of the first order reaction studied (see equations (25) and (26)).

In order to illustrate the dependence of the error upon the ratio between the buffer capacity and A_1, theoretical curves have been calculated for the following cases:

$\omega = \infty$; $BF = 0$ (theoretical, ideal curve)

$\omega = 21k$; $BC = -28.6$; $BC/A_1 = -1.43$; $BF = 50$ μmoles (in 10 ml.)

$\omega = 2k$; $BC = -300$; $BC/A_1 = -15$; $BF = 521$ μmoles (in 10 ml.)

$\omega = 0.5k$; $BC = -1200$; $BC/A_1 = -60$; $BF = 2084$ μmoles (in 10 ml.)

Figure 9 shows the results. They should be considered in connection with the discussion in Section III.3.

Example 2. Splitting of a Peptide Bond.

$$\beta_l = \alpha_m = 0 \qquad i = 1 \qquad k = 1 \qquad \text{(equation 7)}$$
$$r = 1 \qquad s = 1 \qquad \text{(equation 8)}$$

Equation (7) or (8) gives

$$N_{H^+} = (B_1)_f \beta_1 - (A_1)_f \alpha_1; \qquad dN_{H^+}/dt = \beta_1 dB_1/dt - \alpha_1 dA_1/dt$$
$$\Delta pH_c = \pm 0.005$$
$$A_1 = RNH_3^+; \qquad B_1 = R_1COO^-; \qquad A_1 = B_1$$

$$pA_1 \sim 7 - 10; \qquad pB_1 \sim 2 - 4$$

(a) $pSH \gg pH \gg pA_1$. The situation will be as in example 1a, since $\beta_1 = 0$. $\Delta pH_c = -0.005$. If $pA_1 = 7$, $pH = 10$, $\alpha_1 = 0.999$, we find (equation 13), $\gamma \sim 0$, $10^{pS - pH} \sim 0$):

$$BC = -2.3; \quad -BC \cdot \Delta pH_c = -0.012 \ \mu\text{mole.}$$

If, however, $pA_1 = 9$, $pH = 12$, $\alpha_1 = 0.999$, we find:

$$BC = -230; \quad -BC \cdot \Delta pH_c \sim -1.2 \ \mu\text{mole}$$

i. e., the height of the steps in Figure 7 is 6% of the quantity of base added at the end of the reaction (20 μmoles); $\omega/k = 2.6$.

The buffering by the medium at pH 12 is too strong.

(b) $pS < pH \leq pB_1$; i.e., $\alpha_1 = 0$.

$$N_{H^+} = (B_1)_f \beta_1; \qquad dN_{H^+}/dt = \beta_1 dB_1/dt \text{ (titration with acid)}$$
$$\Delta pH_c = +0.005$$

If pH = pB$_1$ = 3, we obtain $\beta_1 = \frac{1}{2}$ and

$$\frac{dN_{H^+}}{dt} = \frac{1}{2}\frac{dB_1}{dt}$$

$BC = -2.3 \cdot V \cdot 10^{(0\,-\,3)} - B_1 \cdot 0.58 = -23 - B_1 \cdot 0.58$ (equation 13),
   $10^{pH\,-\,pSH} \sim 0$)
$-BC\Delta pH_c \sim 0.12 + B_1 \cdot 0.003 \sim 0.15$ μmole for $B_1 = 10$ μmoles
(half-reaction)

$$\omega/k = 20$$

If pB$_1$ = 3, pH = 1 we get $\beta_1 = 0.99$

$BC = -2.3 \cdot V \cdot 10^{(0\,-\,1)} =$

$$-2300 \text{ (equation 13)}, \gamma \sim 0, 10^{pH\,-\,pSH} \sim 0)$$

$$-BC \cdot \Delta pH_c \sim +2.3 \cdot 10^3 \cdot 0.005 = 11.5 \text{ } \mu\text{moles}$$

$$\omega/k = 0.26$$

Hence titration is impossible.

Example 3. Reaction of an Amino Group with CS_2, Acid Formed at the Expense of a Base.

$$\alpha_m = \beta_i = 0 \qquad l = 1 \qquad k = 1 \qquad \text{(equation 7)}$$
$$r = 1, \qquad s = 1 \qquad \text{(equation 8)}$$

Equation (7) or equation (8) gives:

$N_{H^+} = -(B_1)_i\beta_1 - (A_1)_f\alpha_1$; $dN_{H^+}/dt = \beta_1 dB_1/dt - \alpha_1 dA_1/dt$

$B_1 = RNH_2$, $A_1 = RNHCSSH$; $(A_1)_f = (B_1)_i$; $dA_1/dt = -dB_1/dt$
(titration with base)

(a)   pB$_1$ = 8, pA$_1$ = 4, pH = 6 (see 10)

$$\frac{dN_{H^+}}{dt} = -\,(0.99 + 0.99)\frac{dA_1}{dt} \sim -2\frac{dA_1}{dt}$$

(b)   pB$_1$ = 8; pA$_1$ = 4; pH = 8

$$\frac{dN_{H^+}}{dt} = -(0.9999 + 0.5)\frac{dA_1}{dt} \sim -1.5\frac{dA_1}{dt}$$

Example 4. Splitting of a Monoester of Phosphate.

$$\beta_i = \beta_l = 0 \qquad k = 2 \qquad m = 1 \text{ } (s = 1, 2)$$

Equations (7) and (8) give

$$N_{H^+} = (A_1)_i\alpha_1 - (A_2)_f\alpha_2; \quad dN_{H^+}/dt = -\alpha_1 dA_1/dt - \alpha_2 dA_2/dt$$

$$A_1 = ROPO_3H_2; \quad A_2 = H_3PO_4;$$

$$A_1 = A_2; \quad dA_1/dt = -dA_2/dt$$

$$pA_1 = 6.4, pA_2 = 6.8$$

Formation of a weaker acid from a stronger one.   Titration with acid.

(a) $$pH = 6.6$$

$$\frac{dN_{H^+}}{dt} = (0.6131 - 0.3862)\frac{dA_2}{dt} = +0.2263\frac{dA_2}{dt}$$

(b) $$pH = 7.8 \text{ or } 5.4$$

$$\frac{dN_{H^+}}{dt} = 0.052\frac{dA_2}{dt}$$

Example 5. Measurement of Change of Electrostatic Effects on pA and pB. This final example may have some bearing on protein denaturation.

PROTEIN

Initial state — Native structure

y Å

$$RNH_2^+ \quad {}^-OOCR_1 \qquad A_1 = RNH_2^+; \quad B_1 = {}^-OOCR_1$$

histidine   aspartic acid

Final state

z Å

Separation of charges in unfolded structure $z \gg y$

$$RNH_2^+ \qquad {}^-OOCR_1 \qquad A_2 = RNH_2^+; \quad B_2 = {}^-OOCR_1$$

$$pA_2 = 6 \qquad pB_2 = 4.5$$

$$pA_1 = 6 + (\epsilon^2/YDkT)0.4343;$$

$$pB_1 = 4.5 - (\epsilon^2/YDkT)0.4343 \text{ (ionic strength } = 0)$$

$$0.4343 (\epsilon^2/YDkT) \sim 3.0/Y$$

where ϵ is the charge of an electron, D is the dielectric constant (80), k is the Boltzmann constant and T the temperature.

For $y = 3$ Å we find

$$pA_1 = 7; \quad pB_1 = 3.5; \quad pA_2 = 6; \quad pB_2 = 4.5$$

The curve for the value of N_{H^+} corresponding to complete unfolding as a function of pH is shown in Figure 10. It will be seen that there is an uptake of acid below pH 5.25 ($= (6 + 4.5)/2$) where the change from a weaker to a stronger base ($B_1 \rightarrow B_2$) is measured, and an uptake of base above pH 5.25, where the corresponding situation is found for the acids A_1 and A_2. Q is the quantity of separated pairs; hence the curve, if found in an experiment, could be interpreted as $Q/2$ acid groups "appear" at pH 6.5 and $Q/2$ basic groups at pH 4.

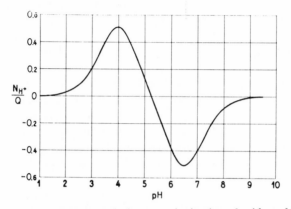

Fig. 10. Effect of electrostatic forces on ionization of acids and bases.

IV. PRACTICAL APPLICATIONS OF THE pH-STAT

1. Some Substitution Reactions of Primary Amino Groups

The first pH-stat constructed at the Carlsberg Laboratory was used for the study of a chemical reaction utilized in the stepwise degradation of peptides. Léonis and Levy (10) have shown that carbon disulfide in alkaline solution reacts with the terminal amino group of peptides, and that subsequent acidification of the resulting peptide dithiocarbamate leads to fission of the amino terminal peptide bond, eliminating the end amino acid as a 2-thio-5-thiazolidone. The latter can be extracted, and the aqueous solution of the remaining peptide subjected to the same series of reactions, leading to the isolation of the 2-thio-5-thiazolidone of amino acid nr. 2, and so on. The kinetics of the first part of this reaction, viz.,

$$RCH \cdot CO \cdot NHR_1 + CS_2 \rightleftharpoons RCH \cdot CO \cdot NH \cdot R_1$$
$$| \qquad\qquad\qquad\qquad\qquad\qquad | $$
$$NH_2 \qquad\qquad\qquad\qquad\qquad NHCSSH$$

has been studied in detail, using the pH-stat to measure the quantity of hydrogen ions liberated (a maximum of 2 per mole of peptide; see Section III.4). A similar method for stepwise degradation was developed by Edman (4). In this method carbon disulfide is replaced by phenylisothiocyanate, but the principle is analogous and leads to the isolation of the amino acids as phenylthiohydantoins. If the coupling with phenylisothiocyanate is carried out at pH-values, where the amino group involved is ionized, it is similarly accompanied by a liberation of hydrogen ions (1 per mole), and may be followed in the pH-stat. Ottesen and Wollenberger (17) made use of this in their study of the yields in the stepwise degradation of some peptides formed during the enzymatic transformation of ovalbumin to plakalbumin.

Andersen (1) has recently investigated the partial substitution of peptides and insulin with phenylisocyanate. Owing to the very fast reaction of this substance with amino groups (and water) use was made of the Lossen rearrangement to generate it slowly in the presence of the reactive group. In alkaline aqueous solutions, pH $\geq$ 8, the potassium salt of dibenzohydroxamic acid is spontaneously converted into benzoate and phenylisocyanate, which latter will react with the amino groups forming the corresponding phenylcarbamyl derivatives. As in the Edman reaction, the rate and extent of the substitution may be followed in the pH-stat, provided the amino groups in question are wholly or partly ionized.

2. Enzymatic Splitting of Carboxylic Acid Ester Bonds

The splitting of carboxylic acid ester bonds rates among the reactions which are most easily followed over a wide pH-range in the pH-stat. As mentioned in the introduction and in Section III.4, the errors are usually small and the original Knaffl-Lenz method has actually been widely used without any automatization whatsoever. The advantages offered by the pH-stat are therefore mainly of the labor-saving kind in this case.

The pH-stat has been used a great deal in studying the esterase activity of proteolytic enzymes (see, e.g., Harris (6)) and, since the splitting of esters is an ideal process for the experimental verification of the theoretical observations in Section III.3 (because the buffer capacity originating from the reacting molecules themselves is practically zero and BC therefore can be kept sufficiently constant), the following experiments were carried out.

The reaction mixtures contained 20 μmoles of benzoyltyrosine ethylester, 1 μg. chymotrypsin and suitable quantities of NaCl or phosphate buffer in 10 ml. 16% methanol. pH_p was 7 (see Sections III.3 and III.4), the temperature 25°C. In Figure 11 curve V represents addition of 0.1 N NaOH at maximum speed (slope $(dM_{H+}/dt)_{max}$). Curves I and II record the uptake of base under ΔpH_c-control. In experiment II, BC was virtually zero (0.1 N NaCl),

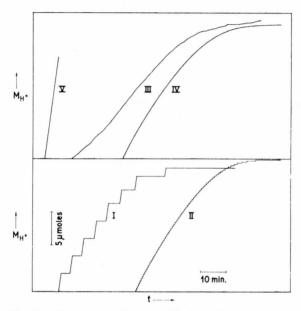

Fig. 11. Rate curves for the splitting of benzoyl tyrosine ethylester by chymotrypsin measured with ΔpH_c-control (I and II) or with Δt_c-control (III and IV).

while in I the reaction mixture was 0.0467 M with respect to phosphate (7 ml. Sørensen buffer 1:1 in 10 ml.) corresponding to a value of BC of -269. Curves III and IV represent similar experiments (III and IV) with Δt_c-control; in IV, BC was zero; in III, -269. x_0 was about 3.

It has already been mentioned that the small steps observed in case of curve II are due to time lags in the response of the system, the pH read on the pH-meter varying 0.1–0.2 pH-unit synchronously with the addition of base. From the height of the steps of curve I we find a value of about 2 μmoles for BC ΔpH$_c$ in this experiment, corresponding to a ΔpH$_c$ of -0.0075, and the actual ΔpH$_c$, ΔpH$_r$, is therefore considerably higher in experiment II. On the basis of equation (28) we find

$$BC\Delta pH_r = BC\Delta pH_c - (\Delta t_a + 2\Delta t_s)\frac{dN_{H^+}}{dt}$$

from which we conclude (Figure 11) that Δt_a and Δt_s are of the order of 10 seconds here, a fact which points to the sluggishness of the response of the glass electrode, possibly combined with insufficient stirring, as the main source of error. The height of the steps indicates a value of 0.3 μmole for $BC\Delta pH_r$ and, since the buffer capacity due to the carboxylic acid liberated is always between zero and -0.5 (Figure 6 and equation 13), ΔpH$_r$ seems to be of the order of 1 pH-unit, viz., a far greater variation than that registered by the pH-meter. In the study of pH-sensitive rate processes it is therefore advisable to add a little buffer to reduce ΔpH$_r$. 5–10 μmoles in 10 ml. $\sim$ 0.0005–0.001 M should be ample.

The conformity with respect to average slope between curves I and II is interesting but may be accidental. Replacing NaCl by phosphate buffer of approximately equal ionic strength may specifically influence the rate of the process.

However, the conformity between curves II and IV is reassuring with regard to reproducibility of results obtained even with different methods of approach. In experiment IV the pH-variations (ΔpH$_r$) are smaller than in experiment II but still considerable, viz., about 0.1 pH-unit corresponding to $\Delta t_c \sim 1$ second. But they are too fast and too small to be registered by the pH-meter and are therefore unable to influence the rhythm of the impulses directing base addition under Δt_c-control (Figure 8). In buffered solutions, experiment III, we find a rather irregular curve the shape of which differs from that of the others in a striking way, which may be partly explained by the theoretical considerations in Section III.3. From equation (27) we find

$$\omega = \frac{3\cdot20}{268\cdot0.1}\,k = 2.2\cdot k$$

so that curve III is comparable to the curve for $\omega = 2k$ in Figure 9, to which it actually bears considerable resemblance. The value of pH$_c$ - pH$_p$ (equation 22) should roughly lie between -0.03 and 0.

The kinks in the curve and the error of the total base consumption are in our opinion typical examples of errors due to drifts of potential magnified by the high buffer capacity. In experiment I such drifts may have occurred but are not so easily observed.

3. Enzymatic Splitting of Amidophosphate

While, as shown in Section III.4, example 4, the splitting of mono-esters of phosphate is not too well registered in the pH-stat, that of amidophosphate by phosphoamidase at pH 4–5:

$$\overset{O^-}{\underset{O}{\overset{|}{^+H_3N-P-O^-}}} + H_2O + H^+ \longrightarrow \overset{O^-}{\underset{O}{\overset{|}{HO-P-OH}}} + NH_4^+$$

is measured with a 100% yield, one hydrogen ion being taken up per molecule split. Acid is consequently used as a reagent (see (14)).

4. Enzymatic Splitting of Peptide Bonds

As mentioned in Section III.4, example 2, the opening of peptide bonds in aqueous solution may be followed with some degree of accuracy by means of the pH-stat if the working pH is kept within certain limits. In acid solution, where the carboxyl group formed has its range of ionization, pH should not exceed the pK-value of this group by more than 1 pH-unit (corresponding to an estimation of only 9% of the group) and it should not be lower than 3. In alkaline solution, where the ammonium group formed has its ionization range, pH should not be more than 1 pH-unit below the pK-value of this group and should not be higher than 11. It will be observed that, since the pK-values of these two groups are about 2–4 and 7–10, respectively, the acid range is much narrower than the alkaline and has not been used in enzymatic work (e.g., pepsin splitting). The alkaline range, however, offers considerable advantages, and it has been used by several authors. Waley and Watson (21), in a study of the tryptic splitting of polylysine, were the first to follow the opening of peptide bonds by continuous titration at constant pH. In the Carlsberg Laboratory the break-down of insulin and ribonuclease by means of the proteolytic enzyme subtilisin has been followed in the pH-stat (18,7).

The method seems, at least in some cases, to be of greater sensitivity than the methods ordinarily used to follow the opening of peptide bonds. During the conversion of ovalbumin into plakalbumin by means of subtilisin the initial reaction consists in the opening of a single peptide bond in the ovalbumin molecule, and the pH-stat has turned out to be sufficiently sensitive to follow the opening of this particular bond with considerable accuracy ((16) see Figure 12).

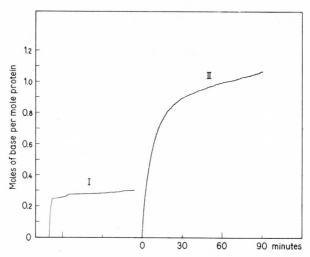

Fig. 12. Reaction between ovalbumin and subtilisin at 30 °C., pH 8 followed in the pH-stat by titration with 0.1 N NaOH. Reaction mixture 10 ml. containing 0.5 g. ovalbumin and 15 μg. subtilisin. Curve I blank reaction prior to addition of enzyme, curve II reaction proper, total consumption 0.9 mole of base per mole protein.

5. Liberation of Acidic or Basic Groups on Denaturation

In the denaturation of proteins the complex rearrangement of the molecules may drastically change the environment of many of the acidic or basic groups situated in the sidechains. This change in environment—whether it is due to disruption of hydrogen bonds in which the groups in question were themselves involved or to rearrangements of the ionic pattern of the molecule with corresponding changes in the electrostatic field surrounding the groups—will undoubtedly influence the acidic and basic properties of the groups and may cause acid or base to be taken up during denaturation at constant pH (see example 5, Section III.4).

Here is obviously a wide and interesting field in which the pH-stat may be useful. We shall refer to a recent article by Harrington (5) in which the liberation of acidic and basic groups upon denaturation of ovalbumin was followed by the pH-stat.

6. Final Remarks

The preceding sections have dealt with the application of the pH-stat to a series of specific problems, but there are naturally a very large number of related cases in which this instrument may be of value for research or routine work. It may suffice to refer to the extensive use of the pH-stat made by Levy (11) for controlling the reaction of amino groups with fluordinitrobenzene to indicate in what directions the widening field of application may go.

V. CONCLUSION

On the preceding pages a review has been given of recent developments in the automatization of the control and measurement of biochemical reactions at constant pH. The technical details of a suitable instrument, the pH-stat, have been described, its merits and faults have been discussed, and the elementary theoretical background for the study of the rate and extension of chemical reactions has been outlined. We are well aware that the solution of the technical problems presented here does not arise from any particular originality on our part, but we believe in the importance of making known to biochemists that instruments of this type do exist and are useful in many fields of biochemistry.

References

1. Andersen, W., *Acta Chem. Scand., 8,* 1721 (1954).
2. Bates, R. G., *Electrometric pH Determinations,* John Wiley and Sons, Inc., New York, 1954.
3. Brønsted, J. N., *Rec. de Trav. Chim. Pay-Bas, 62,* 718 (1923).
4. Edman, P., *Acta Chem. Scand., 4,* 283 (1950).
5. Harrington, W. F., *Biochim. et Biophys. Acta, 18,* 450 (1955).
6. Harris, J. I.. *Nature, 177,* 471 (1956).
7. Haugaard, N., and Haugaard, E. S., *Compt. rend. Lab. Carlsberg, Sér. chim., 29,* 350 (1955).
8. Jacobsen, C. F., and Léonis, J., *Compt. rend. Lab. Carlsberg, Sér. chim., 27,* 333 (1951).

9. Knaffl-Lenz, E., *Arch. Pathol. Pharmakol.*, *97*, 242 (1923), and *Medd. f. K. Vetenskapsakademiens Nobelinst.*, *6*, No. 3 (1923).

10. Léonis, J., and Levy, A. L., *Compt. rend. Lab. Carlsberg, Sér. chim.*, *29*, 57 (1954).

11. Levy, A. L., *Nature*, *174*, 126 (1954); *Methods of Biochemical Analysis*, Vol. II, Interscience, NewYork-London, 1955, p. 360.

12. Lingane, J. J., *Anal. Chem.*, *20*, 285 (1948); *21*, 497 (1949).

13. Longsworth, L. G., and MacInnes, D. A., *J. Bacteriol.*, *29*, 595 (1935).

14. Møller, K. M., *Biochim. et Biophys. Acta*, *16*, 162 (1955).

15. Nielsen, S. O., and Rosenberg, T., *J. Sci. Instr.*, *31*, 401 (1954).

16. Ottesen, M., *Arch. Biochem. Biophys.*, *65*, 70 (1956).

17. Ottesen, M., and Wollenberger, A., *Compt. rend. Lab. Carlsberg, Sér. chim.*, *28*, 463 (1953).

18. Richards, F. M., *Compt. rend. Lab. Carlsberg, Sér. chim.*, *29*, 322 (1955).

19. Rona, P., and Ammon, R., *Biochem. Z.*, *181*, 49 (1927).

20. Sørensen, S. P. L., *Compt. rend. Lab. Carlsberg, Sér. chim.*, *8*, 1 (1909).

21. Waley, S. G., and Watson, J., *Biochem. J.*, *55*, 328 (1953).

22. Whitnah, C. H., *Ind. Eng. Chem., Anal. Ed.*, *5*, 352 (1933).

Assay of
SULFATASES

K. S. Dodgson and B. Spencer, *University of Wales*

CONTENTS (*continued*)

I. INTRODUCTION

The sulfatases are a group of hydrolytic enzymes which liberate sulfuric acid from ester sulfates according to the following equation:

$$R\!-\!O\!-\!SO_3H + H_2O \longrightarrow R\!-\!OH + H_2SO_4$$

The existence and widespread occurrence of these enzymes have been known for many years (75,95,37,38), but methods of assay were laborious and insensitive and, since their physiological functions were not immediately apparent, they did not attract the attention that was given to those enzymes whose biological role was more obvious. Recently there has been an increasing awareness of the importance of the part played by ester sulfate groups in the physiological activities of naturally occurring sulfated compounds, and there has resulted a consequent quickening of interest in the specific sulfatases responsible for their hydrolysis.

The sulfatases can be differentiated according to specificity into five different types.

(*1*) *Glycosulfatase* (*Glucosulfatase*).   Mono-, di-, and trisulfuric acid esters of glucose, galactose, maltose, and other simple carbohydrates are hydrolyzed by this enzyme (95).   These substrates are all synthetic compounds and the natural substrates of the enzyme are unknown.   Glycosulfatase occurs in marine molluscs from subtropical

(95) and temperate waters (20), in certain bacteria (106), and in some vertebrates including mammals (96).

(*2*) *Chondrosulfatase.* Chondrosulfatase liberates sulfuric acid from chondroitin sulfate, the so-called mucoitin sulfate and the sulfated polysaccharide present in the mollusc *Charonia lampas* (33). Chondrosulfatase occurs in a number of putrefactive bacteria (70) and in molluscs (97) but its presence in mammalian tissues is in dispute. The enzyme is always accompanied by a mucopolysaccharase or chondroitinase which breaks down chondroitin sulfate into simpler fragments possessing strong reducing activity. The two enzymes have not yet been completely separated and it is not clear to what extent they are interdependent on each other.

(*3*) *Myrosulfatase.* This enzyme liberates the sulfate radical from potassium myronate (sinigrin) and related mustard oil glycosides.

$$C_6H_{11}O_5SC{=}NC_3H_5$$
$$|$$
$$O \cdot SO_3K$$

Potassium myronate

The enzyme is present together with its substrates in the seeds of the *Cruciferae* (74) and is accompanied by a thioglycosidase from which it can be separated (71). Rather surprisingly the enzyme has not been extensively investigated in spite of its presence in mammalian tissues where its physiological importance is unknown.

(*4*) *Steroid Sulfatase.* This is the most recently discovered sulfatase. It occurs in marine and terrestrial molluscs (49,101,90) and has a narrow substrate specificity, attacking only the 3β-sulfates of the 5α and Δ^5 steroids.

(*5*) *Arylsulfatases (Phenolsulfatases).* These enzymes hydrolyze arylsulfuric acids, e.g., phenyl sulfuric acid, and have been found in bacteria (3), fungi (69), molluscs (95), insects (82), birds (65), and mammals (72).

The existence of a general "alkylsulfatase" has not yet been established with certainty although the isolated observation (108) that (*Bacillus cereus* var. *mycoides,* isolated from soil, converted sodium 2-(2,4-dichlorophenoxy) ethyl sulfate to 2-(2,4-dichlorophenoxy) ethanol may indicate the presence of such an enzyme in this organism.

The specificities of the sulfatases have not yet been fully investigated but no case is known where any one substrate is attacked by more than one type of sulfatase and the distinct nature of the various enzymes seems beyond dispute (13,99). Many of the ester sulfates used in sulfatase studies are synthetic compounds, and the natural substrates of the enzyme are, for the most part, unknown. For this reason the nomenclature of these enzymes must be regarded as provisional until such times as their specificities are fully understood. The physiological functions of the sulfatases are uncertain but the widespread distribution of some of the enzymes in nature suggests that they have important roles to fill. Since 1946 there has been an increased interest in the sulfatases, but the plethora of assay methods and substrates which have been used in the study of these enzymes has resulted in a certain amount of confusion. It is hoped that the present chapter will perhaps bring the problems and difficulties presented into greater prominence and lead to some degree of standardization of assay techniques.

II. GENERAL PRINCIPLES

Methods used in the determination of sulfatase activity have been based on three different principles which involve the measurement of the amount of (1) unhydrolyzed substrate, (2) the liberated desulfated residue, or (3) liberated inorganic sulfate.

1. Determination of Unhydrolyzed Substrate

Considerable use was made of this principle during early studies on the sulfatases (95,75). In general, the enzyme and substrate were incubated together in the presence of barium acetate buffer, and at the end of the incubation period the mixture was immersed in a boiling water bath for a few minutes and precipitated protein and barium sulfate were removed. The remaining substrate was hydrolyzed with hydrochloric acid and the precipitated barium sulfate was separated, dried, and weighed.

This type of method is open to serious objections. Thus, appreciable enzymic destruction of substrate is necessary in order to achieve sufficient difference between test and control determinations, and for this reason incubation periods of several hours and, in some cases, several days must be employed. This means that initial reaction rates cannot be studied. Moreover, the method is wasteful of both substrate and enzyme, and in some cases (23,16) considerable destruction of enzyme can occur during the incubation period.

These disadvantages do not preclude the use of methods of this type in those cases where kinetic considerations are not of primary importance. For instance, in testing the activity of the steroid sulfatase of *Patella vulgata* toward a number of steroid sulfates the substrate remaining after enzyme action was estimated as the chloroform-soluble methylene blue salt (87). The author was careful to point out that the method was unsuitable for accurate kinetic studies.

2. Determination of the Desulfated Residue

Extensive use has been made of this type of method in the study of the arylsulfatases where the liberated phenols can usually be readily determined without appreciable interference from the relatively large amounts of substrate which remain. Unfortunately the method is not generally applicable to those sulfatases which act on substrates containing a number of free "alcoholic" hydroxyl groups since the hydroxyl group which is unmasked as a result of the enzyme action usually confers but little extra chemical reactivity on the desulfated residue. It is difficult to find a chemical reaction or a physical property which is particular to the desulfated residue only. A further difficulty in the cases of chondro- and myrosulfatases is that both the substrate and the desulfated residue may be degraded by other enzymes present in the sulfatase preparations and the determination of the desulfated residue is impossible in these circumstances.

Glycosulfatase activity has been measured by this type of procedure (95), advantage being taken of the fact that glucose-6-sulfate is not fermented by yeast in contrast to glucose, the desulfated residue. After the incubation of enzyme and substrate, yeast was added to the incubation mixture and the carbon dioxide arising from the fermentation of the liberated glucose was measured. However, the method is unwieldy and is difficult to apply when a number of simultaneous experiments have to be performed. There is also a limit to the experimental conditions which can be employed; for example, the efficacy of the yeast enzymes may be impaired by the presence of inhibitors in the original incubation mixture. It seems feasible that the highly specific glucose oxidase (notatin) (56) could replace the yeast to some advantage and the method be adapted to the Warburg apparatus.

The Zimmerman technique (111) has been used to measure steroids liberated from their sulfate esters by steroid sulfatase (87,101).

3. Determination of Liberated Sulfuric Acid

This type of method is applicable to all sulfatases. Nevertheless, the difficulties of measuring minute quantities of inorganic sulfate in the presence of biological material and under the widely varying conditions of enzyme experiment are formidable and at the present time have not been completely resolved. The following methods have been employed.

A. NEPHELOMETRIC METHOD

Glycosulfatase has been studied using this method (95). After incubation of enzyme and substrate the mixture was clarified with mercuric chloride, treated with barium chloride, and the resulting turbidity measured in a nephelometer. Under the conditions used the method was wasteful of both enzyme and substrate, and the author notes that the accuracy is not great. Since these early studies there have been considerable improvements in nephelometric techniques which have increased the applicability and sensitivity of the method, but the original problems inherent in the precipitation of barium sulfate in the presence of biological material under a wide variation of experimental conditions still remain (10,41).

B. ACIDIMETRIC METHOD

An acidimetric method has been used for the determination of glyco- and chondrosulfatases (95,33). Enzyme and the barium salt of the substrate were incubated together in the presence of barium acetate-acetic acid buffer when the following reaction occurred:

$$(R-O-SO_3)_2Ba + (CH_3COO)_2Ba + H_2O \longrightarrow$$
$$2R-OH + 2BaSO_4 + 2CH_3COOH$$

The solution was then titrated potentiometrically with 0.05 N sodium hydroxide and the amount of liberated acetic acid determined by reference to a standard titration curve. Unfortunately somewhat large amounts of enzyme and substrate are required and this limits the usefulness of the method. Moreover, the activity of some sulfatases is affected by the presence of barium ions (26).

C. MANOMETRIC METHOD

The carbon dioxide evolved from sodium bicarbonate by enzymically liberated sulfuric acid can be measured manometrically. This method has been used for the assay of the arylsulfatase activity of sea-urchins' eggs (58) and *Aspergillus oryzae* (59) but is applicable over a limited pH range only.

D. COLORIMETRIC METHOD

After deproteinizing the incubation mixture, the sulfuric acid liberated by the enzyme is precipitated as benzidine sulfate, which is then estimated colorimetrically. The sensitivity and adaptability of this method (18) make it the most suitable for the estimation of the sulfatases.

III. A GENERAL METHOD FOR SULFATASE ASSAY

A method of assay which could be applied to all sulfatases is obviously desirable. Such a method should satisfy the following criteria: It should be sufficiently sensitive to allow incubation periods of 1 or 2 hours to be used, it should permit many determinations to be made simultaneously, and it must be capable of use under widely varying experimental conditions. With these points in mind Dodgson and Spencer (18) examined a number of modifications of the colorimetric micro-benzidine method and evolved a procedure which, although not satisfying the above criteria completely, has been successfully applied to the study of aryl-, glyco- and chondrosulfatases. It seems likely that the method could also be used for the assay of myro- and steroid-sulfatases.

There are many modifications of the micro-benzidine method, most of which have been applied to the determination of the sulfate content of blood. One of these modifications was adapted by Tanaka (104) to the study of the aryl- and glycosulfatases of marine molluscs. In this method the incubation mixture was deproteinized with uranyl acetate at pH 5, the inorganic sulfate liberated by the enzyme was precipitated as benzidine sulfate in the presence of acetone, the washed precipitate dissolved in sodium borate solution, and the color resulting after treatment with naphthoquinone sulfonate was measured colorimetrically. The sensitivity of the method is good and, unlike most other micro-benzidine procedures, it can be used in the presence of phosphate buffers since phosphate is precipitated as uranyl phosphate before the addition of benzidine. However, the need for adjustment of the pH of the incubation mixture before addition of uranyl acetate is troublesome when a number of simultaneous determinations are made. Moreover, the method has not been tested over a wide range of experimental conditions and the limits of its applicability to enzyme studies are therefore unknown.

The method chosen by Dodgson and Spencer (18) for adaptation to sulfatase studies was that entailing the removal of protein from the incubation mixture with trichloracetic acid, precipitation of benzidine sulfate in the presence of ethanol, and colorimetric estimation of the washed benzidine sulfate by diazotization followed by coupling with thymol (42). A number of problems had to be overcome, one of the most serious being the difficulty in some cases of completely removing protein and polysaccharide from the incubation mixture. Traces of these materials which remained in solution were subsequently precipitated when the solution of benzidine in ethanol was added and the resultant precipitate could not be satisfactorily washed free from excess benzidine. The problem was solved by reversing the normal procedure and precipitating protein and polysaccharide with ethanol. After removing the precipitate, trichloracetic acid was added and benzidine sulfate precipitated with a concentrated solution of benzidine in ethanol. A second problem arose from the failure to obtain quantitative precipitation of inorganic sulfate when present in concentrations less than about 10 μg./ml. of the incubation mixture. At the tissue concentrations used in enzyme assay the sulfate present in the control determinations was usually less than this amount and low control values were consequently obtained. In order to surmount this difficulty a fixed quantity of potassium sulfate was incorporated into the trichloracetic acid added to both tests and controls so that at least 15 ug. SO_4^{2-} was present in all cases. It was not possible to add sulfate prior to incubation since sulfate is known to inhibit some sulfatases.

The method finally developed was tested over a wide, though by no means exhaustive, range of experimental conditions and the limits of its applicability roughly established. However, the importance of testing the method (by recovery of added potassium sulfate), whenever conditions of enzyme experiment outside those already examined are to be used, has been stressed and with this proviso in mind the method can be used with most sulfatases. Using the method, the inorganic sulfate liberated from potassium p-acetylphenyl sulfate by rat liver arylsulfatase was, in the same experiment, shown to be quantitatively equivalent to the liberated desulfated residue, p-hydroxyacetophenone, which was measured spectrophotometrically (18).

The method given below is of general application. Modifications to meet individual cases will be found in the relevant sections.

A. APPARATUS

All glassware is cleaned with nitric acid; sulfuric acid-containing mixtures must not be used. Benzidine sulfate is precipitated in selected 15 ml. centrifuge tubes of even taper, with a tip of inside diameter 4–5 mm.

B. REAGENTS

Analytical grade reagents must be used throughout.

(1) *Buffer.* 0.5 M sodium acetate-acetic acid buffer is adjusted to the pH appropriate to the enzyme.

(2) *Substrate.* The required amount of substrate is dissolved in the buffer and the pH readjusted if necessary.

(3) *Absolute Ethanol.*

(4) *Trichloroacetic Acid.* 25 g. trichloroacetic acid and approximately 2.5 mg. potassium sulfate are dissolved in 100 ml. distilled water.

(5) *Benzidine.* A good grade of benzidine is recrystallized at least twice from 95% ethanol (charcoal). 5 g. of the recrystallized material is dissolved in 100 ml. of warm ethanol, the solution filtered and stored in a dark bottle in a warm room. The solution is stable for about 4 weeks.

(6) *Powdered Glass.* Finely powdered glass is washed with distilled water, ethanol, and ether and then dried.

(7) *N Hydrochloric Acid.*

(8) *0.1% Sodium Nitrite.*

(9) *Thymol.* 5 g. thymol is dissolved in 1 liter of 7.5% sodium hydroxide.

C. PROCEDURE

(1) **Incubation of Enzyme and Substrate.** The enzyme preparation (0.6 ml.), contained in a 15 ml. stoppered centrifuge tube, is pre-incubated for 4 min. in a water bath at 37.5°C. and 0.6 ml. substrate solution at the same temperature is added at zero time. After mixing, the tube is incubated at 37.5° for the required period. Enzyme action is subsequently stopped and protein and polysaccharide precipitated by the addition of 4.8 ml. ethanol, the concentration of ethanol in the final mixture thus being 80%. The determination is carried out in triplicate (to cover occasional breakages) with suitable controls in which enzyme and substrate are incubated separately and only mixed immediately prior to the addition of ethanol.

(2) **Precipitation of Benzidine Sulfate.** After standing in the ice chest for 30 min. to allow flocculation of the precipitate the tube is capped and centrifuged at about 2500 g for 5 min. 5 ml. of the clear supernatant is pipetted into a selected 15 ml. centrifuge tube, care being taken not to disturb the precipitate. 1 ml. of the trichloracetic acid solution is added followed by 1 ml. of the benzidine solution. The contents of the tube are mixed by means of a jet of air passing through a fine capillary which is subsequently washed down with a few drops of ethanol. After stoppering, the tube is allowed to stand at 0°C. overnight to allow complete precipitation of the benzidine sulfate.

(3) **Separation and Washing of the Benzidine Sulfate.** A small amount (3–5 mg.) of powdered glass is added to the tube, which is capped and centrifuged at 2500 g for 15 min. The supernatant solution is carefully poured off and discarded. In the absence of powdered glass small particles of benzidine sulfate often break away at this stage, but when powdered glass is present the precipitate packs down tightly on top of the glass and such losses are not experienced. The tube is inverted on filter paper and allowed to drain for 5 to 10 min. The mouth of the tube is wiped with filter paper and the outside washed with acetone. After standing for 1 min. on filter paper the mouth of the tube is washed with ethanol while the tube is held in an inverted position. After draining for 5 min. more on filter paper, the mouth of the tube is again wiped with filter paper and about 10 ml. of ethanol added, care being taken not to disturb the precipitate; otherwise large fragments break away which cannot be washed effectively. The precipitate is broken up and mixed by means of a glass rod which is subsequently washed down with a little ethanol. The benzidine sulfate is separated by centrifuging and, after pouring off the supernatant solution, the tube and contents are treated exactly as before except that instead of adding 10 ml. ethanol, the benzidine sulfate is dissolved in 3 ml. of the hydrochloric acid.

(4) **Colorimetric Measurement.** After standing for a few minutes, 1 ml. of the sodium nitrite solution is added, the whole mixed and, after addition of 5 ml. of the thymol solution, the tube is centrifuged for a short time to separate the powdered glass. The intensity of the red color (λ_{max} 500 mμ) is measured against a reagent blank in a suitable colorimeter. With the Hilger "Spekker" absorptiometer, Chance 0.B.2. glass filters and 2.5 mm. cells are used.

The SO_4^{2-} present is obtained by reference to a calibration curve prepared by diazotizing and coupling known amounts of benzidine in N hydrochloric acid using the volumes and procedures described in this section. In the range 10–70 μg. SO_4^{2-}, the calibration curve prepared in this way does not differ from that prepared by actual precipitation and determination of known amounts of potassium sulfate.

The amount of SO_4^{2-} liberated by 1 ml. of the enzyme preparation in 1 hr. is given by:

$$(T - C) \times 5.88/5.0 \times 1/0.6 \times 1/t$$

or
$$\frac{(T - C)1.96}{t}$$

where T and C are the μg. SO_4^{2-} present in test and control solutions respectively, and t is the time of incubation in hours. The number 5.88 differs from 6.00 because of the shrinkage in volume which occurs when 4.8 ml. ethanol is added to 1.2 ml. aqueous incubation mixture (17).

D. COMMENTS

The method has been successfully tested using enzyme preparations from bacterial (15), fungal, molluscan, and mammalian (18) sources, but with fresh mammalian tissues satisfactory recoveries of added potassium sulfate cannot be obtained when the concentration of the tissue homogenate exceeds 3% (w/v). Sodium acetate-acetic acid and tris(hydroxymethyl)aminomethane-hydrochloric acid buffers are suitable for use with the method. K^+, Na^+, Mg^{2+}, CN^-, Cl^-, and F^- in concentrations of 0.01 M and Fe^{3+}, Ca^{2+}, and PO_4^{3-} at concentrations of 0.001 M do not interfere, but Fe^{3+}, Ca^{2+}, and PO_4^{3-} in higher concentrations cause considerable interference while Ba^{2+}, even in traces, renders the method invalid.

In spite of the value of this technique in the study of the sulfatases the procedure is lengthy and somewhat exacting, and for this reason it has not found general use in cases where the desulfated residue can be readily measured. There is still a need for a simpler method of estimating enzymically liberated sulfate.

IV. GLYCOSULFATASE

1. The Enzyme

The existence in certain tropical molluscs of an enzyme capable of liberating sulfuric acid from glucose-6-sulfate was first noted by Soda and Hattori in 1931 (98). Although a similar enzyme has been shown to occur in bacteria (106,7) and in certain fishes and mammals (96), studies have been largely confined to molluscan preparations. The enzyme attacks a number of simple carbohydrate sulfates but, since the activity was greatest with glucose-6-sulfate, the name "glucosulfatase" was suggested (95). However, glucose-6-sulfate is not known to occur as such in nature, and in view of the diverse character of the carbohydrate sulfates attacked, the name "glycosulfatase" has been proposed (20) as more appropriate until the specificity of the enzyme is more clearly defined and the natural substrates are discovered.

Between 1931 and 1948 a series of publications by Soda and his co-workers described the purification, partial separation from other sulfatases, and properties of the glycosulfatase of the tropical mollusc *Charonia lampas* (*Triton nodiferus*). More recently (20) the enzyme has been found in molluscs which are common to temperate waters, and concentrates have been prepared from the visceral material of *Littorina littorea*, the large periwinkle.

The physiological function of the enzyme is obscure, although in the mollusc it is tempting to suggest a digestive role in view of the presence of sulfated carbohydrates in the seaweeds and marine organisms on which the molluscs feed. Soda (95) has suggested that the enzyme may also play a part in shell formation.

2. The Assay Substrate

Although many substrates of glycosulfatase are known, the accepted substrate for the assay of the enzyme is glucose-6-sulfate. This substrate can be prepared by direct sulfation of glucose with chlorosulfonic acid (94) or with pyridine-sulfur trioxide reagent (30), but the product is not homogeneous and contains varying amounts of a sulfated impurity which may be as high as 30%. This point seems to have escaped the notice of some workers (30,110). The impurity is, however, hydrolyzed by glycosulfatase.

The impure nature of the substrate was first noted by Egami (31) who found that the product prepared by the chlorosulfonic acid method of Soda (94) was hydrolyzed to the extent of about 15% by hydrazine at 37.5°C. in the presence of acetate buffers. No further hydrolysis could be observed by prolonged incubation or by addition of more hydrazine, but addition of more substrate resulted in a further equivalent hydrolysis. Egami concluded that the hydrolyzed material was a sulfated impurity. When glucose is sulfated with the pyridine-sulfur trioxide reagent, up to 30% of the product can be hydrolyzed by hydrazine (20). Chromatography has revealed the presence of two contaminants in glucose-6-sulfate prepared in this way. The concentration of these impurities can be substantially reduced by repeated recrystallization of the brucine salt of glucose-6-sulfate, which can subsequently be reconverted to the potassium salt (20,32).

The impure nature of the substrate was responsible for the anomalous substrate concentration-activity curve obtained by Dodgson and Spencer (20) for the glycosulfatase of *Littorina littorea*. Kinetic problems arising from the use of an impure substrate are evident, and previous kinetic studies (95) on glycosulfatase should therefore be regarded with caution. For this reason the somewhat lengthy method of preparation (IV.2.A) of a substantially pure substrate via the recrystallized brucine salt is given in full. However, the impure substrate can be satisfactorily used for many purposes and a comparatively simple method (IV.2.B) for its preparation is included.

A. SUBSTANTIALLY PURE POTASSIUM GLUCOSE-6-SULFATE

The method is essentially that of Soda (94). A mixture of 7 ml. chlorosulfonic acid and 18 ml. chloroform is added dropwise with stirring to a solution of 20 g. glucose in 75 ml. dry pyridine, the temperature of the reaction being maintained below 10°C. The mixture is then stirred at room temperature for 1 hr. After standing overnight an oil forms which is separated, dissolved in 300 ml. water, and freed from traces of chloroform by concentrating to about 250 ml. *in vacuo* at 40°C. Powdered lead oxide (80 g.) is added and, after mixing, the whole is distilled *in vacuo* to remove pyridine but avoiding undue concentration. The filtered solution is free from pyridine and inorganic sulfate but contains, in addition to the lead salt of glucose-6-sulfate, free glucose, a trace of chloride and lead hydroxide. Lead hydroxide is precipitated by passing carbon dioxide through the solution and, after filtering, chloride is removed by the addition of a solution of silver sulfate. The precipitate is separated by filtration with the help of charcoal. After diluting the filtrate with about 600 ml. water the solution is gassed with hydrogen sulfide until no more lead sulfide is formed. The precipitated lead sulfide is filtered off and excess hydrogen sulfide is removed by passing a stream of air through the solution. The filtrate is then treated with a slight excess of an alcoholic solution of brucine and the whole is concentrated *in vacuo* at 40°C. The first crop of crystals, free brucine, is discarded and after further concentration a sirup remains which solidifies on cooling. This is dissolved in a little hot water and ethanol is added until a slight turbidity appears. On cooling the crystalline salt separates out. The brucine salt is recrystallized from aqueous ethanol five times in order to remove the bulk of the impurity previously mentioned. The brucine salt is dissolved in water, cooled in an ice-bath, and converted into the corresponding potassium salt by the slow addition, with stirring, of the required amount of 2 N potassium hydroxide. The precipitated brucine is filtered off and the filtrate concentrated to about 50 ml. *in vacuo*. It is then poured slowly with stirring into 1 liter of ethanol and, after standing for a few minutes, the precipitated potassium glucose-6-sulfate is filtered off, washed well with ethanol and dried *in vacuo* at 50°C. The salt is very hygroscopic.

B. SIMPLE METHOD FOR IMPURE GLUCOSE-6-SULFATE

The method is based on that of Duff (30). Glucose (10 g.) dissolved in 150 ml. dry pyridine is mixed with 13.7 g. (1.5 moles) pyridine-sulfur trioxide reagent. The mixture is stirred for 4 hr. and allowed to stand overnight in a stoppered flask. Water (200 ml.) is added and sulfuric acid is removed and barium glucose-6-sulfate formed by stirring for 2 hr. with 50 g. barium carbonate. After filtering, the filtrate is concentrated to about 30 ml. *in vacuo* at 40°C. and is poured, with stirring, into 1 liter of ethanol. The precipitate is filtered off, washed well with ethanol, and dried *in vacuo* at 50°. A concentrated solution of the barium salt is converted into the corresponding potassium salt by dropwise addition of the calculated amount of a concentrated solution of potassium sulfate. Barium sulfate is removed, and potassium glucose-6-sulfate is precipitated by pouring the filtrate into 1 liter of ethanol with stirring. The precipitate is separated, washed well with ethanol, and dried *in vacuo*.

The pyridine-sulfur trioxide reagent, $C_5H_5N\diagup^O_{SO_2}$, is conveniently prepared (cf. 4) by passing sulfur trioxide (distilled from "fuming" sulfuric acid) into dry, ice-cold chloroform, with stirring, the gain in weight being noted. The calculated amount of dry pyridine is then added dropwise, with stirring, at 0°C. Suitable precautions are taken to exclude moisture from the apparatus up to this stage. The precipitated pyridine-sulfur trioxide is filtered, washed with dry chloroform, and stored *in vacuo* over phosphorus pentoxide.

3. Method of Assay

The micro-benzidine method described in Section III is suitable, and the technique described below has been used (20) to measure glycosulfatase activity in a number of molluscs common to British waters.

A. THE ENZYME PREPARATION

Molluscs are starved for 24 hr. in aerated sea water to allow the bulk of the waste food material to be eliminated. The appropriate organ is dissected out and washed quickly in ice-cold distilled water to remove contaminating sea water. The tissue is freed from surplus moisture by means of blotting paper, weighed, and homogenized in a known volume of ice-cold 0.5 M sodium acetate-acetic acid buffer, pH 5.8, using a glass homogenizer. The concentration of tissue homogenate should be in the region of 2–4% wet weight/volume.

B. PROCEDURE

The procedure detailed in Section III.C is followed exactly, the substrate (III.B(2)) being 0.04 M potassium glucose-6-sulfate in the acetate buffer (III.B(1)) at pH 5.8 and the incubation period being 2 hr.

C. COMMENTS

The pH of incubation, 5.8, is that found to be optimal for the glycosulfatase of *Littorina littorea* (20), but the substrate concentration used (0.02 M in the incubation mixture) is arbitrary. The true optimum substrate concentration for the *Littorina* enzyme cannot be stated with certainty owing to the impure nature of the substrate but it appears to be in the region of 0.7 M (20). If it is desired to use this higher substrate concentration it is necessary to modify slightly the incubation conditions used in the assay method since SO_4^{2-} cannot be quantitatively recovered when the concentration of potassium glucose-6-sulfate in the incubation mixture is greater than 0.03 M. In the modified method 0.2 ml. enzyme preparation is incubated with 0.2 ml. of 0.14 M substrate solution, both in acetate buffer as before. After incubating for the required period, enzyme action is stopped and protein and polysaccharide precipitated by the addition of 5.6 ml. of 86% (v/v) ethanol, the final concentration of ethanol being 80% as in the original method. The subsequent procedure is as before.

The μg. SO_4^{2-} liberated by 1 ml. of the enzyme preparation is now given by (cf. III.C(4)):

$$(T - C) \times (6.0/5.0) \times (1/0.2) \times (1/t)$$

there being negligible shrinkage in volume when 5.6 ml. 86% ethanol is added to 0.4 ml. incubation mixture.

Almost all the work on glycosulfatase has been done with mollusc preparations and the incubation conditions given may have to be modified considerably for the study of other sources of the enzyme. The introduction of a new assay substrate which can be prepared in such a way as to leave no doubt as to its homogeneity is desirable. Unfortunately, one such substrate, potassium glucose-3-sulfate, which is hydrolyzed by the enzyme cannot be used with the micro-benzidine method since it is unstable in the presence of trichloracetic acid (20).

V. CHONDROSULFATASE

1. The Enzyme

The existence in putrefactive bacteria of an enzyme which is capable of liberating sulfuric acid from chondroitin sulfate was first suspected by Neuberg and Rubin in 1914 (70). An enzyme preparation was subsequently obtained from an organism resembling *B. fluorescens non-liquefaciens* (syn. *Pseudomonas fluorescens non-liquefaciens*) while other putrefactive bacteria, *B. proteus* (syn. *Proteus vulgaris*) and *B. pyocyaneum* (syn. *Pseudomonas aeroginosa*) were also shown to possess the enzyme (67). Since these early studies a similar enzyme has been discovered in the digestive organs of molluscs (97). It is not yet clear whether there is a chondrosulfatase present in mammalian tissues. However, some liberation of $S^{35}O_4{}^{2-}$ following the administration of S^{35}-containing chondroitin sulfate to rats has been observed (29), and there is also a certain amount of somewhat confused evidence which suggests that the enzyme elastase contains more than one component, one of which may be a chondrosulfatase type of enzyme (43,79).

It has not yet been possible to separate completely the mucopolysaccharase (see I(2)), which degrades the polysaccharide chain of chondroitin sulfate, from the chondrosulfatase with which it co-exists in the bacterial and molluscan preparations.* The extent to which these enzymes are interdependent is not yet clear, and kinetic studies of the sulfatase activity are therefore difficult to interpret.

The specificity of chondrosulfatase is not yet clearly understood and, indeed, it is not known whether the different chondroitin sulfuric acids, which have now been shown to be present in mammalian tissues (55), are all attacked by the enzyme. Neuberg and Cahill (66) noted that so-called mucoitin sulfuric acid was also a substrate for the enzyme but the homogeneity of this substrate now appears to be in doubt (cf. ref. 93). Recently, Egami has shown that the cellulose-like polysaccharide sulfate (34) present in the tropical mollusc *Charonia lampas* is hydrolyzed (33) by a chondrosulfatase from this or-

---

* This has now been achieved in the case of the enzymes of *Proteus vulgaris;* see Dodgson, K. S., and Lloyd, A. G., *Biochem. J., 65,* 4P (1957).

ganism.   Early bacterial preparations of chondrosulfatase were reported to attack glucose-6-sulfate and potassium myronate (68), but since these substrates were not attacked by a purified bacterial chondrosulfatase (15) it seems likely that the earlier observations were due to the presence of other sulfatases.   The role of the enzyme in nature is obscure.

2. The Assay Substrate

During the last few years considerable interest has been shown in the chemistry of sulfated polysaccharides, and it is now obvious that the formulation of the chemical nature of these compounds has been oversimplified by workers in the past.   Recently three different types of chondroitin sulfate have been recognized (63,55) and it seems probable that most preparations obtained by simple extraction procedures are unlikely to be homogeneous.

During the past few years chondrosulfatase has been little studied, and until the enzyme has been separated from the mucopolysaccharase with which it is associated there seems little point in insisting on a completely homogeneous substrate.   A product prepared by a modification (15) of the method of Einbinder and Schubert (35) can probably be regarded as satisfactory for initial studies on the enzyme.

Preparation.

The rings of cartilage from fresh bovine trachea are immersed for 10 min. in acetone when the hardened non-cartilaginous material can be removed. The cartilage is washed, coarsely minced, and 150 g. of the mince is macerated in 200 ml. water containing 0.25 g. crude trypsin (British Drug Houses Ltd.) and 0.1 g. thymol, the whole being adjusted to pH 7.8.   After incubation at 37°C. for 72 hr., 1 liter of a 30% solution of potassium chloride is added and the mixture shaken mechanically for 72 hr.   The cloudy extract is decanted and stored at 0°C. while the residue is shaken with a further 1 liter of potassium chloride solution for 72 hr.   The two extracts are combined and dialyzed for 40 hr. against tap water in order to reduce the salt concentration of the solution, thereby increasing the efficiency of the subsequent deproteinization procedure (102).   Glacial acetic acid (20 ml.) and 20 g. potassium acetate are added and the solution is stirred for 30 min. with 20 g. kaolin.   The bulk of the kaolin is removed by centrifugation, the solution clarified by filtering through Filter-Cel, and the filtrate dialyzed for 24 hr. against tap water.   The treatment with acetic acid, potassium acetate, and kaolin is repeated, the solution clarified as before and then concentrated to about 300 ml. *in vacuo* at 40°C.   The solution is poured, with stirring, into 1 liter of ethanol and the whole allowed to stand overnight at

0°C.   The white flocculent precipitate of potassium chondroitin sulfate is
separated, washed well with ethanol and ether, and dried *in vacuo*.   The
product is dissolved in distilled water to give a 3% solution, acidified with
glacial acetic acid (2 ml./100 ml.) and stirred with kaolin (4 g./100 ml.) for
30 min.   The solution is clarified as described before, stirred with a further
quantity of kaolin (4 g./100 ml.), and then clarified.   The filtrate is dialyzed against several changes (100 vol. in all) of distilled water.   This di-
alysis removes traces of inorganic sulfate and is a necessary step if high blank
values in the micro-benzidine assay procedure are to be avoided.   Potassium
acetate (10 g.) is added to each 100 ml. of dialyzate and the potassium chondroitin sulfate is precipitated by the addition, with stirring, of 3 vol. ethanol.
The precipitate is separated, washed with ethanol followed by dry ether, and
dried *in vacuo*.   Yield, 5–7 g.   Analysis (average of three preparations):
N, 2.23; SO_4^{2-}, 14.19; hexosamine, 26.0%; N/S ratio, 1.08.

3. Method of Assay

The micro-benzidine method (III) is suitable.

A. INCUBATION CONDITIONS

The following incubation conditions have been used for the assay of a bacterial chondrosulfatase (15).   The enzyme preparation (0.6 ml.) in 0.2 M
sodium acetate-acetic acid buffer, pH 7.0, is incubated at 37.5°C. for 1 hr.
with 0.6 ml. of a 0.09% solution of potassium chondroitin sulfate in the same
buffer at the same pH.   At the end of the incubation period the sulfate present in test and control is determined as described in Section III.C (2, 3, 4).

B. COMMENTS

The incubation conditions outlined above are those found to be
optimal for the acetone-dried cells of a strain of *Proteus vulgaris* (15).
These conditions may need modification when investigating other
sources of chondrosulfatase activity.   For example, the optimum pH
of the chondrosulfatase of *Charonia lampas* is 5.0; the optimum substrate concentration is not recorded (97).   In their original experiments Dodgson and Spencer (18) indicated that the micro-benzidine
method was applicable up to concentrations of chondroitin sulfate of
0.5% in the incubation mixture.   It is now obvious that these early
observations were made using a partially degraded chondroitin sulfate,
and more recent experiments using freshly prepared substrate (V.2)
have shown that good recoveries of SO_4^{2-} can only be obtained when
the concentration is 0.175% or less.   When higher concentrations are

needed, resort can be made to the use of smaller volumes in the incubation mixture as described for glycosulfatase (IV.3.C).

On a number of occasions when crude mollusc preparations containing large amounts of protein have been examined in this laboratory some difficulty has been encountered during the precipitation of protein following the addition of ethanol to the incubation mixture. The remaining chondroitin sulfate is also precipitated by this procedure and the bulky precipitate, when centrifuged down, is sometimes disturbed when a portion of the clear filtrate is taken for further treatment. This trouble can be avoided by adding 3–5 mg. powdered glass to the mixture before centrifuging. The precipitate packs down tightly on the powdered glass and is not readily disturbed.

VI. MYROSULFATASE

1. The Enzyme

The sulfated thioglycosides, such as sinigrin (potassium myronate), sinalbin and glucocheirolin, which are present in the seeds of the *Cruciferae* can be hydrolyzed by the myrosinase (sinigrinase) of the seeds to give glucose, the respective allyl mustard oil, and potassium hydrogen sulfate (74). Myrosinase is composed of two separable enzymes, a thioglycosidase and a sulfatase which has been termed myrosulfatase (71). Myrosulfatase also occurs in mammalian tissues (76) although not in association with a thioglycosidase.

2. The Assay Substrate

Potassium myronate can be readily prepared from the seeds of black mustard, *Sinapis nigra* (syn. *Brassica nigra*). The following preparation is that of Herissey and Boivin (50). The method of Gadamer (39) is not recommended (64).

Powdered black mustard seed (1 kg.) is boiled for 20 min. with 10 liters of aqueous acetone (2.5 liters of water made up to 10 liters with acetone); this process effectively destroying the endogenous myrosinase. After cooling, the solid material is separated by filtration and the volume of the clear filtrate is then reduced to about 2 liters by distillation on a boiling water bath. The small amount of oil which separates on cooling is removed and, after filtering, the sucrose present in the extract is destroyed by treating the filtrate with 20 g. of fresh baker's yeast for 72 hr. at room temperature.

The fermented solution is neutralized by warming on a boiling water bath with 15–20 g. calcium carbonate and the mixture is filtered and concentrated to a sirup *in vacuo*.   The sirup is dissolved by refluxing with 3 liters of 85% ethanol, and after standing for 24 hr. the solution is filtered and the solvents removed *in vacuo* at 40°C.   The residual material is then extracted six or seven times by refluxing with 300 ml. portions of 95% ethanol.   After each extraction the whole is allowed to stand for 24 hr. before filtering.   All the filtered extracts crystallize out on standing, crystallization being facilitated by scratching or seeding.   Crystals usually continue to form for several days. The glycoside (11–12 g.) is recrystallized from 83% ethanol (10 ml./g. glycoside).

3. Method of Assay

Myrosulfatase has not been investigated in recent years, and the method (76) which has been used in the past is insensitive, wasteful of enzyme and substrate, unsuitable for measuring initial reaction rates, and has been used under arbitrary conditions of pH and substrate concentration.   For details the reader is referred to the original article (76).   No attempt has yet been made to use the micro-benzidine method to study myrosulfatase, but good recoveries of added sulfate can be made from buffered solutions of potassium myronate (18) and there seems little reason why the method should not be used.   Further studies are of course necessary in order to establish the working conditions of the enzyme.

VII. STEROID SULFATASE

1. The Enzyme

Steroid sulfatase was first described by Henri, Thevenet, and Jarrige (49), who found that the intestinal juice of *Helix pomatia* was capable of hydrolyzing the sulfuric acid ester of dehydroepiandrosterone.   The enzyme was subsequently detected in the viscera of the marine mollusc *Patella vulgata* (101) and the African land snail, *Otala punctata* (90).   The only intensive investigation on the properties of the enzyme reported to date is that due to Roy (87), who has examined and prepared concentrates of the *Patella* enzyme.   This study and that of Savard, Bagnoli, and Dorfman (90) have shown that the enzyme has a narrow specificity and will hydrolyze only the 3 β-sulfates of the 5α- and Δ⁵-steroids, other isomeric 3-sulfates not being attacked. This narrow specificity of the enzyme severely limits its usefulness for the hydrolysis of urinary steroid sulfates prior to their assay. The enzyme will not attack true alkyl sulfates such as ethyl or benzyl sulfates, and the original name proposed for the enzyme, "alkylsulfatase" (101), is therefore unsuitable (87). In *Patella* preparations steroid sulfatase is accompanied by other sulfatases, but although complete separation of the enzymes has not yet been achieved there is no doubt as to the distinct nature of the steroid enzyme.

2. The Assay Substrate

The substrate which has been used most for the assay of the enzyme is dehydroepiandrosterone sulfate, which can be conveniently prepared in the following way (87):

Dehydroepiandrosterone (3-β-hydroxyandrost-5-ene-17-one) (50 mg.) is dissolved in 3 ml. dry benzene and an equal weight of pyridine-sulfur trioxide (IV.2.B) added. The mixture is refluxed on a water bath for 90 min., cooled, and diluted with 30 ml. petroleum ether (b.p. 60–80°). After standing for 1 hr. at 0°C. the precipitated pyridinium salt of the steroid sulfate is removed by filtration and washed with petroleum ether. The residue is extracted five times with 2 ml. portions of boiling chloroform in order to separate the soluble pyridinium salt from the excess sulfur trioxide reagent and the extracts are combined and taken to dryness *in vacuo*. The dried material is dissolved in the smallest volume of boiling 70% ethanol and an equal volume of hot potassium sulfate solution (saturated in the cold) is added. Water is added dropwise to the boiling mixture until complete solution is effected. Potassium dehydroepiandrosterone sulfate crystallizes out and is recrystallized from water. The length of time of contact of the sulfate ester with boiling water is kept to a minimum in order to prevent hydrolysis of the ester. Other steroid sulfates may be prepared in the same way.

3. Method of Assay

Two different types of method have been used to determine steroid sulfatase activity. The first type involves the estimation of the residual substrate, while the second depends on the estimation of liberated dehydroepiandrosterone. An example of each type as applied to the assay of concentrates of the steroid sulfatase of *Patella vulgata* is given below.

A. DETERMINATION OF THE RESIDUAL SUBSTRATE (87)

The principle of the method is to extract the substrate remaining at the end of the incubation period as the chloroform-soluble methylene blue salt which is then measured colorimetrically. The liberated dehydroepiandrosterone does not form a methylene blue salt.

(1) Reagents.

Buffer. Sodium acetate-acetic acid buffer (0.5 M) adjusted to pH 4.5.
Chloroform.
Methylene Blue Reagent. Methylene Blue (250 mg.) is dissolved in water, 50 g. sodium sulfate and 10 ml. sulfuric acid are added and the volume made up to 1 liter with water.
75% Ethanol.
Substrate. Potassium dehydroepiandrosterone sulfate, 0.0004 M, in aqueous solution.

(2) Method.

To 0.25 ml. of 0.5 M acetate buffer are added 0.5 ml. substrate solution and 0.25 ml. of the enzyme preparation. After incubation at 37 °C. for 1 hr. the reaction is stopped by immersing the tubes in a boiling water bath for 5 min. A control experiment is made in which enzyme and substrate are incubated separately and mixed at the end of the incubation period immediately before heating in the water bath. After cooling, 1 ml. of the methylene blue reagent is added to each tube and the mixture is extracted with 5 ml. chloroform by shaking in a stoppered tube for 30 sec. Any emulsion is broken by centrifuging, the aqueous layer is removed, and 2 ml. of the clear chloroform layer is added to 10 ml. 75% ethanol. The intensity of the blue color is measured with the Hilger "Spekker" absorptiometer using an Ilford filter No. 608 (700 mμ) and using a reagent blank prepared as described above but omitting enzyme and substrate.

A calibration curve is prepared in the same manner but substituting for the incubation mixture 1 ml. of various dilutions of the steroid sulfate (ranging from 20 to 100 μg.) containing 0.25 ml. 0.5 M acetate buffer, pH 4.5; i.e., the concentration of acetate used in the assay.

The enzyme activity is proportional to the difference between the amounts of potassium dehydroepiandrosterone sulfate remaining after incubation in the presence and absence of enzyme.

(3) Comments.
Recovery of dehydroepiandrosterone sulfate by this method is only about 95% since some slight hydrolysis of the ester occurs when enzyme activity is stopped by treatment at 100°C. for 5 min. The partition of the steroid sulfate-methylene blue com-

plex between the aqueous and chloroform phases is influenced to only a slight extent by the concentrations of electrolytes normally present in enzyme experiments. Sodium chloride (0.1 M) in the aqueous phase increases the partition in favor of the chloroform phase by 10%, while similar concentrations of acetate, sulfate, and phosphate are without effect.

The method can be used with other steroid sulfates as substrates. There is no significant difference between calibration curves prepared with dehydroepiandrosterone, epiandrosterone, pregnenolone, and androsterone sulfates. Many sulfate esters form chloroform-soluble methylene blue salts and an extension of the above method to the assay of sulfatases other than steroid sulfatase may prove feasible.

B. DETERMINATION OF THE LIBERATED STEROID (87)

The principle of the method involves the measurement of the liberated steroid by the Zimmerman technique (62,111).

(1) Reagents.

Ethanol. Absolute ethanol is treated with 4 g./l. *m*-phenylenediamine hydrochloride, allowed to stand in the dark for a week with occasional shaking and then distilled, the head and tail fractions being rejected.

m-Dinitrobenzene. 20 g. is dissolved in 750 ml. 95% ethanol, warmed to 40°C. and 100 ml. of 2 N NaOH is added. After 5 min. the solution is cooled and 2.5 liters of water is added. The precipitated *m*-dinitrobenzene is collected on a Büchner funnel and washed thoroughly with water, sucked dry, and recrystallized twice in succession from 120 ml. and 80 ml. absolute ethanol. When stored in a glass-stoppered brown bottle in the dark it is stable for 10–14 days.

Potassium Hydroxide. 9 g. potassium hydroxide is dissolved in 50 ml. absolute ethanol and filtered through hardened filter paper. The concentration is checked by titration and adjusted between the limits 2.48 and 2.52 N. The solution is stored at 0°C. and must be discarded as soon as the faintest color is discernible.

(2) Method.

The incubation conditions are exactly as described for the methylene blue method (VII.3.A(2)) and the enzyme action is stopped as before by immersing the tubes in a boiling water bath for 5 min. Suitable control determinations are made as described previously. After cooling, 5 ml. chloroform is added, the mixture thoroughly shaken and then centrifuged. 4 ml. of the chloroform layer is pipetted into a test tube and taken to dryness on the water bath, an alundum chip being added to prevent bumping. The residue is dissolved in 0.2 ml. ethanol, and 0.2 ml. *m*-dinitrobenzene reagent is added followed by 0.2 ml. ethanolic potassium hydroxide. The mixture is kept in the dark for 1 hr. at 25°C. and then diluted with 8 ml. ethanol. The resultant pink color in both test and controls is measured with the Hilger "Spekker" absorptiometer against a water blank using an Ilford filter No. 604 (520 mμ). A calibration curve is prepared using concentrations of dehydroepiandrosterone in the range 10 to 80 μg.

C. GENERAL COMMENTS

The incubation conditions described for the assay of steroid sulfatase (final concentration of substrate 0.002 M at pH 4.5) are the optimal conditions for concentrates of the *Patella* enzyme (87). Incubation conditions may well have to be modified for other sources of the enzyme. The limitations of the methods given here have been described by Roy (87) and neither method can be considered completely satisfactory for the assay of the enzyme. It is probable that the micro-benzidine method (18) could be used to measure the sulfuric acid liberated as a result of steroid sulfatase action.

VIII. ARYLSULFATASES

1. The Enzymes and Their Substrates

The first report of arylsulfatase activity can be attributed to Derrien (12), who found that an extract of the snail *Murex trunculus* was capable of converting indoxyl sulfate to indigo. No further study was made until Neuberg and Kurono (69) noted that preparations of the fungus *Aspergillus oryzae* liberated sulfuric acid from potassium phenyl sulfate. The name "sulfatase" was given to the enzyme. Following the discovery of a similar enzyme in mammalian tissues a number of investigations of the specificity of the enzyme were made, and in 1932 Neuberg and Simon (73) suggested that the name "phenolsulfatase" be used to distinguish the enzyme from other sulfatases. More recently (83) the name "arylsulfatase" has been proposed as being more in keeping with the systematic name of the substrates of the enzyme, viz., arylsulfuric acids. The earlier work on arylsulfatases has been reviewed by Fromageot (37,38).

The arylsulfatases have been very much more extensively investigated than other sulfatases; this can be attributed to the ease with which enzyme activity can be measured.   Theoretically the choice of substrate for enzyme assay is unlimited since most arylsulfuric acids can be readily synthesized.   A number of simple and sensitive assay methods (Table II) have been developed, but unfortunately the use of different substrates by the various authors has resulted in a certain amount of confusion regarding the occurrence and properties of the enzymes.   However, recent developments in our knowledge of aryl-sulfatases have done much to explain the conflicting reports which are to be found in the literature and an understanding of the present situation is important when selecting the most suitable method of assay.

The rate of enzymic hydrolysis of different arylsulfates varies considerably and indeed some substrates do not appear to be hy-drolyzed at all (5).   The use of different substrates for enzyme assay need not itself be confusing provided that it is appreciated that the optimum conditions of pH and substrate concentration for the activity of an arylsulfatase will vary with the substrate used.   However, it is now apparent that there are present in nature at least two types of arylsulfatase which possess different relative substrate specificities.

Type 1.   Arylsulfatases of this type occur in mammalian tissues, fungal preparations, and in certain bacteria.   They exhibit ap-preciable activity and affinity toward potassium p-acetylphenyl sul-fate and potassium p-nitrophenyl sulfate but are much less active toward potassium 2-hydroxy-5-nitrophenyl sulfate (nitrocatechol sulfate) (25,28) although the enzymes may actually possess appreci-able affinity for this substrate (26).   These enzymes are inhibited by cyanide but are hardly affected by phosphate or sulfate.

Type 2.   This type of arylsulfatase, which occurs in mammalian tissues and in molluscs, has little activity and affinity toward p-acetylphenyl and p-nitrophenyl sulfates but has considerable activity and affinity toward nitrocatechol sulfate.   Type 2 enzymes are un-affected by cyanide but are strongly inhibited by phosphate and sulfate (85,86).

The danger of using one substrate only for the detection of arylsul-fatase activity will now be apparent since an enzyme which has little activity toward the assay substrate may remain undetected (25). The problems arising from competition for substrate when two iso-dynamic enzymes are present in the same preparation are also ob-vious.

These difficulties have been brought into prominence by the recent

TABLE I

Mammalian Arylsulfatases—Type of Enzyme Studied by Various Workers (see ref. 25)

From an examination of the conditions of assay the particular type of enzyme studied in each case has been inferred and included in the table under the heading "Type of enzyme." Insufficient details are given by Abbot and East (2) to enable a decision to be given. The pH and substrate concentrations shown were those used for assay purposes and are not necessarily optimal. The Type 1 enzyme of mammalian tissues is arylsulfatase C, whereas the Type 2 enzyme is a mixture of arylsulfatases A and B except where otherwise indicated.

Animal	Organ	Method of preparation of enzyme	Substrate—sulfate ester of	Substrate concentration M	pH	Type of enzyme	Ref.
Rat	Liver and other tissues	Centrifuged water extracts	p-Nitrophenol	0.001	5.8	1	(53)
		Extracts (?)			6.6		(2)
		Whole tissue	4-Nitrocatechol	0.0025	6.0	2	(81)
	Liver	Whole tissue homogenates	p-Hydroxyacetophenone	0.007	7.2	1	(23,24)
			p-Hydroxyacetophenone	0.007	7.2	1	(25)
Rat, ox, rabbit, pig, dog, and monkey	Adrenals	Mitochondria	4-Nitrocatechol	0.0075	5.5	2	(107)
		Whole tissue	p-Nitrophenol	0.0005	5.8	1	(40)
Hamster, rat, human, mouse, dog, guinea pig, and rabbit	Various organs	Centrifuged water extracts	6-Benzoyl-2-naphthol	0.0005	6.1	1	(89)
Rabbit	Liver	Sucrose and glycerin extracts	p-Nitrophenol	0.0005	5.9	1	(65)
	Liver and kidney	Glycerin extract	p-Nitrophenol	0.0005	6.1	1	(105)
		Centrifuged NaCl extract	p-Nitrophenol	0.15	6.02	2	(60)
Pig	Kidney	Washed acetone-dried tissue	Phenyl sulfate	0.047	$CaCO_3$	1	(52)
Ox	Liver	Purified centrifuged extracts of acetone-dried liver	4-Nitrocatechol	0.003	4.9	2 (A only)	(84,86)
				0.06	5.7	2 (B only)	

findings (25,28) that mammalian tissues contain at least three distinct and separable arylsulfatases. In rat liver one of these enzymes (arylsulfatase C) is located solely in the microsomes of the rat liver cell and is of Type 1. This enzyme cannot be brought into solution by any of the normal methods which disrupt particulate cellular material (100). The other two enzymes, which are located mainly in the mitochondria of the liver cell, are of Type 2 (arylsulfatases A and B; refs. 85,25) and are released into solution following the rupture of the mitochondrial membrane. It is now clear that in the study of mammalian arylsulfatases the various methods of enzyme preparation and assay used by past workers have often resulted in different enzymes being measured (see Table I).

The individual quantitative assay of the three arylsulfatases of mammalian tissues obviously presents many difficulties. Apart from the competition between the enzymes for the assay substrate, the inhibition of the Type 2 enzymes by endogenous phosphate and sulfate (60), the increase in activity of the Type 2 enzymes following the rupture of the mitochondrial membrane (28), and the anomalous kinetics of arylsulfatase A (85,21,22,88) all detract from the immediate feasibility of such a project. In the case of arylsulfatase C, however, the use of p-acetylphenyl sulfate as substrate, under conditions where the activity of and competition by the Type 2 enzymes is negligible, allows the assay of this enzyme with reasonable accuracy.

Recently the presence of arylsulfatases in a number of different bacteria has been established using phenolphthalein disulfate as a chromogenic substrate (109,3,16). However, the work of Harada, Kono, and Yagi (48) again emphasizes the danger of using only one substrate in such experiments. These workers found that, while many strains of *Escherichia coli* and *Aerobacter aerogenes* were capable of hydrolyzing indoxyl and p-nitrophenyl sulfates, no activity could be detected toward phenolphthalein disulfate. It was concluded that there are present in the bacterial world arylsulfatases which have different substrate specificities. It is not yet clear whether the differences in specificity existing between the bacterial enzymes are comparable to those which distinguish Type 1 and Type 2 arylsulfatases.

The physiological function of the arylsulfatases remains speculative (13,99).

TABLE II

The Optimum Conditions for Assay of Arylsulfatases from Various Sources

Source	Substrate	Substrate concentration M	pH	Buffer	Ref.	Comments
			Type 1			
Bacterial						
Alcaligenes metalcaligenes	APS	0.003	8.75	0.1 M phosphate	(16)	The activity toward NCS is about one fifth of that toward NPS and APS. All are suitable substrates.
	NPS	0.0015	8.75	0.1 M phosphate	(16)	
	NCS	0.015	8.0	0.1 M phosphate	(16)	
Mycobacterium piscium	Phenolphthalein disulfate	0.0025	6.3	Citrate-phosphate	(109)	Use of this diester leads to kinetic complications.
Aerobacter aerogenes	NPS	0.005	7.35	0.1 M acetate	(46)	NPS is a suitable substrate.
Streptococcus alcalophilus	NPS	0.0025	9.6	0.1 M glycine-NaOH	(45)	Care should be taken that no catalysis of the alkaline hydrolysis of NPS occurs (see VIII.6. C(3)).
Fungal						
Aspergillus oryzae (takadiastase)	APS	0.004	6.3	0.5 M acetate	(14)	NPS, APS, and NCS are suitable substrates.
	APS	0.0035	7.6	0.2 M phosphate	(14)	
	NPS	0.005	6.3	0.5 M acetate	(80)	
	NCS	0.0025	5.8	0.5 M acetate	(80)	
	p-Aldehydophenyl sulfate	0.003	5.8	0.5 M acetate	(80)	
	p-Chlorophenyl sulfate	0.0125	6.2	0.5 M acetate	(80)	
	o-Nitrophenyl sulfate	0.005	6.3	0.5 M acetate	(80)	
	m-Nitrophenyl sulfate	0.005	6.3	0.5 M acetate	(80)	
	4-Hydroxy-2-nitrophenyl sulfate	0.002	6.0	0.5 M acetate	(80)	
	Phenyl sulfate	0.02	6.2	0.1 M acetate	(1)	

		pH		Buffer	Ref.
Mammalian					
Rat arylsulfatase C	APS	7.2	0.007	0.5 M acetate	(23)
	NPS	7.0	0.006	0.5 M acetate	(25)
Human arylsulfatase	APS	6.9	0.005	0.5 M acetate	(28)
	NPS	7.3	0.008	0.5 M acetate	(28)

Type 2

		pH		Buffer	Ref.
Mammalian					
Ox arylsulfatase A	NCS	4.9	0.003	0.125 M acetate	(85)
Ox arylsulfatase B	NCS	5.7	>0.06	0.125 M acetate	(86)
Rat arylsulfatase A	NCS	5.0	0.008	0.5 M acetate	(25)
	NPS	5.8	0.12	0.5 M acetate	(25)
Rat arylsulfatase B	NCS	6.0	0.02	0.5 M acetate	(25)
	NPS	6.2	0.12	0.5 M acetate	(25)
Human arylsulfatase A	NCS	5.0	0.006	0.5 M acetate	(28)
Human arylsulfatase B	NPS	6.2	0.07	0.5 M acetate	(28)
	NCS	6.1	0.02	0.5 M acetate	(28)
Molluscan					
Helix pomatia	NPS	5.2	0.0005	0.1 M acetate	(54)
Patella vulgata	APS	5.5	0.065	0.5 M acetate	(14)
	NCS	5.5	0.005	0.125 M acetate	(87)
Littorina littorea	APS	5.5	0.04	0.5 M acetate	(14)

The conditions recorded for APS also give a reasonable measure of enzyme C activity when Type 2 enzymes are present.

Purified preparations of arylsulfatase A from all sources exhibit anomalous kinetics (13). In such cases the optimum conditions for enzyme activity vary with the time of incubation used.

In this table the following abbreviations are used: APS = *p*-acetylphenyl sulfate, NPS = *p*-nitrophenyl sulfate, NCS = nitrocatechol sulfate.

2. Principles Involved in Determining Arylsulfatase Activity

Although Dodgson and Spencer (18) have used the micro-benzidine method to determine the sulfate liberated by arylsulfatases, other equally sensitive and less laborious methods involving determination of the liberated phenolic moiety are preferred. The present discussion will therefore be limited to these methods.

Two different principles have been applied to the determination of the liberated phenol.

(*1*)   The phenol is estimated colorimetrically following a chemical reaction which involves the free phenolic group but which does not affect the parent arylsulfate. Several methods have been described. Phenol released from potassium phenyl sulfate was determined after color formation with Folin-Ciocalteu reagent (1) while 6-bromo-2-naphthol or 6-benzoyl-2-naphthol liberated from their respective sulfate esters was coupled with tetrazotized *o*-dianisidine and the resultant dyes estimated after extraction with ethyl acetate (91,89).

(*2*)   The anionic form of the phenol is estimated spectrophotometrically at wave lengths in the visible or ultraviolet regions of the spectrum where the parent arylsulfate has negligible absorption. The first method using this principle was introduced by Morimoto (65), who measured the *p*-nitrophenol, liberated from *p*-nitrophenyl sulfate, as the yellow anion formed by the addition of alkali. This method has since been extensively modified (see Table II). Other methods include the measurement of the red 4-nitrocatechol anion liberated from dipotassium 2-hydoxy-5-nitrophenyl sulfate (81) and the red phenolphthalein anion liberated from phenolphthalein disulfate (109). The anionic forms of the phenols mentioned are measured at wave lengths in the visible region of the spectrum, but other phenols, which are not colored in the anionic form, can be measured by virtue of their specific absorption in the ultraviolet region. The phenols liberated from *p*-chlorophenyl (80), *p*-aldehydophenyl (80) and *p*-acetylphenyl sulfates (17) have been measured in this way. The selection of suitable phenols has been assisted by the observation of certain empirical relationships between the structure of the phenols, their O-conjugates, and their spectra (17).

3. Limitations of Available Methods

Most of the methods already outlined (VIII.2) are suitable for use with enzyme concentrates of low protein content. With fresh tissue homogenates and other crude enzyme preparations, where protein must be removed prior to estimation of the liberated phenol, the methods have certain limitations. These limitations arise from the failure to achieve complete recovery of the liberated phenol and the incomplete removal of protein after incubation of enzyme and substrate.

A. INCOMPLETE RECOVERY OF THE LIBERATED PHENOL

The failure to recover phenols from fresh tissue homogenates can be attributed to metabolic destruction of the phenols and adsorption of the phenols on protein when the latter is precipitated at acid pH.

Dodgson and Spencer (17) have observed incomplete recovery of p-nitrophenol, 4-nitrocatechol, and p-hydroxybenzaldehyde from fresh rat liver homogenates. This could be attributed to the conversion of p-nitrophenol and 4-nitrocatechol to the corresponding amino derivatives and the simultaneous oxidation and reduction of p-hydroxybenzaldehyde to p-hydroxybenzoic acid and p-hydroxybenzyl alcohol. However, these findings do not preclude the use of the respective sulfate esters of these phenols with homogenates of tissues other than liver, with purified liver preparations or with arylsulfatases from non-mammalian sources.

The use of ethanol to precipitate protein ensures that none of the above phenols is adsorbed onto the precipitate, but when it is necessary to precipitate protein under strongly acidic conditions considerable adsorption of the phenolic cation occurs. This is responsible for the low recoveries of 6-bromo-2-naphthol (17) and 6-benzoyl-2-naphthol (89) from protein-rich enzyme preparations. Many other phenols are no doubt adsorbed onto protein at acid pH, although the parent arylsulfates can be used with purified arylsulfatase preparations where the concentration of protein is low.

p-Hydroxyacetophenone can be quantitatively recovered from all tissues, being neither metabolized nor adsorbed onto protein, and its parent sulfate, p-acetylphenyl sulfate, has been suggested as a suitable substrate for use with fresh tissue homogenates (17).

B. INTERFERENCE DUE TO INCOMPLETE REMOVAL OF PROTEIN

The usual deproteinization procedures sometimes fail to remove protein completely, particularly in the case of fresh tissue homogenates. The residual protein has a strong ultraviolet light absorption at wave lengths below 300 mμ and therefore interferes in those assay methods which depend upon the estimation of liberated phenols by spectrophotometric measurement at these wave lengths. Thus, p-chlorophenol liberated from p-chlorophenyl sulfate absorbs maximally at 245 and 298 mμ, and it cannot be satisfactorily measured unless the protein content of the enzyme preparation is low.

4. Choice of Substrate and Assay Method

The problems that must be considered when choosing a substrate and assay method may now be summarized as follows.

(1)   More than one arylsulfatase may be present in the enzyme preparation.

(2)   Different substrates are required for Type 1 and Type 2 arylsulfatases.

(3)   Phosphate buffers cannot be used with Type 2 enzymes.

(4)   The problem of quantitative recovery of liberated phenols.

(5)   The presence of endogenous inhibitors.

(6)   The possibility of unusual reaction kinetics comparable to those of arylsulfatase A of mammalian tissues.

Present knowledge of arylsulfatases is insufficient to provide complete answers to these problems for all sources of the enzymes, and at the present time only a few arylsulfatases can be quantitatively assayed with certainty. Specific mention of these cases will be made. It is the practice in Cardiff laboratories to use at least two different substrates, p-nitrophenyl or p-acetylphenyl and nitrocatechol sulfates, when examining new sources of the enzyme. These substrates are used in the presence and absence of 0.025 M phosphate, and in this way it is possible to decide whether Types 1 and 2 enzymes are present. However, this procedure fails to distinguish between two arylsulfatases of the same type when they occur together.

5. Preparation of Substrates

A. GENERAL METHOD

Most arylsulfates can be readily prepared by the method of Burkhardt and Lapworth (8) or by simple modifications of this method.

Diethylaniline (100 g., 2.5 moles), or the equivalent quantity of dimethylaniline, in carbon disulfide (100 ml.) is stirred mechanically at $-10°C$. and chlorosulfonic acid (34 g., 1.1 moles) is run in steadily during 15 min., the temperature being maintained below 10°C. The appropriate phenol (1 mole) dissolved or suspended in carbon disulfide (50 ml.) is added and the mixture stirred for 1 hr. The separated carbon disulfide is poured away and the cold viscous residue is run into a solution of potassium hydroxide (22 g. in 150 ml. water) with vigorous stirring, the temperature being maintained below 35°C. The greater part of the diethylaniline and residual carbon disulfide separates out and is removed by shaking with two 200 ml. portions of ether. The inorganic sulfate of the aqueous residue is precipitated by the gradual addition of barium hydroxide saturated in the cold, care being taken to avoid any excess of barium ions. The filtrate is then concentrated to low bulk *in vacuo* at 35°C. Crystals of the potassium salt of the arylsulfate separate out on cooling. The salt is recrystallized several times from small volumes of water until completely free from inorganic sulfate and unchanged phenol.

B. METHOD FOR DIPOTASSIUM 2-HYDROXY-5-NITROPHENYL SULFATE (NITROCATECHOL SULFATE)

The following method is a modification of that of Roy (84).

To a solution of 70 g. potassium hydroxide and 70 g. potassium persulfate in 1 liter of water are added 30 g. *p*-nitrophenol. The reaction mixture is left for 48 hr. at 37°C., acidified to pH 4.0 with sulfuric acid, and the unchanged *p*-nitrophenol extracted with ether. The aqueous solution is made strongly alkaline to litmus with a strong solution of potassium hydroxide and concentrated *in vacuo* at 35°C. to about 300 ml. The solution and any precipitate are poured into acetone (2 vol.) and the mixture filtered. After washing the residue with aqueous acetone (1–2 v/v), the combined filtrates are taken to dryness *in vacuo*. The residue is dissolved in the smallest volume of water and the pH adjusted to 4.2 with glacial acetic acid. The precipitated material is filtered at the pump and is then recrystallized four times from water. The recrystallized material is suspended in water and a concentrated solution of potassium hydroxide is added until the pH rises to about 12. The solution is poured slowly with stirring into 10 vol. ethanol, the precipitated dipotassium salt is filtered off, washed with 90% ethanol, and dried *in vacuo*.

The recrystallization of the monopotassium salt is necessary (22) in order to remove the traces of a sulfated impurity, now known to be nitropyrogallol disulfate, the presence of which was first noted by Roy (88). The presence of this impurity is not responsible for the anomalous kinetics of mammalian arylsulfatase A, as was suggested by Roy (85).

Most arylsulfates undergo autocatalytic degradation over long periods at room temperature, and as a general rule it is advisable to store the compounds at 0°C. whether in the solid form or in solution.

6. Methods of Assay

A. THE MEASUREMENT OF PHENOL LIBERATED FROM PHENYL SULFATE

In this method the liberated phenol is estimated colorimetrically by means of the Folin-Ciocalteu reagent (cf. VIII.2(1)). The method as described is for the assay of the arylsulfatase of takadiastase and is based on the King and Armstrong procedure (57) for the estimation of phenol liberated from phenyl phosphate by phosphatase. A similar method has been used by Abbott (1).

(1) Reagents

Buffer. 0.5 M sodium acetate-acetic acid buffer, pH 6.2.
Substrate. 0.04 M potassium phenyl sulfate in acetate buffer pH 6.2.
Folin-Ciocalteu Reagent (36). This is diluted with 4 vol. of water immediately before use.
Sodium Carbonate Solution. 2.7% in water.

(2) Procedure.

The enzyme solution (0.5 ml.), adjusted to pH 6.2, is pre-incubated for 4 min. at 37.5°C. before addition of 0.5 ml. substrate solution, previously warmed to the same temperature. After incubation for the required period, enzyme action is stopped by the addition of 2 ml. of the diluted Folin-Ciocalteu reagent. The mixture is centrifuged to remove any precipitated protein and to 2 ml. of the clear supernatant is added 4 ml. of the sodium carbonate solution. The mixture is heated for 1 min. in a boiling water bath and immediately cooled in water. The absorption of the blue color is measured in a photoelectric absorptiometer using a Chance OR2 orange filter. A calibration curve is prepared by substituting 1 ml. of various dilutions (in the range 0–30 μg./ml.) of a standard phenol solution. The determination is carried out in duplicate with suitable controls in which enzyme and substrate are incubated separately and only mixed immediately prior to the addition of the Folin-Ciocalteu reagent. The μg. liberated phenol as obtained from the calibration curve must be multiplied by 3 and divided by the time of incubation, in hours, to give the μg. phenol liberated/ml. enzyme solution/hr.

(3) Comments.
This procedure can be used with arylsulfatases from all sources and with many different arylsulfates providing the incubation conditions appropriate to the particular enzyme and sub-

strate are used (see Table II).   The high blank values obtained and the tendency for liberated phenol to be adsorbed on the precipitated protein make the method unsuitable for use with protein-rich enzyme preparations.   On the other hand, with purified preparations where protein concentration is low there is often no need to centrifuge. Many phenols cannot be conveniently obtained in a pure form for the preparation of calibration curves, and in such cases standard solutions of the phenols can be prepared by acid hydrolysis of the respective purified arylsulfates (27).

It should be noted that phenyl sulfate is an unsuitable substrate with at least one Type 1 enzyme (27) and all Type 2 enzymes due to the extremely low rate of enzymic hydrolysis.

B. MEASUREMENT OF p-HYDROXYACETOPHENONE LIBERATED FROM POTASSIUM p-ACETYLPHENYL SULFATE

This method was developed (17,23) for the assay of arylsulfatase activity in fresh rat tissue homogenates.

(1) Reagents.

Acetate Buffer.   0.5 M sodium acetate-acetic acid buffer adjusted to pH 7.2.
Ethanol.
Sodium Hydroxide.   Normal solution.
Substrate Solution.   0.014 M potassium p-acetylphenyl sulfate in the acetate buffer at pH 7.2.

(2) Enzyme Preparation.

The fresh tissue is dissected out and a weighed portion is homogenized in ice-cold acetate buffer for 2 min. using a glass homogenizer.   The pH of the resultant suspension is adjusted if necessary to 7.2 and the whole made up to a suitable volume with acetate buffer.   During these operations the temperature of the suspension is kept below 5°C.

(3) Procedure.

The tissue suspension (0.6 ml.) contained in a 15 ml. centrifuge tube is placed in the water bath at 37.5°C. and after 4 min. 0.6 ml. of the substrate solution, previously warmed to 37.5°C., is added.   After mixing, the tube is stoppered and incubated for 1 hr.   At the end of this period enzyme action is stopped and protein precipitated by adding 4.8 ml. ethanol.   After mixing, the tube is capped and centrifuged at 2500 g for 10 min.   A portion (5 ml.) of the clear supernatant is withdrawn and added to 1 ml. N sodium hydroxide. The absorption of the liberated p-hydroxyacetophenone is measured at

327.5 mμ (the wave length of maximum absorption) in a 1 cm. quartz cell using a suitable spectrophotometer. All determinations are carried out in duplicate and suitable controls are made in which tissue suspension and substrate are incubated separately and only mixed immediately prior to the addition of the ethanol. The calculation is as follows.

$$\mu\text{g. } p\text{-hydroxyacetophenone liberated/ml. enzyme preparation/hr.} = \frac{(E_T - E_C) \times 136 \times 5.88 \times 5.94 \times 10^6}{21,700 \times 5 \times 10^3 \times 0.6}$$

$$= (E_T - E_C) \times 73.1$$

where E_T and E_C are the extinction coefficients (log I_0/I) of the test and control solutions respectively, 21,700 is the molecular extinction coefficient of p-hydroxyacetophenone at 327.5 mμ, and 136 is its molecular weight. The numbers 5.88 and 5.94 represent the shrinkages in volume which occur when 4.8 ml. ethanol is added to the incubation mixture (1.2 ml.) and when 5 ml. of the supernatant is added to 1 ml. sodium hydroxide. The Lambert-Beer law is obeyed in the range of log I_0/I of 0.05 to 1.50 under the conditions of the experiment.

C. MEASUREMENT OF p-NITROPHENOL LIBERATED FROM POTASSIUM p-NITROPHENYL SULFATE

The following method can be used with bacterial and fungal arylsulfatases and with purified preparations of the enzymes from other sources.

(1) Reagents.

Buffer. 0.5 M sodium acetate–acetic acid buffer at the required pH.
Substrate Solution. Potassium p-nitrophenyl sulfate of the desired molarity is dissolved in the acetate buffer.
Sodium Hydroxide. 0.2 N solution in water.

(2) Procedure.

The enzyme preparation (0.5 ml.) and the substrate solution (0.5 ml.) are incubated together at 37.5°C. after having been previously warmed separately to this temperature. After 1 hr. the enzyme action is stopped by the addition of 4 ml. of the sodium hydroxide solution and the liberated yellow-colored p-nitrophenol is measured spectrophotometrically at 400 mμ. The solution is clarified by centrifugation if necessary. The usual control determinations are made (cf. VIII.6.B(3)).

The μg. p-nitrophenol liberated by 1 ml. of the enzyme preparation in 1 hr. is given by:

$$\frac{(E_T - E_C) \times 139 \times 10^6 \times 5}{18,200 \times 10^3 \times 0.5} = (E_T - E_C) \times 76.4$$

where E_T and E_C are the log I_0/I values of the test and control solutions respectively, 18,200 is the molecular extinction coefficient of p-nitrophenol at 400 mμ, and 139 is its molecular weight.

(3) **Comments.** The incubation conditions for the different arylsulfatases are given in Table II. Although the method can be adapted for use with protein-rich enzyme preparations by introduction of ethanol as a protein precipitant (in which case the procedure is exactly as described in Section VIII.6.B(3)), it is unsuitable for use with fresh mammalian liver homogenates (see VIII.3.A).

It has been pointed out (19) that the serum of many mammals contains a thermostable factor which catalyzes the alkaline hydrolysis of potassium p-nitrophenyl sulfate. This non-enzymic hydrolysis has now been shown to depend on the presence of SH groups, and it is possible that it may occur with other biological material. It may therefore be necessary in some cases to measure the liberated p-nitrophenol as soon as possible after the addition of alkali.

A number of modifications of this method (53,60) including a micro adaptation (40) have been reported.

D. MEASUREMENT OF NITROCATECHOL LIBERATED FROM POTASSIUM 2-HYDROXY-5-NITROPHENYL SULFATE (NITROCATECHOL SULFATE)

The following procedure has been used for bacterial and fungal enzymes and concentrates of mammalian arylsulfatases and enzymes from other sources.

(1) **Reagents.**

Buffer. 0.5 M sodium acetate-acetic acid buffer adjusted to the required pH.

Sodium Hydroxide. Normal solution.

Substrate Solution. A solution of the desired molarity of potassium 2-hydroxy-5-nitrophenyl sulfate dihydrate is made using the buffer. The solution is adjusted to the required pH.

(2) **Method.**

The enzyme preparation (0.2 ml.) in a 15 ml. centrifuge tube is preincubated for 4 min. at 37.5°C. before adding 0.2 ml. of the substrate solution which has been previously warmed to the same temperature. After mixing, the tube is stoppered and incubated at 37.5°C. for 1 hr. At the end of the incubation period 2 ml. of the sodium hydroxide solution is added and the mixture clarified by centrifugation if necessary. The red color of the liberated nitrocatechol is measured at 515 mμ (the wave length of maximum absorption of the nitrocatechol anion) within 1 hr. after the addition of the alkali.

The μg. nitrocatechol liberated/ml. enzyme preparation/hr. is given by:

$$\frac{(E_T - E_C) \times 155 \times 10^6 \times 2.4}{11{,}200 \times 10^3 \times 0.2} = (E_T - E_C) \times 160.7$$

where the symbols and figures have the same significance as before (VIII.6.B-(3)).

Alternatively the color can be measured in a simple absorptiometer using a suitable filter and a calibration curve. The 4-nitrocatechol required for the construction of the calibration curve can be conveniently obtained by hydrolysis of nitrocatechol sulfate.

(3) Comments. Table II records the optimum conditions for the assay of arylsulfatases from various sources using this substrate. Mention has already been made (VIII.3.A) that 4-nitrocatechol cannot be quantitatively recovered from fresh tissue homogenates, and this point has also been noted by Roy (84). However, the high activity of mammalian liver toward this substrate has allowed the use of liver homogenates at concentrations at which 4-nitrocatechol could be quantitatively recovered over an incubation period of 1 hr. (25). In such cases the normally stable red color of the nitrocatechol anion fades (84), but this can be prevented by developing the color with an alkaline quinol-sodium sulfite mixture (84) instead of the N sodium hydroxide. The precipitation of protein from crude enzyme preparations as recommended by Roy (84) can usually be dispensed with (16,25).

The Type 2 enzymes have a strong affinity and high activity toward nitrocatechol sulfate (25), and this is the substrate of choice for the assay of this type of enzyme. However, nitrocatechol sulfate cannot be used as an exact measure of Type 2 enzymes in the presence of Type 1 enzymes since the latter often have appreciable activity toward this substrate.

E. DETECTION AND DETERMINATION OF ARYLSULFATASES IN BACTERIAL CULTURES

In recent years the distribution of arylsulfatases among bacteria has been studied using detection and assay methods which have been specially devised for this purpose. Thus, Whitehead, Morrison, and Young (109) incorporated tripotassium phenolphthalein disulfate into the culture broth and, after a period of incubation, alkali was added and the color of the liberated phenolphthalein visually assessed. This principle has been adapted (16) to a plate procedure similar to that used by Bray and King (6) for the study of bacterial phosphatase. It has been pointed out (48) that certain microorganisms are incapable of hydrolyzing phenolphthalein disulfate but are able to hydrolyze p-nitrophenyl and indoxyl sulfates, and it seems clear that arylsulfatases having different relative substrate specificities exist among bacteria (cf. VIII.1). The use of more than one substrate in the detection of enzyme activity is advisable. The recent findings of Japanese workers (47) that a factor present only in certain peptone preparations is needed for the production of arylsulfatase in Enterobacteriaceae make the choice of peptone important when searching for arylsulfatase-producing organisms. Of the Japanese peptones tested, Mikuni peptone is especially rich in the factor, Teruuchi and Funai peptones and polypeptones A and B (Takeda) contain lesser amounts. Other peptones appear to contain only small amounts of the factor and Enterobacteriaceae grown in Difco Bacto-peptone or Witte peptone produce little arylsulfatase. The extent to which this factor is required by other bacteria is not yet known, but when the Japanese peptones cannot be obtained it is advisable to test available peptones for the presence of the factor using a known arylsulfatase-producing bacterium.

(1) Detection of Arylsulfatase-Producing Bacteria.

(a) Plate Method.

Tripotassium phenolphthalein disulfate, prepared by the method of Whitehead, Morrison, and Young (109), is incorporated into the solid media used for making plates to give a final molarity of 0.001. After streaking the plates with an inoculum and incubating at the temperature appropriate to the bacteria, the plates are exposed to ammonia at various stages of growth. Arylsulfatase-producing colonies, or the zones around them, turn red due to the liberated phenolphthalein. If required, active colonies should be subcultured immediately since long exposure to ammonia often results in destruction of the organism.

(b) Lignin Coloration Method.

An ingenious method using indoxyl sulfate (48) has been developed from an original observation of Harada (44). A suitable medium containing 0.001 M potassium indoxyl sulfate is divided into 3 ml. portions to each of which is added a piece (5 x 20 mm.) of lignin-containing paper. The tubes are inoculated and incubated at the desired temperature. At suitable time intervals (usually 1, 3, and 7 days) the paper is removed, washed with water, and the intensity of the red color produced by combination of lignin with the enzymically liberated indoxyl is observed.

(2) Quantitative Assay of Bacterial Arylsulfatase.

(a) *During Growth.*

The following modification of the method of Whitehead, Morrison, and Young (109) is recommended.

Centrifuge tubes graduated at 7 ml. are dried at 105°C., weighed, and 7 ml. of suitable liquid medium containing tripotassium phenolphthalein disulfate (0.001 M) is pipetted into them. Control tubes containing 7 ml. substrate-free medium are also prepared. The tubes are plugged with cotton wool and autoclaved for 20 min. at 30 lb./sq. in., no destruction of substrate occurring under these conditions. All tubes are incubated overnight at 37.5°C., and any tubes showing signs of growth are rejected. The sterile tubes are inoculated with two drops of an 18 hr. culture of the organism under examination and incubated at the required temperature. The tubes are tested at suitable time intervals as follows. The volume of the liquid in each tube is adjusted to 7 ml. with water to compensate for losses due to evaporation and the bacteria are separated by centrifuging. A portion (5 ml.) of each supernatant is mixed with 5 ml. of glycine buffer, pH 10.8 (103), and the red phenolphthalein color measured spectrophotometrically at 560 mμ (or with a suitable filter) using the control tubes as blanks. A calibration curve is prepared using various concentrations of phenolphthalein (ranging from 0 to 100 μg.) in nutrient broth. The separated bacterial cells are suspended in water, separated by centrifugation, dried overnight at 105°C., and the tube weighed. The arylsulfatase activity can be expressed as μg. phenolphthalein liberated and related to the dry weight of the organism.

Since some organisms are capable of destroying liberated phenolphthalein to a certain extent (16), control tubes, prepared as before but containing 70 μg. phenolphthalein, are inoculated, incubated for the same period as the tests, and the remaining phenolphthalein is estimated.

(b) *Grown Cells*

The method is substantially that of Harada, Kono, and Yagi (48).

The grown cells are separated by centrifuging, washed once with an isotonic salt solution, centrifuged, and suspended in a suitable volume of distilled water. The arylsulfatase activity of the suspension can then be estimated using *p*-nitrophenyl sulfate as substrate as described in Section VIII.6.C(2). For conditions of substrate concentration and pH in the incubation mixture see Table II.

F. HISTOCHEMICAL LOCALIZATION OF ARYLSULFATASE ACTIVITY

No completely satisfactory method for the histochemical localization of arylsulfatases has yet been developed but the following summary may be of interest to the reader.

The histochemical localization of mammalian arylsulfatases presents the difficulties normally associated with this type of work, in
particular diffusion of the enzyme and the products of enzyme action.
Seligman, Chauncey, and Nachlas (91) have reported that tissues can
be satisfactorily fixed in formalin (24 hrs. at 4°C.) with only a 40%
loss of activity as measured against 6-bromo-2-naphthyl sulfate.
The arylsulfatase activity of several tissues fixed in this way has been
localized by coupling the 6-benzoyl-2-naphthol liberated from 6-
benzoyl-2-naphthyl sulfate with tetrazotized o-dianisidine (92).
It seems probable that the substrates used by Seligman would be
hydrolyzed primarily by Type 1 arylsulfatases and would be hardly
attacked by the Type 2 enzymes (see VIII.1).

Although diffusion of Type 1 mammalian arylsulfatases is unlikely to occur since they are highly resistant to solubilization techniques (100), Burton and Pearse (9) have criticized the use of 6-bromo-
2-naphthyl sulfate as a substrate on the grounds that the liberated 6-
bromo-2-naphthol diffuses appreciably and combines with tissue structures other than those having enzyme activity.   Pearse (78) has at-
tempted to localize the arylsulfatases of cold formalin-fixed frozen
sections of rat tissues by coupling 2-naphthol, liberated from potassium 2-naphthyl sulfate, with diazotized 4-benzoylamino-2,5-di-
methoxyaniline.   However, no arylsulfatase activity could be detected, and this was wrongly attributed to the "extremely low amounts
of the enzyme in mammalian tissues."   The use of indoxyl sulfate as
a histochemical substrate has been advocated (51), the indoxyl liberated by enzyme action being oxidized to indigo.

A different method of approach and one which can be used with any
sulfate ester is that described by Ohara and Kurata (77), in which
sulfate liberated from the substrate is either precipitated as lead sulfate and visualized as lead sulfide or precipitated with benzidine,
which is then coupled with β-naphthoquinone sulfonate to give a red
color.   With substrates which are hydrolyzed by the Type 2 arylsulfatases these methods must be used with caution.   Using the lead
method with nitrocatechol sulfate as substrate and alcohol-fixed
intestine sections, activity appeared to be located in the brush border.

However, this was subsequently shown to be an artifact arising from diffusion of the enzyme from the tissue into the incubation medium and subsequent absorption of the liberated sulfate at the brush border (11).

References

1. Abbott, L. D., *Arch. Biochem. and Biophys.*, *15*, 205 (1947).
2. Abbott, L. D., and East, M. K., *Federation Proc.*, *8*, 178 (1949).
3. Barber, M., Brooksbank, B. W. L., and Kuper, S. W. A., *J. Pathol. Bacteriol.*, *63*, 57 (1951).
4. Baumgarten, P., *Ber.*, *59*, 1166 (1926).
5. Boyland, E., Manson, D., Sims, P., and Williams, D. C., *Biochem. J.*, *62*, 68 (1956).
6. Bray, J., and King, E. J., *J. Pathol. Bacteriol.*, *55*, 515 (1943).
7. Buehler, H. J., Katzmann, P. A., and Doisy, E. A., *Proc. Soc. Exptl. Biol. Med.*, *78*, 3 (1951).
8. Burkhardt, G. N., and Lapworth, A., *J. Chem. Soc.*, *1926*, 684.
9. Burton, J. F., and Pearse, A. G. E., *Brit. J. Exptl. Pathol.*, *33*, 1 (1952).
10. Cope, C. L., *Biochem. J.*, *25*, 1183 (1931).
11. Dark, A., personal communication.
12. Derrien, M., *Bull. soc. chim. biol.*, *9*, 110 (1911).
13. Dodgson, K. S., *Symposium on the Biochemistry of Sulfur, Roscoff, France*, in press.
14. Dodgson, K. S., Lewis, J. I. M., and Spencer, B., *Biochem. J.*, *55*, 253 (1953).
15. Dodgson, K. S., Lloyd, A. G., and Spencer, B., *Biochem. J.*, *65*, 131(1957).
16. Dodgson, K. S., Melville, T. H., Spencer, B., and Williams, K., *Biochem. J.*, *58*, 172 (1954).
17. Dodgson, K. S., and Spencer, B., *Biochem. J.*, *53*, 444 (1953).
18. Dodgson, K. S., and Spencer, B., *Biochem. J.*, *55*, 436 (1953).
19. Dodgson, K. S., and Spencer, B., *Biochem. J.*, *56*, xiii (1954).
20. Dodgson, K. S., and Spencer, B., *Biochem. J.*, *57*, 310 (1954).
21. Dodgson, K. S., and Spencer, B., *Biochem. J.*, *62*, 30 P (1956).
22. Dodgson, K. S., and Spencer, B., *Biochim. et biophys. Acta*, *21*, 175 (1956).
23. Dodgson, K. S., Spencer, B., and Thomas, J., *Biochem. J.*, *53*, 452 (1953).
24. Dodgson, K. S., Spencer, B., and Thomas, J., *Biochem. J.*, *56*, 177 (1954).
25. Dodgson, K. S., Spencer, B., and Thomas, J., *Biochem. J.*, *59*, 29 (1955).
26. Dodgson, K. S., Spencer, B., and Williams, K., *Biochem. J.*, *61*, 374 (1955).

27. Dodgson, K. S., Spencer, B., and Williams, K., *Biochem. J.*, *64*, 216 (1956).
28. Dodgson, K. S., Spencer, B., and Wynn, C. H., *Biochem. J.*, *62*, 500 (1956).
29. Dohlman, C., personal communication.
30. Duff, R. B., *J. Chem. Soc.*, *1949*, 1597.
31. Egami, F., *J. Chem. Soc. Japan*, *59*, 1034 (1938).
32. Egami, F., *J. Chem. Soc. Japan*, *63*, 763 (1942).
33. Egami, F., personal communication.
34. Egami, F., Takahashi, N., Suzuki, S., Shikata, S., and Nisizawa, K., *Bull. Chem. Soc. Japan*, *28*, 685 (1955).
35. Einbinder, J., and Schubert, M., *J. Biol. Chem.*, *185*, 725 (1950).
36. Folin, O., and Ciocalteu, V., *J. Biol. Chem.*, *73*, 627 (1927).
37. Fromageot, C., *Ergeb. Enzymforsch.*, *7*, 50 (1938).
38. Fromageot, C., in J. B. Sumner and K. Myrback, eds., *The Enzymes*, Vol. I, Pt. 1, Academic Press, New York, 1950.
39. Gadamer, J., *Arch. Pharm.*, *235*, 44 (1897).
40. Glick, D., Stecklein, H. R., and Malmstrom, B. G., *Arch. Biochem. and Biophys.*, *54*, 513 (1955).
41. Guillaumin, C. O., *Bull. soc. chim. biol.*, *22*, 564 (1940).
42. Gupta, P. N. D., *Indian J. Vet. Sci.*, *8*, 119 (1938).
43. Hall, D. A., and Gardiner, J. E., *Biochem. J.*, *59*, 465 (1955).
44. Harada, T., *Mem. Inst. Sci. and Ind. Research, Osaka Univ.*, *6*, 79 (1948).
45. Harada, T., *J. Agr. Chem. Soc., Japan*, *28*, 840 (1954).
46. Harada, T., and Kono, K., *J. Agr. Chem. Soc., Japan*, *28*, 608 (1954).
47. Harada, T., and Kono, K., *Mem. Inst. Sci. and Ind. Research, Osaka Univ.*, *12*, 183 (1955).
48. Harada, T., Kono, K., and Yagi, K., *Mem. Inst. Sci. Ind. Research, Osaka Univ., Japan*, *11*, 193 (1954).
49. Henri, R., Thevenet, M., and Jarrige, P., *Bull. soc. chim. biol.*, *34*, 897 (1952).
50. Herissey, H., and Boivin, R., *J. Pharm. et Chim.*, *6*, 337 (1927).
51. Holt, S. J., *Nature*, *169*, 271 (1952).
52. Hommerberg, C., *Hoppe-Seyler's Z. physiol. Chem.*, *200*, 69 (1931).
53. Huggins, C., and Smith, D. R., *J. Biol. Chem.*, *170*, 391 (1947).
54. Jarrige, P., and Henri, R., *Bull. soc. chim. biol.*, *34*, 872 (1952).
55. Jeanloz, R. W., in Liebecq, C., ed., *Proceedings of the Third International Congress of Biochemistry, Brussels*, Academic Press, New York, 1956, p. 65.
56. Keilin, D., and Hartree, E. F., *Biochem. J.*, *42*, 231 (1948).
57. King, E. J., and Armstrong, A. R., *Can. Med. Assoc. J.*, *31*, 376 (1934).
58. Lindahl, P. E., *Arkiv. Zool.*, *28* (2B), No. 4 (1935).
59. Lowenstein, J. M., and Young, L., *Biochem. J.*, *52*, xxv (1952).

60. Maengwyn-Davies, G. D., and Friedenwald, J. S., *Arch. Biochem. and Biophys.*, *53*, 29 (1954).
61. Malmstrom, B. G., and Glick, D., *Arch. Biochem. and Biophys.*, *40*, 56 (1952).
62. Medical Research Council Committee on Clinical Endocrinology, *Lancet*, *261*, 585 (1951).
63. Meyer, K., and Rapport, M. M., *Science, 113*, 596 (1951).
64. Morell, S., and Link., K. P., *J. Biol. Chem.*, *114*, 123 (1936).
65. Morimoto, K., *J. Biochem.*, *Japan, 26*, 259 (1937).
66. Neuberg, C., and Cahill, W., *Biochem. Z.*, *275*, 328 (1934).
67. Neuberg, C., and Hoffmann, E., *Naturwissenschaften, 19*, 484 (1931).
68. Neuberg, C., and Hoffmann, E., *Biochem. Z.*, *234*, 345 (1931).
69. Neuberg, C., and Kurono, K., *Biochem. Z.*, *140*, 295 (1923).
70. Neuberg, C., and Rubin, O., *Biochem. Z.*, *67*, 82 (1914).
71. Neuberg, C., and Schoenbeck, O., *Biochem. Z.*, *265*, 223 (1933).
72. Neuberg, C., and Simon, E., *Biochem. Z.*, *156*, 365 (1925).
73. Neuberg, C., and Simon, E., *Ergeb. Physiol.*, *34*, 896 (1932).
74. Neuberg, C., and Wagner, J., *Biochem. Z.*, *174*, 457 (1926).
75. Neuberg, C., and Wagner, J., in E. Abderhalden, ed., *Handbuch der biologischen Arbeitsmethoden*, Section IV, Vol. 1, Urban & Schwarzenberg, Vienna, 1927.
76. Neuberg, C., and Wagner, J., *Z. ges. exptl. Med.*, *56*, 334 (1927).
77. Ohara, M., and Kurata, J., *Igaku Seibutsugaka, 16*, 213 (1950).
78. Pearse, A. G. E., *Histochemistry. Theoretical and Applied*, J. & A. Churchill Ltd., London, 1953, p. 281.
79. Pepler, W. J., and Brandt, F. A., *Brit. J. Exptl. Pathol.*, *35*, 41 (1954).
80. Robinson, D., Smith, J. N., Spencer, B., and Williams, R. T., *Biochem. J.*, *51*, 202 (1952).
81. Robinson, D., Smith, J. N., and Williams, R. T., *Biochem. J.*, *49*, lxxiv (1951).
82. Robinson, D., Smith, J. N., and Williams, R. T., *Biochem. J.*, *53*, 125 (1953).
83. Robinson, D., Spencer, B., and Williams, R. T., *Biochem. J.*, *48*, xxvii (1951).
84. Roy, A. B., *Biochem. J.*, *53*, 12 (1953).
85. Roy, A. B., *Biochem. J.*, *55*, 653 (1953).
86. Roy, A. B., *Biochem. J.*, *57*, 465 (1954).
87. Roy, A. B., *Biochem. J.*, *62*, 41 (1956).
88. Roy, A. B., *Biochem. J.*, *62*, 35P (1956).
89. Rutenberg, A. M., and Seligman, A. M., *Arch. Biochem. and Biophys.*, *60*, 198 (1956).
90. Savard, H., Bagnoli, E., and Dorfman, R. I., *Federation Proc.*, *13*, 289 (1954).

91. Seligman, A. M., Chauncey, H. H., and Nachlas, M. M., *Stain Technol.*, *26*, 19 (1951).
92. Seligman, A. M., Nachlas, M. M., and Cohen, R., *Cancer*, *10*, 240 (1950).
93. Smith, H., and Gallop, R. C., *Biochem. J.*, *53*, 666 (1953).
94. Soda, T., *Bull. Chem. Soc., Japan*, *8*, 37 (1933).
95. Soda, T., *J. Fac. Sci., Tokyo*, *3*, 149 (1936).
96. Soda, T., personal communication.
97. Soda, T., and Egami, F., *J. Chem. Soc., Japan*, *59*, 1202 (1938).
98. Soda, T., and Hattori, C., *Bull. Chem. Soc. Japan*, *6*, 258 (1931).
99. Spencer, B., *Symposium on the Biochemistry of Sulfur, Roscoff, France*, 1956, in press.
100. Spencer, B., Dodgson, K. S., Rose, F. A., and Thomas, J., *Résumés des communications, third international cóngress of biochemistry, Brussels*, sect. 4, No. 20 (1955).
101. Stitch, S. R., and Halkerston, I. D. K., *Nature*, *172*, 398 (1953).
102. Strandberg, L., *Acta Physiol. Scand.*, *21*, 222 (1951).
103. Talalay, P., Fishman, W. M., and Huggins, C., *J. Biol. Chem.*, *166*, 757 (1946).
104. Tanaka, S., *J. Biochem. Japan*, *28*, 37 (1938).
105. Tanaka, S., *J. Biochem., Japan*, *28*, 119 (1938).
106. Tanko, B., *Biochem. Z.*, *247*, 486 (1932).
107. Viala, R., and Gianetto, R., *Can. J. Biochem. Physiol.*, *33*, 839 (1955).
108. Vlitos, A. J., *Contrib. Boyce Thompson Inst.*, *17*, 127 (1953).
109. Whitehead, J. E. B., Morrison, A. R., and Young, L., *Biochem. J.*, *51*, 585 (1952).
110. Wolfrom, M. L., and Montgomery, R., *J. Am. Chem. Soc.*, *72*, 2859 (1950).
111. Zimmerman, W., *Hoppe-Seyler's Z. physiol. Chem.*, *245*, 47 (1936).

Determination of
SERUM ACID PHOSPHATASES

WILLIAM H. FISHMAN AND HAROLD M. DAVIDSON, *Tufts University School of Medicine*

I. INTRODUCTION

The determination of the activity of enzymes in the serum is becoming an increasingly important application of biochemistry in medicine, as illustrated by these few examples; serum amylase (24) and lipase (18) in pancreatic disease, alkaline phosphatase in diseases of bone (11,48) and liver (16,37,68), acid phosphatase in carcinoma of the prostate (35,39) and recently, transaminase in coronary heart disease (47). In all of these it should be emphasized that the activity measured is a reflection not only of the potency of the serum enzyme protein but also of many factors which operate both *in vivo* and *in vitro*. The slightest change in any one of seemingly minor conditions can result in an alteration in the final number of units of activity found. Consequently, the need exists for adhering to precisely standardized conditions for the determination of serum enzyme activity, requirements which are more exacting than those for the determination of entities such as serum protein or glucose. It is contended that many of the theoretical and practical considerations discussed in this chapter concerning serum acid phosphatase apply directly to the accurate determination of any other enzyme in serum.

The enzyme, acid phosphatase, is classified as one which hydrolyzes a monoester of ortho phosphoric acid at an acid pH (67,73).

$$R-O-\overset{\displaystyle O}{\underset{\displaystyle O}{\overset{\|}{\underset{\|}{P}}}}-OH \ + \ H_2O \ \longrightarrow \ R-OH \ + \ H_3PO_4$$

Information regarding the properties of acid phosphatases is lacking since these enzymes have so far not been prepared in a pure state. However, the enzyme from human prostate in contrast to the mixture of acid phosphatases in *serum* has received systematic study and highly purified preparations have been obtained (13,20,23,52,56,58, 60). It is reported to be a protein of low molecular weight. Its isoelectric point is pH 4.5 (23), where it is also most stable against inactivation by heat or silver (28). However, in very dilute solution it undergoes rapid inactivation (62). Phosphamidase is consistently present in purified acid phosphatase (22).

The serum acid phosphatase is widely believed to possess significance with respect to cancer of the prostate. In 1925, Demuth (22) first observed that human urine had the capacity to hydrolyze hexosediphosphate at an acid pH (5.0). Ten years later, the tissue source of the enzyme was found by Kutscher and Wolbergs (53) to reside in the prostate gland. This tissue possessed an extraordinarily high concentration of the enzyme which hydrolyzed a variety of phosphate esters in a medium of pH 4 to 6. The relationship of the presence of skeletal metastases from cancer of the prostate and elevated serum acid phosphatase levels was discovered by Gutman and Gutman (35,36,39). The metastatic tissue contained acid phosphatase which exhibited the same properties as that of the prostate and the serum. Clinical improvement which followed usually when these patients were treated with estrogens was often accompanied by a fall in the serum acid phosphatase (44). These findings support the view that acid phosphatase is a biochemical characteristic of the cancer which originates from the prostate gland.

The value of the serum acid phosphatase determination to the clinician has proved greatest in the realm of differential diagnosis, prognosis and hormonal therapy. As a result the serum acid phosphatase assay has become a routine procedure in most hospitals and clinics in the country.

The definition of the biochemical problems in determining serum acid phosphatase is dependent on an understanding of the needs of the clinician. In the past, elevated serum acid phosphatase levels were observed in only about 50% of patients with metastatic cancer of the prostate and rarely in subjects whose disease remained localized to the prostate. Disease states other than cancer of the prostate have also been associated from time to time with elevated serum acid phosphatase, thus rendering the interpretation of such values less clear. In addition, falsely high levels of serum acid phosphatase occur not infrequently as a result of hemolysis, the erythrocyte being relatively rich in acid phosphatase. Since it is stated that the earlier the clinician can recognize cancer of the prostate the greater is the possibility of successful surgical and chemotherapeutic measures, it is imperative that the biochemical objective be the refinement of present methods or the development of new ones which will raise the clinical accuracy of the enzyme assay to the maximum.

Two procedures have received widespread acceptance. One is based on the measurement of phenol liberated from phenyl phosphate (50) which is the substrate employed for the measurement of L-tartrate sensitive serum acid phosphatase (29), and the other is founded on the analysis of inorganic phosphate released from β-glycerophosphate (10).

260　　　W. H. FISHMAN AND H. M. DAVIDSON

In this report, theoretical and practical considerations with regard to the determination of serum acid phosphatases will be followed by a detailed description of the Fishman-Lerner method. A discussion of some problems in this field which remain unsolved is also included.

II. THEORETICAL CONSIDERATIONS

1. Serum Acid Phosphatase—A Mixture of Enzymes

While acid phosphatases prepared from a variety of tissues have many properties in common, striking differences in their behavior have been noted. Davies (19) first observed that acid phosphatase from erythrocyte and spleen hydrolyzed α- and β-glycerophosphates at distinctly different rates. The marked ability of ethanol to inhibit prostatic acid phosphatase (54) was used by Herbert (41) in assays designed to measure prostatic acid phosphatase in serum. Abdul-Fadl and King (1) found that formaldehyde inhibited erythrocytic but

TABLE I

Summary of the Effect of Different Treatments on the Acid Phosphatase of Prostate and Red Blood Cells (2)

Treatment	Prostatic acid phosphatase	Red-cell acid phosphatase
Alcohol incubation	Inhibition 90–100%	Inhibition 70–80%
Copper (0.0002 M)		
Acetate buffer	Inhibition 8%	Inhibition 96%
Citrate buffer	No effect	Inhibition 90%
Cyanide	Slight activation	Slight activation
Cysteine	Slight activation	Slight activation
Formaldehyde (0.5%)	No effect	Inhibition 100%
Fluoride (0.01 M)	Inhibition 97%	Inhibition 10%
Hydrolysis of α- and β-glycerophosphoric esters	β slightly $> \alpha$	$\alpha > \beta$
Iron (0.0005 M)		
Acetate buffer	Inhibition 80%	Inhibition 9%
Citrate buffer	No effect (or slight activation)	No effect
Magnesium (0.01 M)	No effect (or slight activation)	Inhibition
Manganese	Slight inhibition	Slight inhibition
L-Tartrate	Inhibition	0

not prostatic acid phosphatase whereas L-tartrate inhibited prostatic but not erythrocytic acid phosphatase. In a later study (2),
these authors noted a number of points of difference which support
the thesis that the properties of the latter two enzymes are not
identical (Table I).

The nature of the buffer is of importance in influencing the effect of

TABLE II

Efficiency of L-Tartrate Inhibition of Serum Acid Phosphatase Whether or Not
Enriched with Purified Acid Phosphatase (29)

Patient	Total	Plus L-tartrate	"Prostatic"	Serum + prostatic acid phosphatase	Mixture + L-tartrate	"Prostatic" found	"Prostatic" calculated
T.	1.4	1.2	0.2	13.5	1.3	12.2	12.3
R.	1.1	0.9	0.2	11.4	1.1	10.3	10.5
F.	1.1	0.9	0.2	12.8	1.1	11.7	11.9
N.	1.1	0.9	0.2	9.0	1.5	7.5	8.1
K.	0.5	0.4	0.1	8.4	0.5	7.9	8.0
G.	0.7	0.6	0.1	9.9	0.6	9.3	9.3
W.	1.4	1.1	0.3	12.6	1.2	11.4	11.5
O.	0.9	0.5	0.4	11.1	0.6	10.5	10.6
Wa.	1.0	0.8	0.2	22.2	0.7	21.5	21.4
Wh.	1.1	0.9	0.2	21.6	1.1	20.5	20.7
O'H.	0.7	0.6	0.1	25.5	0.7	24.8	24.9
C.	0.7	0.5	0.2	28.2	0.7	27.5	27.7
V.	0.7	0.6	0.1	12.6	0.6	12.0	12.0
P.	0.5	0.3	0.2	10.8	0.2	10.6	10.5
Y.	1.5	1.0	0.5	8.7	0.6	8.1	7.7
M.	0.2	0.1	0.1	9.6	0.1	9.5	9.5
Ca.	1.0	1.1	0.0	10.2	1.0	9.2	9.2
J.	1.6	1.3	0.3	10.2	1.3	8.9	8.9
B.	2.1	1.7	0.4	10.2	1.7	8.5	8.5
Q.	1.1	1.0	0.1	14.7	1.0	13.7	13.7
C.							
Jan. 21	28.2	1.8	26.4	37.8	2.0	35.8	36.0
Feb. 25	1.8	0.5	1.3	11.7	0.6	11.1	11.2
July 3	0.9	0.8	0.1	10.8	1.2	9.6	10.0
July 7	0.7	0.4	0.3	8.7	0.4	8.3	8.3
H.							
July 3	38.4	3.2	35.2	41.4	2.8	38.6	38.2
July 8	37.2	2.2	35.0	42.0	3.4	38.6	39.8
D.							
July 2	37.8	3.0	34.8	49.2	2.7	46.5	46.2
July 7	33.6	1.6	32.0	37.8	1.9	35.9	36.2

inhibitors, activators, and the rate of hydrolysis. For example, 0.0005 M iron in acetate buffer inhibits 80% of the activity of prostatic acid phosphatase but has no effect in citrate buffer (2). The hydrolysis by this enzyme of phosphorylcholine and β-glycerophosphate is much more rapid in citrate than in acetate (59).

The addition of certain of these inhibitors, e.g., L-tartrate, Cu^{2+}, to serum does cause a reduction in measurable acid phosphatase, a fact which indicates that the serum acid phosphatase represents a mixture of acid phosphatases (29,2).

2. Serum "Prostatic" Acid Phosphatase

The following observations support the view that in male subjects the fraction of the serum acid phosphatase inhibited by L-tartrate is mainly of prostatic origin. (1) Purified prostatic acid phosphatase is completely inhibited in 0.02 M L-tartrate at pH 4.9 (29). (2) L-Tartrate invariably inhibits "prostatic" acid phosphatase of serum when assayed with phenylphosphate whether or not the serum had been enriched with purified prostatic enzyme (29) (Table II). (3) Massage of the prostate gland often results in a transient increase in the amount of serum acid phosphatase which is inhibited by L-tartrate (14,27). (4) Elevated levels of serum acid phosphatase in patients with cancer of the prostate consist mainly of tartrate-inhibited acid phosphatase (14). For these reasons serum acid phosphatase inhibited by tartrate is termed "prostatic" in order to indicate the probable tissue source in males, the small amounts of this component in female sera being due to other sources (1). The increased acid phosphatase in cancer of the breast in females which is rarely seen is not inhibited to an appreciable extent by L-tartrate (26).

3. Transferase Phenomena

The simple hydrolysis of substrate leads to the formation of two products in equimolar amounts. It has been generally assumed that the measurement of either product is an indication of the hydrolytic activity of the enzyme. This is not necessarily a valid assumption in view of the information uncovered regarding phosphate group transfer.

The discovery by Axelrod (5) that phosphatases are capable of catalyzing the transfer of phosphate from the substrate to an acceptor alcohol has introduced an important consideration (transferase) in the interpretation of the activity of hydrolases as usually measured. In his experiments more phenol than inorganic phosphate accumulated in the digests containing an acceptor alcohol. Therefore it is important to establish the presence or absence of such group transfers in the system under study in order to know the significance of measuring just one product of the hydrolytic reaction.

A picture of the reactions possible in the absence and in the presence of an acceptor alcohol is provided by the following equations:

(a) $R'OPO_3H_2 + H_2O \longrightarrow R'OH + H_3PO_4$ hydrolysis

(b) $R'OPO_3H_2 + R''OH \longrightarrow R'OH + R''OPO_3H_2$ transfer

(c) $R''OPO_3H_2 + H_2O \longrightarrow R''OH + H_3PO_4$ hydrolysis

where R represents an alkyl or aryl group.

Equimolar liberation of $R'OH$ and inorganic phosphate will occur under the following circumstances: (1) when (a) is the only reaction, and (2) when (b) and (c) occur in addition to (a) but the rate for reaction (b) is equal to or less than the rate for (c); i.e., the product formed by transfer, $R''OPO_3H_2$, is being hydrolyzed as rapidly as it is formed. Equimolar liberation of $R'OH$ and inorganic phosphate will not occur in the presence of an acceptor when the rate for (b) is greater than that for (c). Under these conditions, the concentration of $R'OH$ will exceed that of inorganic phosphate by an amount equal to the concentration of $R''OPO_3H_2$ present in the digest.

It is important to note that in the presence of acceptor the inorganic phosphate liberated is the product of hydrolysis of two substrates $(R'OPO_3H_2$ and $R''OPO_3H_2)$, whereas the hydroxylated moiety $R'OH$ formed is the product of both hydrolysis and transfer, reactions (a) and (b). Also, in view of the fact that transfer reactions in the presence of hydrolysis increase the amount of one product and reduce the other, it appears advisable to determine both products of hydrolysis in any new study of acid phosphatase, e.g., in kinetic studies on activation and inhibition of hydrolysis. Consequently, if unrecognized acceptor substances are present in the assay digest, the results may be incorrectly interpreted. An example of a study in which these factors were considered is that of Barrueto, Davison-Reynolds, Walker, and Lemon (6) who determined the molar concentrations of nitrophenol and inorganic phosphate upon hydrolysis of p-nitrophenyl phosphate by serum. They concluded that there was only a small amount of transfer occurring with unspecified acceptor alcohols of serum.

III. PRACTICAL CONSIDERATIONS

1. General Comments

With regard to the serum acid phosphatase, the most important consideration is that of maintaining accuracy. This is certainly the case for the Fishman-Lerner method utilizing L-tartrate inhibition. Here, the conditions require a sufficient liberation of phenol from the substrate so that the extent of inhibition can be noticed. This requirement is met when duplicate readings in the presence of inhibitor are safely out of the region of variation of the readings for digests without inhibitor. An advantage of the L-tartrate technique is that it does not include erythrocytic acid phosphatase, and so hemolyzed sera can be assayed without difficulty.

The elimination of the requirement for precipitating the serum proteins would materially reduce the number of manipulations and thereby increase the convenience of procedures based on phenyl phosphate hydrolysis. Several attempts designed to accomplish this objective are recorded in the literature and these and similar efforts of this laboratory are dealt with in a later section.

2. Time of Hydrolysis

The period of hydrolysis is of critical importance in satisfying the requirement for accuracy. Since serum contains a substantial amount of phosphate and phenol (plus other substances which give a Folin-Ciocalteu reaction) an appreciable reading is noted in the controls tubes lacking substrate. Accordingly, the degree of hydrolysis of the substrate should be sufficiently great to provide readings which are well above those of the control digests. This can be ensured in the case of phosphatase-poor sera by a long enough period of hydrolysis (*vide infra*). Thus, in the case of partitioning serum acid phosphatase into L-tartrate sensitive and L-tartrate insensitive components, a three-hour period is essential to render accurate the measured differences. Since the rate of hydrolysis by the non "prostatic" component decreases with time, one should not expect exact agreement in the units of *total* acid phosphatase calculated from data obtained with the same serum incubated for different lengths of time (Figure 1).

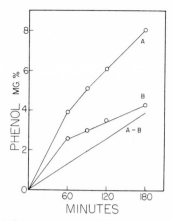

Fig. 1. Pooled female sera enriched with purified prostatic acid phosphatase. Curve A, serum plus prostatic acid phosphatase. Curve B, serum alone. Curve A — B, activity of purified prostatic acid phosphatase.

3. Methods Requiring Precipitation of Protein

Since the only known route to the measurement of acid phosphatase in serum is through its action on substrate, the choice of method to a large extent actually depends upon the substrate employed. Therefore, the utility of any method would reflect in large part the advantages and disadvantages of the substrate and of the methods available for measuring the desired product.

As may be seen from the equation (a) expressing the hydrolysis catalyzed by acid phosphatase two products are formed, an hydroxy compound and inorganic phosphate. Attention will be given first to those substrates whose hydrolysis is measured in terms of the release of inorganic phosphate and later to the ones in which determination of the liberated alcohols or phenol is the important feature of the assay.

A. PHOSPHATE RELEASE AS A BASIS FOR ENZYME ASSAY

If the inorganic phosphate produced on hydrolysis is to be measured, then theoretically, any hydrolyzable phosphate ester would be suitable. However, in practice, glycerophosphate has been used almost exclusively for this purpose, probably because it is already the standard substrate for the assay of alkaline phosphatase in serum. Yet, glycerophosphate is less efficiently split by acid phosphatase of serum than phenyl phosphate or nitrophenyl phosphate (Table III), a fact which has favored the wider adoption of phenolic phosphates as substrates.

Since glycerophosphate as supplied commercially is a mixture of α and β forms, there are objections to the use of a mixed substrate, particularly in studies concerned with the quantitative partition of the components of the acid phosphatase mixture in serum. The consistent use of pure isomers would go far toward overcoming this objection.

The outstanding advantage in using glycerophosphate, an alcoholic ester, is its stability in comparison to the phosphate esters of phenols. Since the routine measurement of glycerol is impractical, phosphate produced by hydrolysis is determined. Citrate ion interferes in the determination of inorganic phosphate and so cannot conveniently be used as a buffer whèn the assay is based on this determination.

B. RELEASE OF A PHENOL AS A BASIS FOR ENZYME ASSAY

Although theoretically any phenolic phosphate ester might serve as substrate, the simplest of these, phenyl phosphate, is widely employed, the liberated phenol being determined by means of the Folin-Ciocalteu reaction.

Other substrates for the acid phosphatase determination have been proposed because their use appeared to simplify the procedure in one way or another. Binkley, Shank, and Hoagland (9) have proposed using tyrosine phosphate instead of phenyl phosphate mainly because a reference standard is more easily prepared with anhydrous tyrosine than with phenol which for the most accurate work must be standardized by the method of Koppeschaar (51). The units of activity for serum with tyrosine phosphate as substrate are almost identical to those defined for phenyl phosphate.

Seligman and co-workers (69) have proposed a method using β-naphthyl phosphate as substrate. Two molecules of β-naphthol produced by hydrolysis form an insoluble colored complex with tetrazotized diorthoanisidine. The colored product must be extracted with ethyl acetate from the deproteinized serum mixtures and then determined colorimetrically. Other components of serum do not interfere in the color reaction. The advantages of the method are stated to reside in the stability of the reagents and the requirement of a single control. The necessity of tedious solvent extractions of the colored product makes this procedure unattractive for routine use.

4. Relative Merits of Substrates and Buffers

The data assembled in Table III show that the hydrolysis in

TABLE III

Comparison of Important Features in Methods Presently Used for Determining
Serum Acid Phosphatase

I Substrate[a]	II Buffer	III Normal mean	IV mM./liter/ hr.	V Relative rate of hydroly- sis	VI Molar extinc- tion coeffi- cient $\times$ 10^{-3} [b]	VII $\dfrac{IV \times VI}{208}$
Glycero- phosphate	Acetate	0.19^c	0.061	1.0	3.40^d	1.0
Phenyl phosphate	Citrate	2.05^e	0.22	3.6	11.9^f	13
p-Nitrophenyl phosphate	Citrate	0.25^g	0.25	4.1	21.1^h	25
p-Nitrophenyl phosphate	Acetate, Mg^{2+}	1.54^g	1.54	25	21.1^h	160
β-Naphthyl phosphate	Acetate	1.0^i	0.69	11	31.6^j	100
Phenolphthalein diphosphate	Acetate	5.9^k	0.038^l	0.62	24.6^m	4.5

[a] Sodium salt.
[b] Calculated from data in the literature except in the case of phosphorus and phenol; E = optical density $\times$ M.W./grams per liter $\times$ cell thickness (cm.).
[c] mg. phosphorus/100 ml. serum/hr. (12).
[d] Phosphorus in Fiske and Subbarow determination (30) at 625 mμ.
[e] mg. phenol/100 ml. serum/hr. (12).
[f] Phenol in Folin-Ciocalteu determination (31) at 660 mμ.
[g] millimoles p-nitrophenol/liter serum/hr. (4,43).
[h] p-Nitrophenol in alkaline solution at 400 mμ (43).
[i] 10 mg. β-naphthol/100 ml. serum/hr. (69).
[j] $E/2$ of product formed from condensation of two molecules of β-naphthol and tetrazotized diorthoanisidine, 540 mμ (70); the quantitative conversion of β-naphthol to dye stuff is assumed.
[k] 5.9 units = 0.6 mg. phenolphthalein/100 ml. serum/hr. (45,55).
[l] 0.0188 mM. phenolphthalein $\times$ 2.
[m] Phenolphthalein, pH 10.6 to 10.9, "Filter S 53" (55).

citrate of phenyl phosphate (which is more efficient than hydrolysis of glycerophosphate in veronal-acetate) is practically equivalent to that of p-nitrophenyl phosphate in citrate although much lower than that of p-nitrophenyl phosphate in acetate containing magnesium ion. Also it is seen from Table III that the molar extinction for phenol in the Folin-Ciocalteu reaction is about four times greater than that of phosphorus in the Fisk and Subbarow determination. This fact coupled with the greater rapidity of hydrolysis of phenylphosphate makes for great sensitivity when the latter substrate is used in preference to glycerophosphate—an important feature when dealing with sera of low activity. No serious problems have been encountered in the assay of phosphatase-rich sera with phenyl phosphate. Table III also indicates that there is only a small advantage with regard to sensitivity when p-nitrophenyl phosphate is used instead of phenyl phosphate with citrate buffer. Due to the paucity of information on serum acid phosphatase assayed with p-nitrophenyl phosphate in acetate with magnesium, it is not possible at present to evaluate the usefulness of this particular system.

5. Performance of Methods Designed to Eliminate Precipitation of Protein

A. REVIEW OF PROPOSED METHODS

An assay not requiring deproteinization before determining the product of hydrolysis would be of great practical advantage in the clinical laboratory. Such a method calls either for a substrate that decomposes enzymatically into a colored product or for a procedure of color development with reagents that do not precipitate proteins. Three methods which seem to possess practical potentialities from the latter point of view are discussed in this section.

Two other proposed procedures are based on the substrates, phenolphthalein phosphate (45) and rosolyl phosphate (71).

With regard to phenolphthalein phosphate there is no simple relation between the amount of color produced and the concentration of enzyme because no indicator is formed unless both phosphate groups are split from the substrate. Linhardt and Walter (55) have pointed out that a linear relationship does exist between the logarithm of phenolphthalein liberated and the logarithm of the units defined by Huggins (45). They have also pointed out that the fading of the indicator in alkaline solution can be avoided by controlling the pH between 10.6 and 10.9. Commercial preparations of phenolphthalein phosphate do not always have the same amount of mono- and di-phosphate esters, and so the unit must be re-established with each new lot of substrate.

Rosolyl phosphate, which is rather poorly hydrolyzed in comparison to phenolphthalein phosphate, has been proposed as a suitable substrate only for serum with high activity (67).

There is little information yet concerning the fluorimetric determination of phosphatase activity in serum using the substrates eosin phosphate, fluorescein phosphate and 4-methyl-7-oxycoumarin phosphate prepared by Neumann (63).

B. AMINOANTIPYRENE METHODS

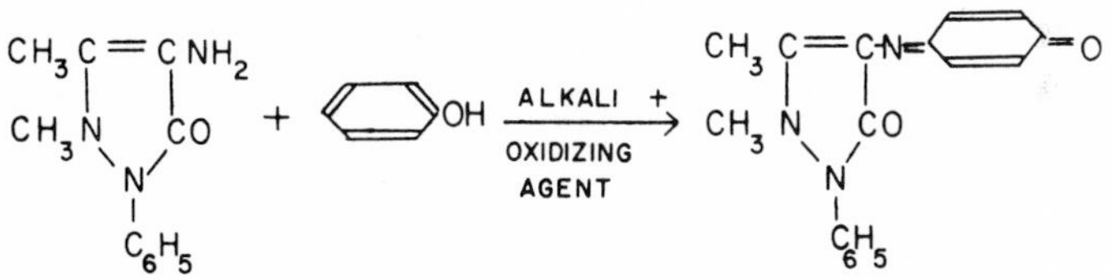

Fig. 2. The reaction of phenol with 4-aminoantipyrene.

The use of 4-aminoantipyrene as a phenol reagent was reported by Emerson (25) and modified later by Gottlieb and Marsh (33). This reagent condenses with phenol to give a product which can then be oxidized to yield a red or purple colored compound. It is asserted that there is no reaction with protein. Grifols (34) applied this principle to the measurement of phenol liberated in the assay of serum alkaline phosphatase using ferricyanide in alkali as the oxidizing agent. A careful study by Powell and Smith (66) revealed in 4 out of 4 subjects good agreement with the King-Armstrong (50) procedure in phosphatase-rich sera of prostatic cancer but in 2 out of 4 normal subjects the results of the two methods differed. In their view, the main difficulty was that of getting full color development which required adjustments in the concentrations of 4-aminoantipyrene, citrate, carbonate, and bicarbonate. They also found that serum protein had to be included in the standard solutions of phenol. Kind and King (49) noted increasing optical density in their digests at the pH for the development of color, 10.2. This was ascribed to the action of alkaline phosphatase. They recommended a final pH of 11.5 to stop this interference. The presence of plasma proteins was considered to have a minimal effect on the color and therefore plasma was not included in the phenol standards. Two out of four normal sera showed poor agreement between the aminoantipyrene method and that of King and Armstrong.

The experience with the aminoantipyrene methods in this laboratory was as follows: Aminoantipyrene produced color with serum incubated without substrate. It is not known whether this is due to reaction with serum proteins. When care was taken to mix the solution thoroughly after each addition of reagents, troublesome precipitates were avoided. Curves relating phenol concentration to optical density were linear whether or not serum was present even at very low concentrations of phenol. Good agreement was obtained for total serum acid phosphatase when its activity ranged above 2 King-Armstrong units employing the King-Armstrong procedure as the method of reference. However, attempts to utilize the amino-antipyrene method for determining "prostatic" acid phosphatase in the range between 0 to 1.0 King-Armstrong unit, where accuracy is an essential requirement, were unsuccessful.

C. DIAZO METHODS

Attention to the formation of dye colors by coupling phenol with stabilized diazotates was first directed by Gomori (32). Later, Kaplan and Narahara (46) reported a procedure for determining serum acid phosphatase in which the phenol liberated from phenyl phosphate was coupled with Diazo Blue to yield a reddish color. The average figure for normal male subjects was 1.0 King-Armstrong unit which is definitely below the accepted value of 3.5 units.

For purposes of making the Fishman-Lerner method presented below more convenient, the measurement of phenol by diazo coupling seemed to offer the best approach. It is of some interest that it took six months of intensive work to bring us to the point where this objective appeared in view. Some of the findings are listed briefly to illustrate the problems that arise when adapting conditions validated in one method into a procedure designed for selective estimation of serum phosphatase of prostatic origin. Thus, a higher concentration of the diazo reagent than stated by others (32,46) was required for full color development. The reagent must be prepared at low temperature (5°C.) and exact measurement of the diazo reagent is essential for obtaining reproducible results.

D. NITROPHENYL PHOSPHATE PROCEDURES

Hudson, Brendler, and Scott (43) and Andersch and Szczypinski (4) have adapted the micro determination of alkaline phosphatase with p-nitrophenyl phosphate (8) to the determination of serum acid phosphatase. These methods require only 0.1 or 0.2 ml. of serum and a period of incubation as short as thirty minutes. The chief disadvantages in the use of p-nitrophenyl phosphate seem to be related to its lack of purity and instability, it being necessary to extract free nitrophenol with ether from the substrate solution. The fact that such solutions of substrate would contain a variable amount of inorganic phosphate which reduces the hydrolytic rate is not generally appreciated. Interference by chromogens present in hemolytic or icteric sera is another troublesome feature. Perhaps the adoption of the highly stable monosodium salt of the ester instead of the disodium salt would eliminate some of the objections to the use of this substrate (40).

With regard to practical considerations, the lack of necessity for removing serum proteins and the simplicity of color development are two attractive features which have lured a number of investigators into adopting p-nitrophenyl phosphate for measuring "prostatic" acid phosphatase in serum (17,42,64). Such methods have been used by these investigators in surveys of male populations with and without cancer of the prostate and have led to the establishment of limits of normal which differ in each series. Moreover, the clinical correlations, especially in the series studied by the latter two workers, have not measured up to their expectations. We attribute this to the shortened incubation period adopted by these workers without recognizing the consequences to the values of the "prostatic" fraction.

The experience in this laboratory with the nitrophenyl phosphate substrate has been disappointing. Some 70 sera from patients with and without cancer of the prostate were assayed for total and prostatic acid phosphatase by two methods, the Cline (nitrophenyl phosphate) and the Fishman-Lerner procedures. The data showed no consistency at normal and "borderline" ranges of activity and at high acid phosphatase levels, the nitrophenyl phosphate substrate released only a third to a sixth of the nitrophenol expected in view of the figures obtained with the phenyl phosphate substrate. Hill (42) found also only a minimal correlation in the results of these methods.

We have noted a rapid "falling-off" in the rate of hydrolysis of this substrate by serum enriched with prostatic acid phosphatase.

From a practical point of view it is desirable to develop conditions which would reduce the number of manipulations in the procedure so that the determination of serum acid phosphatase would be more convenient and rapid. At the present time, the most promising approach is that utilizing azo dye formation from the phenol released enzymatically, a step which would eliminate protein precipitation from the Fishman-Lerner method. It should be stressed, however, that it is dangerous to substitute this or any other technique for color development before careful comparison of its accuracy, both laboratory and clinical, with the standard procedure.

Aside from color development, it is equally dangerous and inadvisable to adopt without rigorous testing and control conditions from a properly validated procedure into a second procedure. This may be illustrated by the observation that 0.02 M L-tartrate (a concentration commonly employed with the substrates phenyl and p-nitrophenyl phosphate) is not an efficient inhibitor of the hydrolysis of nitrophenyl phosphate whereas it completely inhibits the action of acid phosphatase on phenyl phosphate (65).

IV. CHOICE OF METHOD

Most hospital laboratories utilize the procedure in which phenyl phosphate is the substrate and in which a unit of activity is defined as the liberation of 1 milligram of phenol per hour by serum under standard conditions (King-Armstrong). One virtue of the Fishman-Lerner procedure is that the "prostatic" component is expressed in K.-A. units and is thus familiar to the individuals whose responsibility it is to interpret these values. In addition, it provides a figure for total acid phosphatase which is reliable in view of the incorporation into the method of a number of controls which take into account phenolic constituents of the serum and the extent of the spontaneous hydrolysis of the substrate (7). In view of the fact that the Fishman-Lerner technique is the method of choice in this and other laboratories (21,27,61,72,74) and because its use without modification yields similar results in clinical studies and since it is interpretable in the standard K.A. units, this procedure is presented in detail.

V. FISHMAN-LERNER METHOD

1. Principle

The hydrolysis of phenyl phosphate is measured in the absence and in the presence of L-tartrate. The difference found in the amount of phenol liberated is believed to represent the inhibition of acid phosphatase of prostatic origin and so reflect the concentration of the latter enzyme in serum. The analytical procedure is based on the modification by Benotti et al. (7) of the Gutman and Gutman (38) version of the King-Armstrong method (50).

2. Reagents

Citrate buffer, pH 4.9. 18.9 g. of citric acid $\cdot 1H_2O$ (Merck, C.P.) is dissolved in 500 ml. of H_2O and 180 ml. of 1 N NaOH and 100 ml. of 0.1 N HCl are added. The pH of the solution is checked and adjusted to 4.9 (glass electrode) with 1 N NaOH or 0.1 N HCl. The volume is then made up to 1 liter with distilled water and the buffer stored in the refrigerator in a glass-stoppered bottle.

Substrate. Disodium phenyl phosphate (Paul-Lewis Laboratories, Madison, Wisconsin). A 1% aqueous solution of substrate is prepared fresh every 2 weeks in routine work or when the reagent blank contains more than 0.015 mg. of phenol from the decomposition of substrate. The dry substrate and the solution are stored in the refrigerator.

Phenol reagent (Folin-Ciocalteu (31) 2 N with respect to acidity). In a 2000-ml. round flask, connected to a condenser and supported by a heating mantle, a mixture of 100 g. sodium tungstate ($Na_2WO_4\cdot 2H_2O$), 25 g. sodium molybdate ($Na_2MoO_4\cdot 2H_2O$), 700 ml. distilled water, 50 ml. 85% phosphoric acid (H_3PO_4), 100 ml. conc. hydrochloric acid is refluxed for 10 hours. The heating may be interrupted overnight. After the mixture is cooled, the condenser is removed and the following additions are made: 150 g. lithium sulfate ($Li_2SO_4\cdot H_2O$), 50 ml. distilled water and about 10 drops bromine. This is boiled for 15 minutes or until the odor of bromine has disappeared. After cooling, the volume is adjusted to 1 liter with distilled water and filtered through paper on a conical filter. One volume of this reagent is diluted with two volumes of water and stored in the refrigerator in a brown glass bottle.

The undiluted Folin-Ciocalteu reagent is also available commercially, e.g., Boston Medical Laboratory or Mahady and Company in Boston.

Sodium carbonate (anhydrous, Merck reagent). A 20% aqueous solution is prepared. It must be filtered daily before using.

Standard aqueous phenol solution containing 0.01 mg. of phenol per ml. A solution of phenol in 0.1 N HCl is prepared which contains approximately 1 mg. per ml. of "crystallized phenol" (Mallinckrodt analytical reagent). Twenty-five milliliters of this solution is transferred to a 250-ml. Erlenmeyer flask, 50 ml. of 0.1 N sodium hydroxide is added and the solution is heated to 65° on a hot plate. To the hot solution, 25 ml. of 0.1 N iodine solution is added, the flask stoppered and allowed to stand at room temperature for 30 to 40 minutes. Five milliliters of concentrated HCl is added and the excess iodine is titrated with 0.1 N thiosulfate solution. Each ml. of 0.1 N iodine (ml. of iodine added minus ml. of thiosulfate used in titration) corresponds to 1.567 mg. of phenol. On the basis of the titration data the solution of phenol is diluted with 0.1 N HCl so that 1 ml. contains 0.01 mg. of phenol.

0.2 M L-tartrate. 3.002 g. of tartaric acid (c.p. Baker's "analyzed" and Merck's "reagent" are both L(+)-tartaric acid) is dissolved in 50 ml. of H_2O. Approximately 35 ml. of 1 N NaOH is added. The pH is checked and adjusted to 4.9 (glass electrode) and the solution is made up to 100 ml. The solution is stored in the refrigerator in a glass-stoppered bottle and only an amount required for the day's analyses is taken.

3. Apparatus

Coleman Junior spectrophotometer, 660 mμ filter, constant temperature water bath at 38°.

4. Procedure

Four digests are prepared in Pyrex test-tubes as follows: Digest A (serum blank), 10 ml. of H_2O and 0.5 ml. of serum; Digest B (substrate blank) 8 ml. citrate buffer, 1 ml. of 0.2 M L-tartrate, 0.5 ml. of H_2O and 1.0 ml. of substrate; Digest C (total), 0.5 ml. of serum, 9 ml. of buffer, 1 ml. of substrate; Digest D (tartrate), 0.5 ml. of serum, 8 ml. of buffer, 1 ml. of 0.2 M L-tartrate, and 1 ml. of substrate. In all of these, substrate is the last addition.

The tubes are stoppered and mixed well. (Rubber stoppers must be washed and boiled in alkali and then rinsed after each run.) Digests B, C, and D are placed in a water bath at 38° and the time recorded. Digest A is treated with 4.5 ml. of phenol reagent and filtered after 15 minutes. The length of incubation time is variable: 0.5 hour for values expected to exceed 20 King-Armstrong units, 1.0 hour for 6 to 19 units, and 3 hours for values expected to be lower than 6 units. The rate of hydrolysis at least insofar as the prostatic fraction is concerned, is linear for periods of at least three hours. At the end of the incubation period, 4.5 ml. of dilute phenol reagent is added separately to Digests B, C, and D. The mixtures are centrifuged for fifteen minutes at 2000 r.p.m.

As a check with each day's determinations a standard is prepared (2.0 ml. of standard aqueous phenol (0.01 mg. phenol per ml.), 5 ml. of H_2O, 3 ml. of phenol reagent). Color development results after adding 2.5 ml. of 20% Na_2CO_3 to 10 ml. of the supernates of the four digests, A, B, C, and D, and to the standard. The tubes are stoppered; the contents mixed and then incubated at 38° for five minutes.

Immediately after the 5-minute interval, the optical density of each of these solutions is measured in a Coleman junior spectrophotometer at 660 mμ after adjusting to zero optical density with reagent blank.

Calibration curve. Standard solutions are prepared with increasing amounts of the phenol standard (0.01 mg. per ml.). Each tube, in addition to the standard, contains 3.0 ml. of phenol reagent and water to adjust the volume to 10 ml. To each tube is added 2.5 ml. of 20% Na_2CO_3 solution. After 5 minutes incubation at 38°, the optical density is measured, as described above, including the incubated reagent blank. The concentration of phenol is plotted against optical density to yield a straight line. This curve is readily reproducible.

Calculation. The optical density obtained with Digests A, B, C, and D is substituted in the calibration curve to yield the amount of phenol in mg. present in 10/15 of each digest. From this one computes King-Armstrong units per 100 ml. of serum as below.

$$(1) \quad \frac{C \text{ mg.} - (A \text{ mg.} + B \text{ mg.})}{\text{hr. of incubation}} \times \frac{15}{10} \times \frac{100}{0.5} = T \text{ units per 100 ml. serum}$$

$$(2) \quad \frac{D \text{ mg.} - (A \text{ mg.} + B \text{ mg.})}{\text{hr. of incubation}} \times \frac{15}{10} \times \frac{100}{0.5} = U \text{ units per 100 ml. serum}$$

(3) T units $-$ U units $=$ units of "prostatic" acid phosphatase
per 100 ml. serum

The units defined here are equivalent to the number of milligrams of phenol per hour (King-Armstrong units). Whenever possible, Digests B, C, and D have been analyzed in duplicate.

VI. SOURCES OF ERROR

Errors originate mainly from two sources. One concerns the handling of the blood specimen to the point of diluting the serum for the enzyme assay. The other deals with details in the technique itself.

1. Preparation of Sample

It is important to separate the serum from the clotted blood by centrifugation without delay and to keep the serum refrigerated until use. Woodard (75) points out that acid phosphatase in serum may lose as much as 50% of its activity per hour at summertime room temperatures. "Prostatic" acid phosphatase is also unstable under these conditions. Rosenmund (67) observed that acid phosphatase is stable in serum even at 37°C. if the pH is lowered from 7.4 to 6.0. Lowering the pH of the fresh serum would appear to be a useful precaution in situations where sera are left unrefrigerated for long periods of time before assay. Sera should be free of contaminating white and red cells. This may require a second centrifugation of the serum.

2. Other Variables (Dilution, Buffer, and Time)

The effect of dilution on the activity of the acid phosphatase in the serum is important. If there are activators, stabilizers, and inhibitors present originally in the serum, the effect of each would change with dilution of the serum and their net effect on activity might also change.

Considerations such as these help explain the fluctuations in activity seen when serum is assayed at varying dilutions. Such effects have been reported by Brayer and Trunnell (15) who assayed acid phosphatase in sera diluted ten to eighty times.

The wide variety of activations and inhibitions which they observed upon assaying incubation mixtures consisting only of substrate (glycerophosphate) buffered with hydrochloric acid might not necessarily have been observed with another substrate or a different buffering system. The activation of prostatic acid phosphatase by citrate ion as well as other organic acids with an hydroxyl, ketone or thiol group in the alpha position has been demonstrated by Anagnostopoulos (3). A buffer ion which fully activates the enzyme under investigation is ideal for purposes of enzymes assay although it follows that with

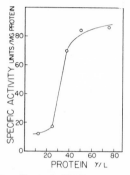

Fig. 3. The effect of dilution on activity. The enzyme was partially purified prostatic acid phosphatase which liberated 80–90 mg. of phenol from phenyl phosphate/mg. protein/hr. The phenol liberated was determined by the Folin-Ciocalteu reaction.

such a buffer it would be difficult to observe the presence of native inhibitors or activators of that enzyme. The situation with regard to dilution and buffers becomes even more complicated when one considers the heterogeneity of the serum acid phosphatase.

The difference in behavior of individual components of the acid phosphatases of serum during the course of incubation is illustrated in an experiment in which the effect of dilution on partially purified prostatic acid phosphatase was under investigation. In the experiment described in Figure 1 prostatic acid phosphatase was added to pooled female sera. The production of phenol from phenyl phosphate was determined at intervals during a period of three hours in the serum and in the mixture of serum and added enzyme. In the presence of serum the rate of hydrolysis of phenyl phosphate by the added prostatic component of the mixture was constant (derived Curve A−B); however, there appeared to be a gradual decline in activity for the non-prostatic acid phosphatase fraction.

We do not include a curve for enzyme alone because at the high dilutions of enzyme needed for this experiment, the purified preparation is inactive. Since purified acid phosphatase is inactivated at high dilutions (under 0.1 γ protein per ml.) (Figure 3) this fact must be taken into account when using highly diluted solutions of this purified enzyme as a control in serum studies. The experiment also indicates that the partially purified preparation of prostatic acid phosphatase was neither activated nor inhibited in any unique way by female sera.

Because highly purified preparations of prostatic acid phosphatase were fully activated in solutions containing approximately two micrograms of albumin per milliliter (0.0002%) it is unlikely that the prostatic component of serum would be inactivated within a wide range of dilutions in studies involving the estimation of that enzyme in serum (7.5% protein). Other studies in this laboratory with serum indicate that dilution does not influence the "prostatic" component but does lead to a lower non-"prostatic" fraction. Since, in addition, the latter component decreases in activity with time, both dilution and length of time of incubation become important considerations in estimating the contribution of this fraction to the total activity.

3. Technical Errors

The exact measurement of the serum taken for analysis is the critical step with regard to overall accuracy. The use of scrupulously clean pipettes and adherence to quantitative technique are essential.

Whenever possible, total and "prostatic" serum acid phosphatase are determined in duplicate. Duplicate readings should never differ by more than one or two transmission units. Should variance greater than this be encountered, the determination is repeated.

In the event of serum so rich in acid phosphatase that the transmission reading does not fall on the calibration curve, it is not permitted to dilute the digest for a second reading. The determination must be repeated. If the serum is only moderately elevated, e.g., above 4.0 K.-A. units, one can incubate the repeat digest for 1 hour instead of 3. If the serum is far above this level, it is necessary to dilute the serum with pooled aged female serum and follow the regular procedure. In either instance, the calculation should take into account the new dilutions.

Occasionally more color may be present in the tubes containing L-tartrate as compared to the digests lacking tartrate, leading to a negative or reversed value.   This has been found due to deterioration of the tartrate solution.

VII. DEFINITION OF NORMAL AND ABNORMAL VALUES

The decision of ascribing normality to a certain number of units of enzyme activity is based on a number of considerations.   First, from the statistical viewpoint, a rule of thumb, widely accepted, indicates that a value differing from the mean by two standard deviations usually occurs in 5% of the population and is considered "possibly

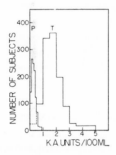

Fig. 4. Units of total (T) and "prostatic" (P) acid phosphatase in the serum of 1100 patients without cancer of the prostate.

abnormal" (12), whereas a value of 3 standard deviations from the mean is stated to be "probably abnormal" since it appears in only 1% of the population.   Next, it is important to understand the necessity of employing for the normal distribution study, a population of the same age and sex as that of the diseased patients.   Many errors in the interpretation of diagnostic tests are explained on this basis.   Thirdly, it is necessary to consider known though infrequent sources of error which are not referable to the analysis itself, e.g., hemolysis, temperature inactivation.   Finally, there is the judgment to be made on the basis of the clinical problem itself.   Is it more important to strive for a close to 100% correlation of disease with abnormal values even if this requires lowering the dividing value to the point where the number of false positives becomes considerable.

In the case of total and prostatic acid phosphatase the distribution curves (see Figure 4) indicate a homogeneous population. For prostatic acid phosphatase the mean and its standard deviation is 0.15 ±, 0.2, and for total acid phosphatase 1.8 ± 0.8 King-Armstrong units.

It seems reasonable therefore to regard 0.6 and more units of prostatic acid phosphatase in the serum as probably abnormal (26).

There is little argument as to which method to use when one is analyzing an acid-phosphatase-rich serum from a patient with prostatic carcinoma. All will register positive. The situation is much different in the accurate measurement of phosphatase-poor sera where important medical consequences ride on the analytical result. It is in this equivocal range of high normal to low abnormal values for total acid phosphatase that one finds the majority of patients with cancer of the prostate (26).

VIII. THE QUESTION OF NORMAL LEVELS IN METASTATIC CANCER OF THE PROSTATE

One is impressed by the fact that serum "prostatic" acid phosphatase levels often do not bear any relationship to the extent of spread of the disease (26,57). Thus, it is not uncommon to observe a normal or slightly elevated value in a patient with widespread bony metastases and on the other hand, occasional patients with localized cancer of the prostate may have marked elevations in their enzyme level. A number of explanations have been proposed: (1) the blood and lymph drainage from the cancerous areas may be the limiting factor so that although the amount of enzyme in the tumor is high, its entry into the blood stream is not uniform; (2) the prostatic cancer tissue itself may be low in acid phosphatase and be a poor producer of the enzyme; (3) the presence of a serum inhibitor of prostatic acid phosphatase has been suggested (its concentration would then be the factor controlling the measurable activity. The same considerations would apply to a serum activator); (4) the extent of excretion of the enzyme by the kidneys may be a variable; and (5) it has been proposed that the enzyme undergoes considerable heat inactivation at the pH of blood, so that what is measured in the enzyme assay is only a fraction of the active enzyme protein which has originally entered the circulation; (6) the possibility of an endogenous acceptor for the phosphate enzymatically released from the substrate has been suggested. Its concentration would greatly affect the amount of phenol liberation.

Possibilities 3, 5, and 6 are most readily open to biochemical enquiry. Work in this laboratory has been unsuccessful in demonstrating in the blood serum inhibiting or activating principles operative during the determination at pH 5.0. London, McHugh, and Hudson (57) favor the heat-inactivation concept.

The possibility is considered, elsewhere (26), that the phosphatase entering the blood from a malignant prostate gland may have its source in the benign areas of this tissue which have undergone compression or partial obstruction by the growing tumor.

IX. SUMMARY AND CONCLUSION

Evidence is presented that serum acid phosphatase is a mixture of which one member can be measured quantitatively by selective inhibition, an approach of unique value in designing accurate enzymodiagnostic procedures. Specifically, this review concerns the theoretical and practical nature of the Fishman-Lerner procedure for measuring acid phosphatase of prostatic origin with the inhibitor L-tartrate. The background information including group transfer is discussed. New experiments from this laboratory and a critique of the significance of the method in diagnosing cancer of the prostate are also presented.

The work of the authors reported herein has been supported by Grants No. C-1964 and No. CS-9082 of the U. S. Public Health Service, National Institutes of Health, Bethesda, Maryland. The help of L. Stolbach in developing the diazo method is acknowledged.

References

1. Abdul-Fadl, M. A. M., and King, E. J., *Biochem. J.*, *41*, xxxii (1947); *42*, xxviii (1948); *J. Clin. Pathol.*, *1*, 80 (1948).
2. Abdul-Fadl, M. A. M., and King, E. J., *Biochem. J.*, *45*, 51–60 (1949).
3. Anagnostopoulos, C., *Bull. Soc. Chim. Biol.*, *35*, 575 (1953).
4. Andersch M. A., and Szczypinski, A. J., *Am. J. Clin. Pathol.*, *17*, 571–574 (1947).

5. Axelrod, B., *J. Biol. Chem.*, *172*, 1 (1948).
6. Barrueto, R. B., Davison-Reynolds, M. M., Walker, B. S., and Lemon, H. M., *Am. J. Clin. Pathol.*, *24*, 1144 (1954).
7. Benotti, J., Rosenberg, L., and Dewey, B., *J. Lab. Clin. Med.*, *31*, 357 (1946).
8. Bessey, O. A., Lowry, O. H., and Brock, M. J., *J. Biol. Chem.*, *164*, 321 (1946).
9. Binkley, F., Shank, R. E., and Hoagland, C. L., *J. Biol. Chem.*, *196*, 253 (1954).
10. Bodansky, A., *J. Biol. Chem.*, *101*, 93–104 (1933).
11. Bodansky, A., and Jaffe, H. L., *Arch. Internal Med.*, *54*, 88 (1934); *Am. J. Diseases Children*, *48*, 1268 (1934).
12. Bodansky, M., and Bodansky, O., *Biochemistry of Disease*, 2nd ed., The Macmillan Company, New York, N. Y., 1952.
13. Boman, H. G., *Biochim. et Biophys. Acta*, *16*, 245 (1955).
14. Bonner, C. D., Homburger, F., and Fishman, W. H., *Surg., Gynecol. Obstet.*, *99*, 179 (1954).
15. Brayer, F. T., and Trunnell, J. B., *Texas Repts. on Biol. and Med.*, *10*, 946 (1952).
16. Cantarow, A., and Nelson, J., *Arch. Internal Med.*, *59*, 1045 (1937).
17. Cline, J. K., Burke, L. S., Cobb, W. R., Wilkinson, M. A., and Johnson, R. B., *J. Urol.*, *73*, 384 (1955).
18. Comfort, M. W., and Osterberg, A. E., *J. Lab. Clin. Med.*, *20*, 271 (1934).
19. Davies, D. R., *Biochem. J.*, *28*, 529 (1934).
20. Davison, M. M., Asimov, I., and Lemon, H. M., *Am. J. Clin. Pathol.*, *23*, 833 (1953).
21. Day, E., Ying, S. H., Schwartz, M. K., Whitmore, W. F., Jr., and Bodansky, O., *Proc. Am. Assoc. Cancer Research*, *2*, 12 (1955).
22. Demuth, F., *Biochem. Z.*, *159*, 415 (1925).
23. Derow, M. A., and Davison, M. M., *Science*, *118*, 247 (1953).
24. Elman, R., *Arch. Irternal Med.*, *48*, 828 (1931); *J. Am. Med. Assoc.*, *118*, 1265 (1942).
25. Emerson, E., *J. Org. Chem.*, *3*, 153 (1938).
26. Fishman, W. H., Bonner, C. D., and Homburger, F., *New Eng. J. Med.*, *255*, 925 (1956).
27. Fishman, W. H., Dart, R. M., Bonner, C. D., Leadbetter, W. F., Lerner, F., and Homburger, F., *J. Clin. Invest*, *32*, 1034 (1953).
28. Fishman, W. H., and Davidson, H. M., unpublished experiments.
29. Fishman, W. H., and Lerner, F., *J. Biol. Chem.*, *200*, 89 (1953).
30. Fiske, C. H., and Subbarow, Y., *J. Biol. Chem.*, *66*, 375 (1925).
31. Folin, O., and Ciocalteu, V., *J. Biol. Chem.*, *73*, 627 (1927).
32. Gomori, G., *J. Lab. Clin. Med.*, *34*, 275 (1949).
33. Gottlieb, S., and Marsh, P. B., *Ind. Eng. Chem.*, *18*, 16 (1946).
34. Grifols, J. A., *Brit. Med. J.*, *2*, 295 (1951).

35. Gutman, A. B., and Gutman, E. B., *Proc. Soc. Exptl. Biol. Med.*, *88*, 470 (1938); *J. Clin. Invest.*, *17*, 473 (1938).
36. Gutman, A. B., Gutman, E. B., and Robinson, J. N., *Am. J. Cancer*, *88*, 103 (1940).
37. Gutman, A. B., Olson, K. B., Gutman, E. B., and Flood, C. A., *J. Clin. Invest.*, *19*, 129 (1940).
38. Gutman, E. B., and Gutman, A. B., *J. Biol. Chem.*, *136*, 201 (1940).
39. Gutman, E. B., Sproul, E. E., and Gutman, A. B., *Am. J. Cancer*, *28*, 485 (1936).
40. Helferich, B., and Stetter, H., *Ann. Chem.*, *558*, 234 (1947).
41. Herbert, F. K., *Biochem. J.*, *88*, xxiii (1944); *39*, iv (1945); *Quart. J. Med.*, *15*, 221 (1946).
42. Hill, J. H., *Am. J. Clin. Pathol.*, *26*, 120 (1956).
43. Hudson, P. B., Brendler, H., and Scott, W. W., *J. Urol.*, *58*, 89 (1947).
44. Huggins, C., and Hodges, C. V., *Cancer Research*, *1*, 293 (1941).
45. Huggins, C., and Talalay, P., *J. Biol. Chem.*, *159*, 399 (1945).
46. Kaplan, A., and Narahara, A., *J. Lab. Clin. Med.*, *41*, 825 (1953).
47. Karmen, A., Wróblewski, F., and LaDue, J. S., *J. Clin. Invest.*, *34*, 131 (1955).
48. Kay, H. D., *J. Biol. Chem.*, *89*, 249 (1930).
49. Kind, P. R. N., and King, E. J., *J. Clin. Pathol.*, *7*, 322 (1954).
50. King, E. J., and Armstrong, A. R., *J. Can. Med. Assoc.*, *31*, 376 (1936).
51. Koppeschaar, W., in F. P. Treadwell and W. T. Hall, eds., *Analytical Chemistry*, 9th ed., Wiley, New York, 1948.
52. Kutscher, W., and Pany, J., *Hoppe-Seyler's Z. physiol. Chem.*, *255*, 169 (1938).
53. Kutscher, W., and Wolbergs, H., *Hoppe-Seyler's Z. physiol. Chem.*, *236*, 237 (1935).
54. Kutscher, W., and Worner, A., *Hoppe-Seyler's Z. physiol. Chem.*, *239*, 109 (1936).
55. Linhardt, K., and Walter, K., *Röntgen und Laboratoriumspraxis*, *7*, 113 (1954).
56. London, M., and Hudson, P. B., *Arch. Biochem. and Biophys.*, *46*, 141 (1953).
57. London, M., McHugh, R., and Hudson, P. B., *Cancer Research 14*, 718 (1954).
58. London, M., Sommer, A., and Hudson, P. B., *J. Biol. Chem.*, *216*, 81 (1955).
59. Lundquist, F., *Acta physiol. Scand.*, *13*, 322 (1946); *14*, 263 (1947); *Nature*, *158*, 710 (1946).
60. Lundquist, F., Thorsteinsson, T., and Buus, O., *Biochem. J.*, *59*, 69 (1955).
61. Mathes, G., Richmond, S. G., and Sprunt, D. H., *J. Urol.*, *75*, 143 (1956).
62. Møller, K. M., *Biochim. et Biophys. Acta, 16*, 162 (1955).

63. Neumann, H., *Experentia*, *4*, 74 (1948).
64. Ozar, M. B., Isaac, C. A., and Valk, W. L., *J. Urol.*, *72*, 90 (1955).
65. Peacock, A., private communication.
66. Powell, M. E. A., and Smith, M. J. H., *J. Clin. Pathol.*, *7*, 245 (1954).
67. Rosenmund, H., *Helvetica Med. Acta*, Ser. A, Suppl. xxxiii, 20 (1955).
68. Rothman, M. M., Meranze, D. R., and Meranze, T., *Am. J. Med. Sci.*, *192*, 526 (1936).
69. Seligman, A. M., Chauncey, H. H., Nachlas, M. M., Manheimer, L. H., and Ravin, H. A., *J. Biol. Chem.*, *190*, 7 (1951).
70. Seligman, A. M., and Nachlas, M. M., *J. Clin. Invest.*, *29*, 31 (1950).
71. Sols, A., and Monche, J., *Bull. Soc. Chim. Biol.*, *31*, 161 (1949).
72. Storer, R. V., *Supplement to Evaluation of Phosphatase and Exfoliative Cytology in the Early Diagnosis of Prostate Cancer*, Australia Science Publishing Company, Melbourne, 1953.
73. Walker, B. S., Lemon, H. M., Davison, M. M., and Schwartz, M. K., *J. Clin. Pathol.*, *24*, 807 (1954).
74. Whitmore, W. F., Jr., Bodansky, O., Schwartz, M. K., Ying S. H., and Day, E., *Proc. Am. Assoc. Cancer Research*, *2*, 53 (1955).
75. Woodard, H. Q., *J. Urol.*, *65*, 688 (1951).

DETERMINATION OF AMINO ACIDS
by Use of Bacterial Amino Acid Decarboxylases

ERNEST F. GALE, *University of Cambridge*

I. GENERAL PRINCIPLES

1. Reaction

An amino acid decarboxylase is an enzyme which attacks a specific amino acid, $R \cdot CHNH_2 \cdot COOH$ according to the equation:

$$R \cdot CHNH_2 \cdot COOH \longrightarrow R \cdot CH_2NH_2 + CO_2$$

2. Estimation of Carbon Dioxide

1. In those cases where a specific enzyme can be prepared free from other CO_2-liberating enzymes and where the forward reaction

proceeds to completion, or to a constant proportion of theoretical yield, estimation of the CO_2 liberated can be used for measurement of the amino acid present. The method can be used in conjunction with any suitable gasometric technique. Estimations are commonly carried out in conventional Warburg manometers but have also been performed in the Van Slyke apparatus, Cartesian divers, and Conway units.

2. The essential components of the reaction mixture other than the amino acid preparation to be tested consist of a suitable buffer solution and a suspension or solution of the decarboxylase preparation in buffer solution. Many of the bacterial decarboxylases exhibit sharp pH optima (9) and if the reaction pH deviates as much as 1 pH unit from the optimum, the rate of decarboxylation may be 20%, or less, of that at the optimum. Consequently it is desirable to use strong buffer solutions and adjust all components of the reaction mixture to the optimum pH before setting up estimations. The pH optima for the various decarboxylases vary between pH 4.0 and 7.0.

3. Evolution of CO_2 from an aqueous solution is quantitative only if the pH is below ca. 5.8 and estimation of retained CO_2 is necessary if the pH at the end of the reaction is above that value. When the Warburg manometer is used, retained CO_2 can be released at the end of the reaction by adding acid (0.2 ml. 8 N H_2SO_4) from a second side bulb (26). The majority of the amino acid decarboxylase preparations are unaffected by the presence of oxygen in the reaction vessel and estimations may be carried out in air; in certain cases the reaction mixture may contain autoxidizable components and estimations must then be carried out in nitrogen. Control estimations should be carried out in the absence of the amino acid to be estimated, particularly in those cases where residual CO_2 is estimated at the end of the reaction by the addition of acid. The decarboxylase preparations themselves normally give rise to negligible CO_2 output.

It has not so far been possible to demonstrate any reversal of decarboxylase action under the conditions used for amino acid assay, although claims have been made that reversal of histidine decarboxylase can be demonstrated by the use of isotopes. Consequently, CO_2 evolution should correspond to the theoretical value and, in practice (when CO_2 retention is negligible), is found to represent 97–98% of theory.

4. The decarboxylase method can be used to estimate the [14]C

content of the 1-COOH of the corresponding ^{14}C-labeled amino acid
by trapping and estimating the radioactivity of the CO_2 liberated.
In the author's laboratory it has been found convenient to carry out
the decarboxylation in a Conway unit (3). A planchette containing
0.1–0.2 ml. of standard baryta (approximately 0.2 N) is placed in the
central compartment of the unit; in order to facilitate even spreading
of the radioactive material on the planchette, this can be charged
with a disk of lens tissue together with one drop each of 1% cetyltrimethylammonium bromide and 1% polyvinyl alcohol solutions.
Suitable amounts of buffer and decarboxylase preparation are placed
in the outer chamber and the lid greased and placed in position.
The sample to be estimated is delivered into the outer chamber without mixing with the other reagents. The unit is sealed, rotated to
mix the reagents in the outer chamber, and incubated at 37°C. for
60 minutes. The planchette is then removed, dried, and counted as
usual. The addition of thymolphthalein to the baryta will indicate
whether its capacity is exceeded during the incubation (22).

3. Specificity of Method

1. **Specificity of Enzyme.** Each amino acid decarboxylase will
attack only the L-isomer of its amino acid substrate. If the structure
of the substrate is represented as R·CHNH$_2$·COOH, decarboxylation
will occur only if both —NH$_2$ and —COOH groups are unsubstituted,
and the enzyme displays specificity toward the nature of R. For
some of the enzymes R is a unique structure and the estimation is
then strictly specific for one amino acid; for other decarboxylases
minor modifications such as the addition of hydroxyl groups to R
may alter the rate of reaction but not prevent decarboxylation. For
example, histidine decarboxylase is not known to attack any naturally
occurring substance other than histidine, whereas tyrosine decarboxylase attacks tyrosine, phenylalanine and 3,4-dihydroxyphenylalanine.
If the list of amino acids which form substrates for decarboxylases
(Table I) is inspected, it can be seen that many of them possess a
polar group in the ω-position of the R structure; in such cases this
polar group must also be unsubstituted if decarboxylation is to occur.
During early investigations of these enzymes (9) it was thought that
only amino acids possessing three polar groups could form substrates
for decarboxylases but the later discovery by King (13) of enzymes
attacking leucine and valine has disproved this hypothesis.

Glutamic acid decarboxylase provides an example of an enzyme whose specificity has been subjected to considerable investigation (8,9,14,15,20). The enzyme does not attack D-glutamic acid, diethyl-L-glutamic ester, N-methyl-L-glutamic acid, N-acetyl-L-glutamic acid, α-L-glutamylglycine, γ-L-glutamylglycine, glycyl-L-glutamic acid, α-L-glutamyl-L-glutamic acid (or any glutamic acid or glutamyl peptide tested), glutathione, α-ketoglutaric acid, L-aspartic acid, L-asparagine, L-isoasparagine, L-isoglutamine, carbamyl-L-glutamic acid, pyrrolidone-carboxylic acid, γ-ethylamide-glutamic acid, pyruvic acid, glucosamine, creatine, creatinine, succinamide, any other naturally occurring amino acid, purine, or purine derivative. The preparation of glutamic acid decarboxylase consisting of a suspension of Cl. welchii SR 12 decarboxylates γ-ethyl-L-glutamic acid and γ-methylamide-L-glutamic acid at 2.5 and 6.1%, respectively, of the rate of glutamic acid decarboxylation (20); attacks L-glutamine with the liberation of both ammonia and carbon dioxide (14) and, in the presence of pyruvic or other keto acids, decarboxylates L-aspartic acid to α-alanine (20); it is highly probable that these activities are due to other enzymes in the preparation acting in conjunction with glutamic acid decarboxylase rather than to the action of the decarboxylase itself.

2. Specificity of the Enzyme Preparation. From the point of view of specificity, ideally the best preparation is the pure enzyme. However, the isolation and purification of an enzyme is usually too laborious to form the basis of a method of assay, and it usually suffices to obtain a crude preparation of the enzyme in which the decarboxylase is the only enzyme yielding CO_2 from the reaction mixtures to be assayed. The preparations described below constitute such materials and when incubated, under the conditions described, with the solutions and extracts normally encountered in biological and biochemical work, will liberate CO_2 from the specific amino acid substrates only. Thus they will not normally give rise to significant gas evolution in the presence of glucose or other fermentable carbohydrates, keto acids, phosphate esters, etc., but, if such substances are present in the solutions to be assayed, it is advisable to set up appropriate controls.

The usual sources of highly active amino acid decarboxylase preparations are bacteria and, although it is occasionally possible to find a specific organism possessing only one of these enzymes, untreated organisms frequently contain more than one (9). Consequently, except in the cases specified below, untreated suspensions of organisms will decarboxylate more than one amino acid. Nevertheless such preparations, which may be highly active, can be used for the assay of an amino acid in simple solution. For example, if it is desired to assay solutions containing ornithine as the only amino acid it may be more convenient to prepare a suspension of a suitable strain of *Esch. coli* than to grow the more difficult *Cl. septicum* although the preparation may not be so specific. Most coliform organisms possess decarboxylases (9) and it requires little work to obtain a strain active toward any of the amino acids listed in Table I (other than tyrosine which is decarboxylated only by rare strains); the organisms listed in this article and in Table I are those which can be used for the preparation of specific decarboxylases.

The specificity of a given enzyme preparation will depend upon (a) the strain of organism used, (b) the conditions under which it is grown, (c) the conditions under which it is tested, and (d) the treatment of the organism subsequent to harvesting from the culture medium. Since it is desirable in routine assay procedures to have as little preparative detail as possible, attempts have been made to utilize (a), (b), and (c) to obtain suspensions of organisms which will act as specific decarboxylases without further treatment. Where this has not proved possible, some simple treatment such as acetone powdering has been tested since enzymes vary in their resistance to this treatment and frequently an organism which is non-specific in suspensions of intact cells will yield an acetone powder containing only one active decarboxylase.

Since strains of organisms vary widely in their enzymic composition and in the activity of the enzymes they produce, it is desirable to use, in the first place at any rate, strains whose activity and specificity have already been established. Suitable organisms, listed in Table I, have been deposited in the National Collection of Type Cultures, Chemical Research Laboratory, Teddington, Middlesex, England, and can be obtained from the Curator.

The enzymic activity of a bacterial cell varies with the conditions under which it is grown and many of the decarboxylases (marked * in Table I) are formed best when growth occurs in an acid medium (9). A good yield of cells with high activity is obtained by growing the organism in a rich medium containing sufficient glucose to last until growth has been completed and harvested; many initial failures to produce active decarboxylase preparations are due to insufficient glucose in the medium, resulting in cells being harvested from media

TABLE I

Preparation and Properties of Specific Amino Acid Decarboxylase Preparations

Amino acid	Organism (NCTC No.)	Growth conditions				Preparation	Storage life
		Medium	Temp., °C.	Time, hr.	Final pH		
*Lysine	Bact. cadaveris (6578)	Casein digest Glucose	25	30	5.0–5.3	Acetone powder 10 mg./test	1–3 months in desiccator
*Arginine	Esch. coli (7020)	Casein digest Glucose	25	30	5.0–5.3	Acetone powder 10 mg./test	1–3 months in desiccator
*Histidine	Cl. welchii var. BW21 (6785)	Casein digest Glucose Yeast extract Minced muscle	37	16	4.0–4.3	Acetone powder 30 mg./test; or extract	2–3 months in desiccator
*Ornithine	Cl. septicum Pasteur (547)	Casein digest Glucose Yeast extract Minced muscle	37	16	5.3–5.5	Cell suspension 20–30 mg./test	2–3 days in ice chest
*Tyrosine	S. faecalis (6782)	Casein digest Glucose Yeast extract	37	16	4.8–5.0	Acetone powder 10 mg./test	2–6 weeks in desiccator
*Glutamic acid	Cl. welchii var SR12 (6784)	Casein digest Glucose Yeast extract Minced muscle	37	16	4.0–4.5	Cell suspension 20 mg./test	1 month in ice chest
	Esch. coli ATC No. 4157	Casein digest Glucose Yeast extract	30	20	5.0–5.3	Acetone powder 30 mg./test	1–3 months in desiccator
*Aspartic acid	Cl. welchii var. SR12	As for glutamic acid decarboxylase					
Diaminopimelic acid	Esch. coli ATCC No. 9637	Salt solution Glucose (0.2%)	37	18		Acetone powder 40 mg./test	

Assay conditions

	Buffer system	CO_2 evolution as % theory	Calculation: 100 μl. CO_2 arise from mg. amino acid	mg. amino acid-N
Lysine	0.2 M phosphate pH 6.0 + acid-tip	(92)	0.652	0.125
Arginine	0.2 M phosphate-citrate at pH 5.2	98 95	0.775	0.249
Histidine	0.2 M acetate pH 4.5	96	0.692	0.188
Ornithine	0.2 M phosphate-citrate at pH 5.5 + acid-tip	98	0.590	0.125
Tyrosine	0.2 M phosphate-citrate at pH 5.5	96	0.81	0.063
Glutamic acid	0.2 M acetate pH 4.5	98	0.656	0.063
Aspartic acid	0.2 M acetate pH 4.9 + pyruvate	96	0.596	0.063
Diaminopimelic acid	0.1 M phosphate pH 7.2 + acid-tip	94	0.85	0.125

in which the pH has not fallen below 5. Suitable media for production of active enzyme preparations are given below and in Table I,
but it must be remembered that any alteration designed to increase
the yield (e.g., increasing the nitrogen content or the buffering capacity) will probably necessitate increasing the glucose content of the
medium. Cells harvested from such acid media contain high decarboxylase activities while many other activities are depressed by the
acidity. In those cases where the decarboxylases are optimally
active at acid pH values, suspensions of the organisms in buffer at the
optimum pH can be used as specific decarboxylases without further
treatment.

II. PREPARATIONS

Organisms. Organisms suitable for the preparation of various
specific decarboxylases are listed in Table I.

The following notes are included for workers not familiar with the
use of bacteria in biochemical preparations: All cultures must be
grown and maintained in sterilized media and handled with aseptic
precautions; no precautions against contamination need be taken
once the organisms are harvested. Where the harvested organisms
are suspended in buffers of pH 4.5 or less, or are treated with acetone,
the preparations are rendered non-viable. Thick suspensions of
viable organisms, especially of the potentially pathogenic clostridia,
constitute a possible danger and care should be taken concerning sterilization and disposal of equipment and waste suspensions. No
hazard arises from the use of these organisms as long as normal care
is exercised in the way of personal cleanliness, use of plugged pipettes,
and immersion of used apparatus in antiseptic or cleaning fluid after
contamination.

The listed organisms fall into three groups: coliforms, clostridia,
and faecal streptococci. Coliform organisms are nutritionally non-
exacting and grow copiously on simple media; both clostridia and
streptococci are nutritionally fastidious and require media containing
most of the natural amino acids and numerous growth factors, the
latter usually being supplied by addition of a yeast extract to the
medium. Organisms are usually supplied either as dried cultures or,
in the case of clostridia, as spore cultures in broth containing pieces of

meat.   The organisms should first be inoculated into a fully nutrient medium and incubated until growth is visible.   If daily cultures are required, these can be maintained by subculture into fresh liquid medium each day.   It is advisable, however, to set up a "cellar" or reference culture which can be used should the liquid transfers become contaminated.   The coliform and streptococcal organisms can be maintained on slants of nutrient agar and will normally remain viable for about one month on such slants.   Clostridia should be maintained in tubes of broth containing pieces of minced heart muscle.   When bulk cultures are to be grown it is advisable to start growth in liquid culture 1–2 days before and to inoculate the bulk medium with 0.5–1% by volume of a liquid culture in a state of active growth.

Culture Conditions. The optimum conditions for growth of organisms required for decarboxylase preparations will vary in different laboratories owing to differences in media components, media used for maintenance of sub-cultures, bacteriological procedures, etc., and the following instructions constitute a general guide, the details of which may have to be modified in the light of experience.

Culture Media. The enzymes marked * in Table I develop best in acid media; this is most conveniently achieved by addition of glucose to the medium as explained above.   The components of the various media are as follows:

A1. Tryptic Digest of Casein. Various commercial preparations made by enzymic digestion of casein are available and are usually used at a final concentration of 1–2% by weight.   If digests are to be used indefinitely and in large quantities, it is more economical to prepare them in the laboratory from "physiological casein."   In the author's laboratory, a tryptic digest is made as follows: 1 kg. "physiological casein" is suspended in 10 liters water and solid Na-HCO_3 added until the pH is approximately 7.8.   A suspension of defatted minced pancreas is then added and the whole incubated at 37° in the presence of chloroform and toluene for 16–20 days, the pH being maintained at 7.8 by the addition of alkali at intervals.   At the end of this period, the digest is left at room temperature for 2 days and then filtered.   The filtrate is adjusted to pH 5.5 with conc. HCl, steamed for 1 hour, left to cool and again filtered.   This inactivates the proteases and precipitates the greater part of the free tyrosine.   The filtrate is neutralized to approx. 7.5 and diluted for use with 2 volumes of water.   Such incomplete digests support growth more effectively than acid hydrolyzates of casein; the preparation described above contains growth factors, etc., from the pancreatic material in addition to the casein breakdown products.

A2. Acid Hydrolyzate of Casein. The following method is that advised by McIlwain and Hughes (18): 170 ml. conc. HCl is mixed with 80 ml. 15% titanous chloride and added to 200 g. casein, mixed rapidly and then autoclaved at 120° for 45′ minutes. The solution is cooled and adjusted to pH 6–6.5 by addition of *ca.* 240 ml. 40% NaOH; a bulky precipitate forms. Small samples are taken and tested by the addition of acid and alkali for further precipitate formation. When optimal conditions for precipitation are obtained, the bulk is boiled for 10 min., cooled and left at room temperature for 3 hr. before filtering through paper pulp on a Buchner funnel. The hydrolyzate is further treated before use as a basal medium as follows: 45 g. KH_2PO_4 is added to the bulk filtrate, followed by 1 g. oxalic acid and the pH adjusted to 7.6. Water is added to 1 liter, the whole boiled for 5 min., cooled and then filtered after standing for 2–3 hr.

Acid hydrolysis destroys tryptophan and cysteine and if casein hydrolyzates are used for growth of organisms without fortification with other sources of amino acids, it is necessary to add these amino acids to the media.

B. Yeast Extract. Extracts of yeast are added as a general source of growth factors to media for the growth of streptococci and clostridia. Various commercial preparations are available and can be used at a final concentration of approx. 0.1%. Commercial "marmite," used by some authors, is an autolyzate of brewer's yeast preserved by addition of salt; it has a variable composition. For growth of clostridia, Krebs (15) recommends a high concentration of an extract prepared by autoclaving baker's yeast with an equal volume of water and filtering off the sediment.

C. Glucose. This is normally made up in concentrated solution (20–30%) and sterilized separately in acid solution (1 drop syrupy $H_3PO_4/100$ ml.).

D. Salt Solution. Media containing casein digest or hydrolyzate are usually adequately buffered while the presence of trace elements is ensured by the use of tap water for dilution or presence of yeast extracts. Umbreit and Gunsalus (27) recommend the addition of 0.25% KH_2PO_4 to the medium for glutamic decarboxylase formation in *E. coli.*

Specific preparations of diaminopimelic acid are best obtained from coliform organisms grown in a salt medium; Dewey *et al.* (4)

recommend the following: K_2HPO_4, 7 g.; KH_2PO_4, 3 g.; trisodium citrate, 0.5 g.; $(NH_4)_2SO_4$, 1.0 g.; $MgSO_4$, $7H_2O$, 0.01 g.; $FeSO_4$, $7H_2O$, trace; glucose, 2.0 g.; water to 1 l., final pH 7.4.

E. *Peptone Infusion.* 500 g. minced heart muscle (ox or horse) is added to 500 ml. boiling water containing 10 g. commercial peptone and 5 g. NaCl; this is maintained at 100° for 20 min. and then strained through muslin before filtering. The filtrate is neutralized to bromthymol blue, heated to 90° to precipitate calcium phosphates, filtered hot and the pH finally adjusted to 7.6.

F. *Minced Meat.* The minced heart preparation remaining in the muslin during the preparation of the peptone infusion is used. Its presence markedly improves the growth of clostridia. The amount of meat added to the medium by various authors differs widely; in the present author's laboratory about 10 g. wet weight minced meat is added to each liter flask of medium so that the bottom of the flask is just covered with pieces of meat, but Krebs (15) recommends addition of 80 g. minced meat per liter of medium.

Suitable media for the various organisms listed in Table I are made up as follows:

Coliform organisms	Al, C, D	(glucose 2–3%)
Streptococcus faecalis	Al, B, C, D	(glucose 1%)
Clostridia	Al, B, C, D, E, F	(glucose 3%)

The medium recommended for growth of clostridia by Krebs (15) is as follows: 80 ml. casein hydrolyzate (A2); 100 ml. peptone infusion broth (E); 150 ml. yeast extract (B); 80 g. minced meat (F); water 560 ml.; 50 ml. 20% glucose (C).

The optimum concentrations of the various components may vary with different commercial or laboratory sources and should be found by experience; it is important to adjust the glucose content in all cases so that the pH at harvesting is of the order shown in Table I.

In all cases (other than diaminopimelic acid decarboxylase preparations) growth takes place anaerobically and the media can be dispensed in flasks leaving little or no air space above the medium. Clostridia will grow well under such conditions if flasks are inoculated with actively growing cultures; media should not be left for more than a few hours after sterilization, otherwise they absorb oxygen from the air and this may hinder the onset of rapid growth.

Time of Incubation. The development of decarboxylases in coliform organisms frequently takes place more efficiently at low temperatures than at high; consequently 25° is normally used for these organisms. The activity of the enzymes decreases once active growth has ceased and it is desirable to harvest organisms just at the time that growth is ceasing. This is not very critical with coliform and streptococcal cultures but may be very important with clostridia; the glutamic acid decarboxylase activity of *Cl. welchii* may disappear completely if the culture is left for as long as 2 hr. after growth has ceased. Optimal periods of incubation differ with the particular medium employed and must be found by experience. In the author's laboratory, glutamic acid decarboxylase preparations are made from *Cl. welchii* grown in a medium containing casein digest, meat and 2% glucose; 10 hr. growth at 37° or 16 hr. at 30° give highly active preparations whereas 16 hr. at 37° frequently gives inactive suspensions; however, if the richer medium described by Krebs (14,15, as above) is used, 16 hr. at 37° provides optimal conditions. As a rough guide for use with the clostridia it can be said that, if the medium is thick with organisms and bubbles of gas are still rising in the medium, active suspensions will be obtained; if organisms are sedimenting out at the bottom of the flask and no gas is forming in the medium, then incubation has probably continued too long.

Washed Suspensions. Cultures are centrifuged at *ca.* 4000 *g* for 10 minutes and the supernatant liquid discarded. The pellet of cells is taken up in distilled water or 1% saline in volume approximately equal to $1/10$ that of the medium harvested, and centrifuged down again. The washed pellet is suspended in the appropriate buffer solution at a suspension density of the order indicated in Table I. Storage properties of washed suspensions vary; all preparations will normally retain their decarboxylase activities for 3–5 days if kept in the ice chest. Krebs (14) states that the glutamic decarboxylase activity of *Cl. welchii* suspensions, after growth in the enriched medium, remains unimpaired for a month in the ice chest; similar preparations have remained active in the author's laboratory for 6–8 months. Meister (20) states that such preparations can be stored at 5° for 6–8 months if lyophilized and then resuspended in 0.2 *M* acetate buffer, pH 4.9, immediately prior to use. It is of interest that suspensions harvested from comparatively simple media (A, C, F only) have a much shorter storage life.

Acetone Powders. The washed organisms are suspended in water to make a thick cream and then pipetted as rapidly as possible into 5 volumes of cold acetone. The mixture is stirred until coagulation occurs and left to sediment; when the bulk of the organisms has sedimented, the supernatant is siphoned off and the remainder of the suspension collected on a Buchner funnel. Gentle suction is applied until the bulk of the liquid is removed but suction is not continued until the cake cracks, otherwise subsequent washing with acetone is rendered ineffective. The cake is washed on the filter twice with acetone and once with ether. After the ether washing, the cake is sucked dry, broken up and spread out on a plate to dry in air. The dry material is powdered, finally dried over sulfuric acid *in vacuo* and stored in a desiccator in the cold. For use, the powder is re-suspended in the appropriate buffer solution at a dry weight density as indicated in Table I. The storage life of acetone powders varies from a few days to several years; the cause of variation in storage life is not known but is certainly related to the efficiency of desiccation during preparation.

Extraction of Enzyme from Acetone Powder. This is necessary in the case of histidine decarboxylase only and is dealt with below in the notes on that enzyme.

III. ESTIMATION OF AN AMINO ACID IN THE WARBURG MANOMETER

The general procedure for estimation of an amino acid in solution by the appropriate decarboxylase preparation is as follows: 0.5 ml. of decarboxylase preparation in the appropriate buffer is placed in one side-bulb of a Warburg manometer; in the main compartment is placed 1.5 ml. of the correct buffer solution and 1.0 ml. of the solution to be assayed, adjusted approximately to the pH of the buffer solution. If the reaction pH is greater than 5.8 (or if the final pH is likely to rise above this value) 0.2 ml. 8 N H_2SO_4 is placed in the second side-bulb. A control manometer is assembled with all components other than the amino acid solution, this being replaced by an equivalent amount of water. The manometers are equilibrated in a water bath maintained at 37°. After equilibration, the enzyme preparation is tipped into the main compartment and readings are taken until gas evolution ceases or falls in rate to that shown in the control manometer. The acid in the second side-bulb is then tipped into the main compartment in experimental and control manometers and final readings taken when gas evolution has ceased. The amino acid content is then calculated from the CO_2 evolution in the assay manometer, corrected for any evolution in the control manometer and for the % theoretical output shown in Table I. It is advisable to perform each assay in duplicate or triplicate. The amount of amino acid substrate that can be accurately estimated by the usual Warburg technique is 5–20 μmole L-amino acid.

IV. NOTES ON THE ESTIMATION OF SPECIFIC AMINO ACIDS

The estimation of histidine will be described in detail as an example of the application of the method; notes will then be given concerning particular features, precautions or complications involved in the estimation of other amino acids by decarboxylase preparations.

1. Histidine

Organism. *Cl. welchii* B W 21 (N.C.T.C. No. 6785).

Growth medium. 3% casein digest, yeast extract, 3% glucose, meat.

Growth conditions. 16–20 hr. growth at 37°; in large bulk cultures it is advisable to ensure anaerobiosis at the beginning of incubation by addition of 1 drop thiolactic acid/liter of medium (6).

Preparation. Suspensions of cells harvested under these conditions possess an active histidine decarboxylase and also some glutamic acid decarboxylase activity. If an acetone powder of the suspension is prepared, the glutamic acid decarboxylase activity disappears in most cases; if any residual activity remains, the histidine decarboxylase can be extracted as below and the preparation is then specific. The instructions given by Epps (6) for acetone treatment and extraction of the enzymes are as follows: the thick suspension of organisms is stirred into 3 volumes of acetone at room temperature; after 30 minutes the precipitate is filtered off and washed on the filter with acetone, a mixture of equal volumes acetone and ether, and finally with ether. The powder is dried, suspended at 40 mg. dry weight/ml. in 0.05 M borate buffer pH 8.5 and incubated overnight at 37°. The suspension is then centrifuged at 4000 g for 30 minutes and the clear yellow supernatant solution taken as decarboxylase preparation.

Assay conditions. Optimum pH 4.5; suitable buffer solution, 0.2 *M* acetate pH 4.5; atmosphere, air; CO_2 evolution = 96% theory.

Notes. A preparation which is approximately 10 times as active as the *Cl. welchii* preparation has been described by Rodwell (23) using a *Lactobacillus* sp. as enzyme source. The intact cells possess decarboxylating activity toward lysine and ornithine in addition to histidine, and no information is given concerning the specificity of acetone powder preparations or extracts therefrom.

2. Arginine

Arginine decarboxylase is best prepared and stored as acetone powder of *Escherichia coli* N.C.T.C. No. 7020. The strain is important as No. 7020 is the only organism so far described which is specific for the decarboxylation of arginine alone. Washed suspensions of freshly harvested cells can be used for assay purposes although the pH optimum is critical and somewhat variable with culture conditions; more consistent results are obtained with acetone powder preparations.

3. Aspartic Acid

Two types of decarboxylase for aspartic acid have been described: (*1*) enzymes removing the 1-COOH to yield β-alanine (α-decarboxylation), (*2*) enzymes removing the 4-COOH to yield α-alanine (γ-decarboxylation). α-Decarboxylation was first described by Virtanen and Laine (29) as a property of *Rhizobium leguminosarum* and suspensions of the organism were used for aspartic acid assay. The reaction appears to have been a slow one, and Virtanen used a method involving trapping and estimation of CO_2 evolved over several days incubation. No application in Warburg manometers has been recorded. Mardashev and co-workers (19), in papers seen in abstract only, report an active aspartic acid decarboxylase in acetone powder preparations of a "pseudomycobacterium," but the availability of the organism is not known. The formation of β-alanine from aspartic acid has been reported for a number of bacteria, but the reaction has been on a mμmole scale and not suitable for aspartic acid assay.

γ-Decarboxylation of aspartic acid was reported by Meister, Sober, and Tice (20) to occur in the presence of washed suspensions of *Cl. welchii* SR12 used, as below, for estimation of glutamic acid. The reaction was enhanced by the presence of small amounts of keto acids such as pyruvic or α-ketoglutaric acids, and could be prevented by the presence of keto fixatives such as semicarbazide. The preparations used by Gale (8) and Krebs (14,15) for glutamic acid decarboxylase have no action on aspartic acid unless keto acids are added; if keto acids are present, decarboxylation as described by Meister et al. occurs and can be used to estimate aspartic acid in the usual way. Glutamic acid decarboxylase is prepared as described below, suspended in 0.2 M acetate buffer pH 4.8 and placed in the side-bulb of the manometer. The aspartic acid solution is placed in the main compartment together with 0.1 ml. sodium pyruvate (50 μmole) and acetate buffer of such strength that the final concentration is 0.5 M. The usual procedure is then followed.

4. Glutamic Acid

The glutamic acid decarboxylase preparation used by Gale (8), Krebs (14), and Meister et al. (20) consists of a thick suspension of cells of Cl. welchii SR 12; the strain is important as most Cl. welchii strains possess histidine decarboxylase in addition to glutamic acid decarboxylase (7). Strains of Esch. coli, such as American Type Collection No. 4157, have been isolated which, after acetone treatment, yield preparations specific for glutamic acid decarboxylation. A commercial preparation of such an acetone powder has been listed under the United States Patent Office No. 2,687,369. Acetone treatment of the Cl. welchii suspension results in loss of most of the activity. As mentioned above, the Cl. welchii suspension attacks aspartic acid in the presence of small amounts of keto acids and, although such reactions can be eliminated by suitable washing of the cells, it is simpler to prevent their occurrence by adding an inhibitor or keto fixative to the reaction mixture. Cetyltrimethylammonium bromide or the commercial preparation thereof (cetavlon, CTAB) in final concentration 0.25% prevents aspartic acid decarboxylation while enhancing the activity of the suspension toward glutamic acid or glutamine (14), and may be regarded as the inhibitor of choice for assay of glutamic acid in biological materials. The assay system is set up in manometers as usual and 0.5 ml. 2% (or other suitable concentration) cetavlon added to the contents of the main compartment.

5. Glutamic Acid and Aspartic Acid Present Together

Meister, Sober, and Tice (20) give the following procedure for estimating glutamic and aspartic acids in the presence of each other. Manometer cups with two side bulbs are employed, 0.5 ml. glutamic acid decarboxylase preparation being placed in one and 0.1 ml. solution containing 50 μmole sodium pyruvate at pH 4.9 in the other. The main compartment contains the material to be assayed, acetate buffer pH 4.9 and 0.5 ml. semicarbazide solution. This last is prepared by dissolving 0.401 g. semicarbazide hydrochloride in 100 ml. solution containing equal amounts of 0.4 M sodium acetate at pH 4.9 and 0.072 N NaOH. After equilibration, the decarboxylase preparation is added to the contents of the main compartment and the reaction allowed to proceed to completion; the CO_2 output corresponds to the glutamic acid present. When this first stage of the reaction is over, the pyruvate is added from the second side bulb; this reacts with the semicarbazide and provides excess keto acid to promote aspartic acid decarboxylation. The second gas evolution is followed to completion and the CO_2 output corresponds to the aspartic acid present. Alternatively two manometers may be set up for each assay, each containing 0.1 ml. sodium pyruvate (0.66 g. in 10 ml. 0.2 M acetate pH 4.9) and the other components of the reaction mixture except that semicarbazide (or cetavlon) is present in one manometer only; gas output is measured in both manometers, that in the presence of semicarbazide (or cetavlon) corresponds to glutamic acid, that in the absence of inhibitor corresponds to the sum of glutamic acid and aspartic acid.

6. Glutamine

Cl. welchii suspensions decarboxylate glutamine with the liberation of both CO_2 and ammonia; it appears that the organism possesses a glutaminase which first deamidates glutamine to glutamic acid which is then decarboxylated in the usual way. Glutamine can be estimated by the liberation of either CO_2 or ammonia in the presence of the *Cl. welchii* suspension set up as for glutamic acid assay (14). If both glutamic acid and glutamine are present together, the CO_2 output gives a measure of both substances while ammonia liberation gives a measure of the glutamine present.

7. β-Hydroxyglutamic Acid

The glutamic acid decarboxylase preparation liberates CO_2 from certain isomers of β-hydroxyglutamic acid (7); Umbreit and Heneage (28) have recently provided evidence that the enzyme responsible for decarboxylation of the hydroxy-acid is different from the decarboxylase attacking glutamic acid itself.

8. Lysine

Lysine decarboxylase is prepared as an acetone powder of *Bact. cadaveris* Gale. Breed has pointed out that this organism is incorrectly named and has reclassified it as *Paracolobactrum aerogenoides;* it should be pointed out that there is no evidence that organisms listed in the American Type Culture Collection under this name can be used for the estimation of lysine and, as far as the author is aware, no investigation of their decarboxylating activities has been made. In the present case it may be more satisfactory to ensure accuracy of estimation by using the incorrectly named organism.

Intact cells of this organism possess a feeble arginine decarboxylase but this activity is usually lost on acetone treatment; if a trace of activity survives, this disappears if the acetone powder is kept in the ice chest for 2–3 days before use. The acetone powder retains its lysine decarboxylase activity for many weeks. The preparation attacks hydroxy-lysine slowly and consequently lysine assays on gelatine preparations may be high.

9. Ornithine

Many strains of *Esch. coli* and similar organisms possess ornithine decarboxylase but strains of *Cl. septicum* are the only organisms recorded which are specific for ornithine decarboxylase without further treatment. The activity is somewhat unstable and preparations should be used within a few days of harvesting; the enzyme also dissociates readily and assays should be carried out in the presence of pyridoxal phosphate (final concentration 1–3 μg./ml.). The most satisfactory results are obtained in 0.2 M phosphate buffer pH 6.0 but, if glucose or other fermentable sugars are present in the assay sample, these will give rise to CO_2 evolution. Such fermentation reactions can be avoided by using well washed cells and carrying out the assay in citrate buffer at pH 5.5 instead of phosphate at pH 6.0.

10. Tyrosine/Phenylalanine

The tyrosine decarboxylase preparation attacks phenylalanine at 5–10% of the rate at which tyrosine is decarboxylated (17) and this introduces error into estimations of tyrosine in mixtures containing phenylalanine. The error can be approximately corrected if a control manometer is set up containing phenylalanine as substrate and the assay manometers are read until the rate of CO_2 evolution therein falls to that recorded in the phenylalanine control. The preparation also attacks L-3,4-dihydroxyphenylalanine (5).

11. Diaminopimelic Acid

The use of diaminopimelic acid decarboxylase for analysis of biological extracts is complicated by the fact that the enzyme is easily inhibited by salts, heavy metals, or other amino acids (4); consequently it is necessary to clean up solutions before assay either by electrodialysis or passage through columns of appropriate exchange resin. The diaminopimelic decarboxylase differs from those so far described in that it is formed in neutral growth media and is optimally active at neutral pH values. Most organisms which contain the enzyme also possess lysine decarboxylase and so will decarboxylate diaminopimelic acid to cadaverine with the liberation of two molecules CO_2 per molecule diaminopimelic acid. The formation of lysine decarboxylase can be suppressed by growth in a simple medium free from lysine and at a neutral pH. The salt solution recommended for this purpose is given above (p. 294); Dewey, Hoare, and Work (4) grow a suitable coliform organism in this medium for 18 hr. at 37° under full aeration, and prepare an acetone powder from the harvested cells.

Diaminopimelic acid decarboxylase attacks meso-diaminopimelic acid but since most preparations also contain a diaminopimelic racemase, CO_2 evolution takes place from both meso- and LL-forms (12) and both substances will be estimated if present in extracts from biological material.

12. Valine and Leucine

It has been reported by King (13) that strains of *Proteus* will decarboxylate valine and leucine to the corresponding amines. As far as the present author knows, no details have been published concerning the use of preparations of these enzymes for analytical purposes.

V. APPLICATIONS OF THE DECARBOXYLASE METHOD

Amino Acid Constitution of Proteins. The decarboxylase method can be applied with considerable accuracy to the estimation of amino acids in protein hydrolyzates (8). Hydrolysis of protein should be carried out in 5 N HCl and the bulk of the free acid removed after hydrolysis by evaporation *in vacuo;* care must be taken to neutralize the hydrolyzate approximately to the pH of the decarboxylase reaction before analysis. Since the decarboxylases are specific for the L-isomer of their substrates, racemization occurring during hydrolysis will introduce error into the subsequent assays. Hydrolysis in HCl under the conditions described by Chibnall, Rees, Williams, and Boyland (2) introduces little racemization of the amino acids listed in Table I. Considerable humin formation occurs with proteins containing carbohydrate material and this may result in a decrease in the assay of tyrosine; alkaline hydrolysis results in a high degree of racemization of this amino acid.

Peptide Breakdown. The decarboxylases will not attack amino acids forming part of peptide structures, and this fact has been utilized by Zamecnik and Stephenson (30) and by Rowlands, Gale, Folkes, and Marrian (24) to follow the rate of enzymic hydrolysis of peptides containing suitable residues. The decarboxylase preparation is added to a mixture containing a suitable peptide and the peptidase enzyme; the whole is maintained at a pH at which both peptidase and decarboxylase are active. If the amount of decarboxylase added is such that the rate of decarboxylation is not a limiting factor, then the rate of CO_2 output can be taken as a measure of the rate of liberation of the free amino acid substrate from peptide combination.

Preparation of D-Amino Acids from Racemic Mixtures. Since the decarboxylases attack the L-isomer only and are not inhibited by the presence of the D-isomer, the preparations can be used to destroy the L-isomer in a racemic mixture of amino acid substrates. The D-isomer can then be isolated from the reaction products. The method has been used for the preparation of D-lysine by Neuberger and Sanger (21) and for D-glutamic acid by Camien, McClure, and Dunn (1).

Estimation of Free Amino Acid Content of Cells. The decarboxylase preparations are unable to penetrate the walls of intact, living cells. Consequently, if suspensions of such cells are incubated with a decarboxylase preparation, any CO_2 evolution occurring as a result of the presence of the enzyme must arise from amino acid on the surface of the cells, in the intercellular water or diffusing out of the cells. If the walls of the cells are destroyed, ruptured, or damaged, any free amino acid remaining inside those cells will become accessible to the enzyme and an output of CO_2 over and above that obtained with intact cells will be obtained and provide a measure of the free amino acid within the intact cells. Cell wall damage may be accomplished by mechanical disintegration, treatment at 100° for 10-15 minutes, or treatment with 5% trichloracetic acid or detergent substances such as cetyltrimethylammonium bromide. Methods for the assay of free internal amino acids in bacteria and yeasts have been described by Gale (10) and Taylor (25), and the use of a decarboxylase in conjunction with suspensions of staphylococci or streptococci for studying the lytic action of detergent substances has been described by Gale and Taylor (11).

Transamination Reactions. Many transamination reactions involve glutamic acid as one of the components:

$$R \cdot CHNH_2 \cdot COOH + HOOC \cdot CH_2 \cdot CH_2 \cdot CO \cdot COOH =$$
$$R \cdot CO \cdot COOH + HOOC \cdot CH_2 \cdot CH_2 \cdot CHNH_2 \cdot COOH$$

Consequently, estimation of glutamic acid by the corresponding decarboxylase can be used as a means of following such transamination reactions (16). Krebs (15) has devised a method for the estimation of aspartic acid, asparagine, and α-ketoglutaric acid by combining glutamic acid decarboxylase with other systems.

Pyridoxal Phosphate Assay. The decarboxylases possess pyridoxal phosphate as prosthetic group and in some cases, e.g., tyrosine decarboxylase, it is possible to remove the prosthetic group leaving an inactive apo-decarboxylase preparation (5). The apoenzyme is activated by pyridoxal phosphate and the rate of decarboxylation is proportional to the concentration of pyridoxal phosphate over a limited range.

References

1. Camien, M. N., McClure, L. E., and Dunn, M. S., *Arch. Biochem.*, *28*, 220 (1950).
2. Chibnall, A. C., Rees, M. W., Williams, E. F., and Boyland, E., *Biochem. J.*, *34*, 285 (1940).
3. Conway, E. J., *Microdiffusion Analysis and Volumetric Error*, Crosby Lockwood & Son, Ltd., London, 1950.
4. Dewey, D. L., Hoare, D. S., and Work, E., *Biochem. J.*, *58*, 523 (1954).
5. Epps, H. M. R., *Biochem. J.*, *41*, 605 (1944).
6. Epps, H. M. R., *Biochem. J.*, *39*, 42 (1945).
7. Gale, E. F., *Biochem. J.*, *35*, 66 (1941).
8. Gale, E. F., *Biochem. J.*, *39*, 46 (1945); *Nature, 157*, 265 (1946).
9. Gale, E. F., *Adv. Enzymol.*, *6*, 1 (1946).
10. Gale, E. F., *J. Gen. Microbiol.*, *1*, 53 (1947).
11. Gale, E. F., and Taylor, E. S., *J. Gen. Microbiol.*, *1*, 77 (1947).
12. Hoare, D. S., and Work, E., *Biochem. J.*, *61*, 562 (1955).
13. King, H. K., *Biochem. J.*, *54*, xi (1953).
14. Krebs, H. A., *Biochem. J.*, *43*, 51 (1948).
15. Krebs, H. A., *Biochem. J.*, *41*, 605 (1950).
16. Lichstein, H. C., Gunsalus, I. C., and Umbreit, W. W., *J. Biol. Chem.*, *161*, 311 (1945).
17. McGilvery, R. W., and Cohen, P. P., *J. Biol. Chem.*, *174*, 813 (1948).
18. McIlwain, H., and Hughes, D. E., *Biochem. J.*, *38*, 187 (1944).
19. Mardashev, S. R., Semina, L. A., Etinoff, R. N., and Baliasnaia, A. I., *Biokhimiya, 14, i*, 44 (1949).
20. Meister, A., Sober, H. A., and Tice, S. V., *J. Biol. Chem.*, *189*, 577, 591 (1951).
21. Neuberger, A., and Sanger, F., *Biochem. J.*, *38*, 125 (1944).
22. Plackett, P., and McQuillen, K., personal communication.
23. Rodwell, A. W., *J. Gen. Microbiol.*, *8*, 224, 233 (1953).
24. Rowlands, R., Gale, E. F., Folkes, J. P., and Marrian D. H., *Biochem. J. 65*, 519 (1957).
25. Taylor, E. S., *J. Gen. Microbiol.*, *1*, 85 (1947).
26. Umbreit, W. W., Burris, R. H., and Stauffer, J. F., *Manometric Techniques and Tissue Metabolism*, Burgess Publishing Co., Minneapolis, 1949.
27. Umbreit, W. W., and Gunsalus, I. C., *J. Biol. Chem.*, *159*, 333 (1945).
28. Umbreit, W. W., and Heneage, P., *J. Biol. Chem.*, *201*, 15 (1953).
29. Virtanen, A. I., and Laine, T., *Enzymologia 3*, 266 (1937).
30. Zamecnik, P. C., and Stephenson, M. L., *J. Biol. Chem.*, *169*, 349 (1947).

Determination of
SUCCINIC DEHYDROGENASE ACTIVITY *

THOMAS P. SINGER,† AND EDNA B. KEARNEY, *Edsel B. Ford Institute for Medical Research*

* The original investigations reported have been supported by grants from the National Institutes of Health, United States Public Health Service, from the American Heart Association, and by a contract between the Office of Naval Research, Department of the Navy, and the Edsel B. Ford Institute for Medical Research, Nonr-1656(00).

† Established Investigator of the American Heart Association.

I. INTRODUCTION

Succinic dehydrogenase was discovered by Thunberg in 1909 in the course of a survey of the various compounds capable of undergoing dehydrogenation by cell preparations in the presence of methylene blue as electron acceptor (52). The ubiquitous occurrence and high activity of the enzyme focussed attention early on its probable importance in general metabolism, but the key role of the dehydrogenase in the terminal oxidation of carbohydrates, fats, and amino acids was clearly recognized only after the events of the tricarboxylic acid cycle were clearly established. Meanwhile, the brilliant investigations of Keilin and Hartree (27–31) revealed the main features of the electron transport system with which the oxidation of succinate is linked *in vivo*. It was established that the oxidation of succinate to fumarate in animal tissues is linked to O_2 via cytochrome c and cytochrome oxidase and that even in cell-free, colloidal preparations this chain of enzymes acts as an organized, multi-enzyme system whose overall activity depends not only on the integrity of each component but also on the integrity of the link between these components. The entire chain of enzymes was named "succinic oxidase," while the term "succinic dehydrogenase" was retained for the primary dehydrogenase which accepts electrons from succinate. A scheme of electron transport within the succinic oxidase chain (Scheme 1) was

SCHEME 1. THE SUCCINIC OXIDASE SYSTEM (after Keilin and Hartree)

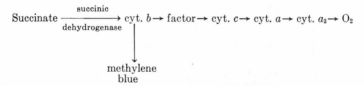

postulated by these investigators on the basis of spectroscopic evidence and the use of suitable inhibitors, the main features of which were verified by the subsequent investigations of Ball, Chance, Keilin and Hartree, Slater, Stotz, and their colleagues. While these studies shed considerable light on the nature and components of the succinic oxidase system, definitive information on the chemical nature and mechanism of action of succinic dehydrogenase itself could not be gained until the enzyme was solubilized and separated from the other members of the succinic oxidase chain. The apparent failure of many investigators to accomplish this end, despite major efforts, in retrospect may be largely ascribed to the assay procedures used, which utilized electron acceptors that either required the simultaneous presence and cooperation of various electron transport enzymes and which therefore failed to react directly or reacted only very slowly with the dehydrogenase itself (e.g., cytochrome c, methylene blue, brilliant cresyl blue, indophenol and tetrazolium dyes). Another commonly used acceptor has been ferricyanide, whose reactivity with the dehydrogenase may vary considerably depending on the source of the enzyme, its degree of purity, and the nature of contaminating proteins present (24,41,47) (cf. below). Although there are reports by Hogeboom (19) and Morton (36) of varying degrees of solubilization of the dehydrogenase as judged by the ferricyanide assay, it was the finding that phenazine methosulfate provides a generally reliable assay for the dehydrogenase in particulate and soluble preparations from a very large array of animal tissues and microorganisms which truly facilitated isolation of the dehydrogenase as a soluble protein. The enzyme has since been prepared in essentially homogeneous state from animal tissues (42,45) and in highly purified form from yeast (47). As detailed elsewhere (21–23, 43,44), the enzyme from both sources is a ferroflavoprotein (in accord with earlier predictions of the role of riboflavin in succinic dehydrogenase (1,3,28)), containing 4 atoms of non-hemin iron per mole of flavin. The enzyme catalyzes the *reversible* oxidation of succinate to fumarate, and the events of electron transfer on the surface of the enzyme appear to proceed according to the relations shown in Scheme 2. The kinetics of the action of the isolated dehydrogenase and the action of inhibitors simulate earlier findings with particulate preparations quantitatively.

SCHEME 2. PROPOSED MECHANISM OF ACTION OF SUCCINIC DEHYDROGENASE

Succinate + flavin $\longrightarrow$ fumarate + leucoflavin

Leucoflavin + $2Fe^{3+}$ $\longrightarrow$ flavin + $2Fe^{2+}$ + $2H^+$

$2Fe^{2+}$ + $2H^+$ + acceptor $\longrightarrow$ $2Fe^{3+}$ + reduced acceptor

The "succinic dehydrogenase complex" (SDC), i.e., the chain of enzymes which pass electrons from succinate to cytochrome c, has also been purified as a *particulate* entity by Green et al. (17), as judged by an increased specific activity compared with the mitochondrial starting material. This type of preparation, by virtue of the fact that it contains a number of electron transfer proteins, possibly cemented by phospholipid bridges (10), shows, of course, different electron acceptor requirements than soluble preparations of the primary dehydrogenase, but the pattern of succinate oxidation by such preparations does not differ appreciably from those observed with Keilin-Hartree preparations or with the pure dehydrogenase. Another type of preparation, capable of catalyzing succinate oxidation and with still different acceptor specificity, is the recently reported "electron transport particle" (ETP) (5,14,16) which is presumably a purified form of the entire succinic oxidase chain, linking succinate to molecular O_2; it is known to oxidize succinate and DPNH by way of the cytochrome chain defined by the studies of Keilin and Hartree (11,28). In between these complex particles and the primary dehydrogenase stand a number of less well-defined preparations, derived from SDC, ETP, or mitochondria by treatment with bile salts, or degradation with alkali or proteolytic enzymes (2,5,16,37). Such preparations differ from succinic dehydrogenase in the invariable presence of hemoproteins and the consequently greater latitude in acceptor specificity, as compared with succinic dehydrogenase. Since these preparations differ among each other in the degree of intactness of the dehydrogenase as well as in the kind and relative number of electron transport proteins they contain, and, therefore, with respect to the dyes with which they react maximally, no attempt will be made here to describe their assay.

II. ASSAY OF THE PRIMARY DEHYDROGENASE

1. Reactions of the Dehydrogenase with Various Dyes

Regardless of source or purity, in all preparations hitherto investigated, the primary dehydrogenase reacts maximally with phenazine methosulfate according to reaction (1); under aerobic conditions the leuco dye is instantly reoxidized (reaction 2) (2,7,24,40,41,47). Since the dehydrogenase shows no obvious requirements for anions (except

Succinate + phenazine methosulfate ⟶ fumarate +
                                          leucophenazine methosulfate   (1)

Leucophenazine methosulfate + O_2 ⟶
                                          phenazine methosulfate + H_2O_2 (2)

for phosphate, cf. below), presumably the other salts, such as the methochloride, would be equally suitable. Phenazine ethosulfate gives the same maximal activity (V_{max} at infinite dye concentration) as does the methosulfate but the apparent affinity of the former dye for the dehydrogenase is much smaller; hence at the dye concentration recommended in the manometric assay (II.B) the turnover of the enzyme in the presence of the phenazine ethosulfate is much smaller than with phenazine methosulfate.* It is of interest that other "cytochrome reducing dehydrogenases" investigated, i.e., yeast lactic dehydrogenase (6) and rat liver choline dehydrogenase (24) also react faster with phenazine methosulfate than any other known acceptor.

The primary dehydrogenase also reacts relatively well with ferricyanide according to reaction (3). In soluble preparations from animal tissues the rate with ferricyanide is 30 to 40% of that with

$$\text{Succinate} + 2 \text{ ferricyanide} \longrightarrow \text{fumarate} + 2 \text{ ferrocyanide} + 2H^+ \quad (3)$$

phenazine methosulfate as acceptor in the presence of protective proteins; in the absence of the latter the rate may be as low as 10%. With soluble succinic dehydrogenase from baker's yeast the rate with ferricyanide, even in the presence of protective proteins, is only 10 per cent of the rate with phenazine methosulfate (47).

A number of other substances, which function relatively efficiently as acceptors in particulate preparations of the dehydrogenase (such as methylene blue, brilliant cresyl blue, 2,6-dichlorophenolindophenol, and neotetrazolium (2,17,28,37)), show no measurable reaction with soluble preparations of the primary dehydrogenase, uncontaminated with hemoproteins, when the dehydrogenase is used in catalytic amounts. It may be safely assumed that efficient functioning of these electron carriers even in particulate preparations involves the mediation of enzymes other than succinic dehydrogenase. Evidence for this concept is available in at least two instances: the succinic dehydrogenases of rat liver mitochondria (40,43) and of *Bact. tularense* (54). In the former case, aqueous suspensions of a mitochondrial acetone powder can utilize phenazine methosulfate, methylene blue, or indophenol dyes as electron acceptors from succinic dehydrogenase, although at unequal rates, whereas the supernatant fluid obtained on centrifugation, which contains all

---

* The naturally occurring phenazine-α-carboxylic acid (18,32), with an unsubstituted tertiary nitrogen, is inactive but the purple product obtained on illumination of phenazine methosulfate seems to be active with beef heart succinic dehydrogenase (35).

312 T. P. SINGER AND E. B. KEARNEY

of the dehydrogenase, can react with phenazine methosulfate only. Soluble preparations from *Bact. tularense* oxidize succinate with methylene blue, indophenol dyes, or phenazine methosulfate as acceptors, but the activities toward either methylene blue or 2,6-dichlorophenolindophenol or both may be removed without impairing the activity toward the phenazine dye (54).

The fact that succinic dehydrogenase is a flavoprotein might lead one to expect some residual activity toward molecular O_2 and dyes such as methylene blue. This is indeed the case. The highly purified dehydrogenase from beef heart is autooxidizable, the rate being about $1/_{5000}$ that obtained with phenazine methosulfate (42). Very recently, Dr. Massey in this laboratory has demonstrated that such preparations also react with methylene blue anaerobically; while the relative velocities have not been compared exactly, the reaction rate is of the order of $1/_{100}$ as fast as with phenazine. With O_2 and methylene blue a direct reaction with the leucoflavoprotein appears to be involved, while phenazine methosulfate and ferricyanide accept electrons from the iron moiety of the enzyme (43). Possibly, if high enough concentrations of the enzyme are used, similar slow side-reactions may also be observed with other dyes and cytochrome *c*, but these reactions proceed by clearly different mechanisms from the rapid ones found in preparations of the "succinic dehydrogenase complex."

2. The Phenazine Methosulfate Method

A. PREPARATION AND PROPERTIES OF PHENAZINE METHOSULFATE (9,26)

Reagents.

(*1*) *Phenazine*, available from Eastern Chemical Co., 34 Spring Street, Newark, N. J.

(*2*) *Dimethyl sulfate*, Matheson or Eastman. Redistill and use the fraction boiling at 186°–188°, unc.

(*3*) *Nitrobenzene*, Eastman. Use without redistillation.

Synthesis.

Throughout the procedure it is essential to work rapidly and to exclude light as much as feasible. The total working time, including one recrystallization, is about 90 minutes. Ninety milliliters of nitrobenzene is heated to the boiling point to remove traces of water. When cooled to about 120°, 5 g. of phenazine is added. After the solution has cooled to 100°, 22.5 ml. of dimethyl sulfate is added in one batch and the solution is kept at 100° for 7 minutes. After cooling to about 0 to 5° the crystals are rapidly filtered on a sintered glass funnel and washed with 60 ml. of ice-cold ether. The second batch of crystals, which form when the wash ether is mixed with filtrate, is collected and worked up separately. The first batch of crystals is rapidly recrystallized from a minimum volume of boiling 95% alcohol. After cooling to 0°, the recrystallized methosulfate is collected on a sintered glass funnel, washed with a minimal volume of ice-cold absolute alcohol, then copiously with ether, and recrystallized a second time from alcohol. The second batch of crystals may require 3 recrystallizations, but usually 2 suffice. The crystals are dried over H_2SO_4 in the dark. They should be orange in color, giving a yellow-orange solution (no greenish hue) and should be freely soluble in water.

Properties.

In the dry state the methosulfate is stable for years if protected from light. Solutions should be kept frozen in water, *not* in neutral buffers, and may be preserved for several months in the dark. In actual use the only important precaution is to protect solutions from light. The dye is therefore conveniently added to Warburg vessels as one of the last components before the beginning of a manometric experiment.

The methosulfate is autooxidizable, E_h (pH 7.38) = 0.080 V. Reoxidation of the leuco dye produces H_2O_2. Since phenazine methosulfate inhibits catalase practically completely, when working with —SH enzymes, such as succinic dehydrogenase, it is imperative to make provisions to overcome the effect of H_2O_2 on the enzyme (cf. section II.2.B).

B. MANOMETRIC ASSAY

Reagents.

(1) Phenazine methosulfate, 1% solution in glass distilled water. The solution may be preserved in the frozen state, protected from light.

(2) Phosphate buffer, pH 7.6, 0.3 M, in glass distilled water.

(3) Sodium or potassium succinate, 0.2 M, neutral. The reagent is prepared from analytical reagent (Merck preferred) succinic acid in glass distilled water.

(4) HCN, 0.01 M, pH about 8, in glass distilled water, prepared from KCN by addition of 0.85 equivalent HCl.

Apparatus.

Conventional Warburg equipment is used with the rate of oscillation adjusted to permit O_2 uptake at the rate of 15 cu. mm. per min. without the diffusion of O_2 becoming the limiting factor. Wide angle vessels with raised center wells (or no center well), having a large surface/liquid volume ratio, and a volume of 15 to 25 ml. are preferred.

Method.

To the main compartment of a Warburg vessel phosphate buffer (0.5 ml.), enzyme, and water (to give 2.2 ml. volume) are added and the side arm receives 0.3 ml. of succinate and 0.2 ml. of phenazine methosulfate. Immediately before placing the vessel on the manometer, 0.3 ml. cyanide is added to the main compartment and the manometer is placed in the water bath (at 38°) with the stopcock closed, so as to minimize the escape of cyanide, pressure being released as necessary. After 7 minutes equilibration the contents of the side arm are tipped in and readings are taken at 2 and 7 minutes after tipping. The amount of enzyme is so chosen as to give 30 to 60 cu. mm. O_2 uptake per 5 min. When vessels of smaller volume are used, the reagents are scaled down proportionately.

The pH stated is optimal for succinic dehydrogenase from mammalian tissues at 38°. With yeast succinic dehydrogenase the apparent pH optimum at 38° is 7.7 (pH measured at 38° in the presence of the complete reaction mixture). With other sources of the enzyme the pH optimum must be individually determined. Phosphate is included in the reaction mixture since it has been shown (25,42) that the soluble primary dehydrogenase is 2 to 3 times as active in the presence of a high concentration of phosphate as in other buffers tested. This apparent stimulation appears to be a function of the electron acceptor used (35).

The soluble, primary dehydrogenase from baker's yeast is equally active in phosphate, tris(hydroxymethyl)aminomethane and imidazole buffers in the phenazine assay. If the distilled water used in the preparation of the enzyme or of the reagents or of one of the reagents is contaminated by trace metals, histidine buffer or versene + phosphate may give a higher activity than phosphate buffer alone.

Phenazine methosulfate reacts rapidly with sulfhydryl compounds, including the —SH groups of proteins, and thus inactivates succinic dehydrogenase when the dye is allowed to react with the enzyme in

the absence of succinate.   For this reason the dye is placed in the
side arm and added simultaneously with the substrate.

The reason for the inclusion of HCN in the reaction mixture is as
follows.   The H_2O_2 generated in the reoxidation of the leuco dye
(reaction (2)) oxidizes the —SH groups of the dehydrogenase even

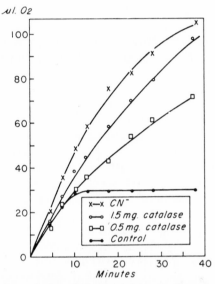

Fig. 1. Comparison of the effect of catalase + ethanol and of cyanide in
maintaining the initial reaction rate in the phenazine methosulfate assay.
Standard manometric assay conditions but no cyanide present, except as
indicated.   The enzyme was a relatively crude preparation of the soluble
dehydrogenase from beef heart mitochondria.   Cyanide, where present,
was $1 \times 10^{-3} M$, and 0.05 ml. 95% ethanol was added in the experiments
with catalase.

in crude preparations containing large amounts of catalase, since
catalase is almost completely inhibited by phenazine methosulfate
at the concentration used here (24).   The resistance of succinic
dehydrogenases to inactivation by H_2O_2 varies somewhat, depending
on the source of the enzyme and the impurities present, but, in general,
it is advisable to protect the enzyme from the effect of peroxide.
Massive amounts of added catalase in the presence of a trace of
ethanol (Figure 1) accomplish this purpose as judged by the maintenance of linear rate for a longer period than in the unprotected control,

but cyanide and 8-hydroxyquinoline (Figures 1 and 2) are more satisfactory. Cyanide is assumed to act by reduction of the disulfide
linkages formed by the action of H_2O_2 (reaction (4))

$$\begin{array}{c} R\!-\!R' \\ | \quad | \quad + \text{HCN} \longrightarrow \\ S\!-\!S \end{array} \quad \begin{array}{c} R\!-\!\!-\!\!-\!R' \\ | \qquad | \\ SH \quad SCN \end{array} \qquad (4)$$

Possibly, the enzyme may be active when one member of a pair of
—SH groups is converted to the thiocyanate form.

Despite the presence of cyanide or of catalase + ethanol, the rate
seldom remains perfectly linear for more than 7 to 8 minutes. One

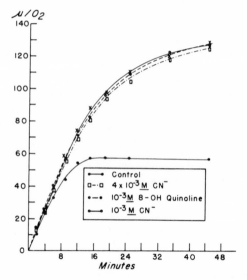

Fig. 2. Comparison of the effects of cyanide and 8-hydroxyquinoline in
maintaining the initial rate (from (24)). Experimental conditions as in Fig.
1.

reason for this may be the accumulation of fumarate, a good com-
petitive inhibitor of the primary dehydrogenase (42). In general,
the higher the activity during the initial 5 min. period, the greater
is the relative decline during the ensuing periods. This decline
may be minimized by coupling succinic dehydrogenase with appropriate enzymes to remove fumarate by conversion to a non-
inhibitory product, such as aspartate. This has been accomplished
(24) by the addition of crystalline fumarase and highly purified malic

dehydrogenase and a transaminase which catalyzes the reaction between oxalacetate and cysteinesulfinate. Under these conditions
reactions (5–9) occur.

$$\text{Fumarate} + H_2O \overset{\text{fumarase}}{\rightleftharpoons} \text{malate} \tag{5}$$

$$\text{Malate} + \text{DPN} \overset{\text{malic de-}}{\underset{\text{hydrogenase}}{\rightleftharpoons}} \text{oxalacetate} + \text{DPNH} + H^+ \tag{6}$$

$$\text{DPNH} + H^+ + O_2 \overset{\text{phenazine}}{\underset{\text{methosulfate}}{\longrightarrow}} \text{DPN} + H_2O_2 \tag{7}$$

$$\text{Oxalacetate} + \text{L-cysteinesulfinate} \overset{\text{transaminase}}{\rightleftharpoons} \text{aspartate} + \beta\text{-sulfinylpyruvate} \tag{8}$$

$$\beta\text{-Sulfinylpyruvate} \overset{\text{spontaneous}}{\longrightarrow} \text{pyruvate} + \text{sulfite} \tag{9}$$

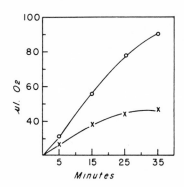

Fig. 3. Comparison of the oxidation of succinate to fumarate with the
coupled reaction of succinate and L-cysteinesulfinate by soluble beef heart
preparations. Lower curve, 0.02 M succinate, 0.05 M phosphate, pH 7.6,
and 1 mg. phenazine methosulfate present. Upper curve, same +0.02 M
L-cysteinesulfinate, 4×10^{-4} M DPN, and the following enzymes added in
excess: crystalline fumarase, highly purified malic dehydrogenase and oxalo-
acetic-glutamic transaminase. (The latter enzyme catalyzes the oxaloace-
tic-cysteinesulfinic transamination.) Temperature, 38°C. (from (40)).

Although this device helps maintain linearity for prolonged periods in
both particulate preparations of the succinic dehydrogenase complex
and in purified samples of the soluble dehydrogenase (Figure 3) and
has been successfully used in the initial work on the isolation of the
latter (40), it has been abandoned in favor of a short initial reaction
period with HCN as the only protecting agent, since the numerous

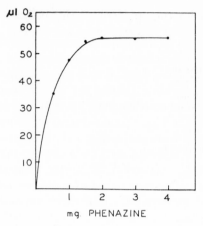

Fig. 4. Relation of the rate of O_2 uptake to phenazine methosulfate concentration. Standard manometric assay conditions: enzyme, soluble extract of rat liver mitochondrial acetone powder; total volume, 3 ml.

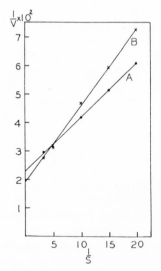

Fig. 5. Determination of the V_{max} with respect to phenazine methosulfate by the double reciprocal method. Standard manometric assay. Abscissa: reciprocal dye concentration, 1/mg. in 3 ml.; ordinate, $1/\mu l$ O_2 uptake in 5 min. Curve A represents a fully active, essentially homogeneous dehydrogenase from beef heart, curve B a partly inactivated, highly purified preparation.

substances required for the above coupled reaction render it unfeasible for a routine method.

The last point to be discussed in connection with the manometric phenazine methosulfate assay is the question of the dye concentration. In a reaction volume of 3 ml., 2 to 3 mg. of phenazine methosulfate gives apparent saturation (Figure 4); higher concentrations are inhibitory. When the activity given by this concentration of the dye is compared with the V_{max} calculated from reciprocal plots (Figure 5), it is found that in fresh preparations of the purified beef heart and yeast enzymes the observed activity is close to the theoretical maximum (85 to 88%). However, in partly inactivated preparations the apparent saturation requirements for the dye may increase (Figure 5, curve B) and the true V_{max} may differ appreciably from the observed velocity at "saturating" concentrations of the dye (35). Hence, it is advisable to perform critical assays at a series of dye concentrations and to calculate the V_{max} by the double reciprocal method.

C. POSSIBLE SPECTROPHOTOMETRIC APPLICATIONS

The marked difference between the absorption of the oxidized and reduced forms of phenazine methosulfate at 387 mμ (Figure 6) suggests the possibility of a sensitive spectrophotometric method for the assay of the primary dehydrogenase. Certain inconvenient properties of the dye have so far prevented the elaboration of a completely satisfactory spectrophotometric assay. Thus turbidity often develops when the dye is reduced under anaerobic conditions: apparently, the leuco dye is relatively insoluble in aqueous media. This difficulty may be circumvented by coupling the reduction of phenazine methosulfate with cytochrome c or 2,6-dichlorophenolindophenol (with which the leuco dye reacts rapidly) and measuring the absorption of the latter compounds.

Another and more serious difficulty encountered when the enzymatic reduction is carried out in Thunberg tube type Beckman cells is that a lag period is generally manifest when succinate is tipped into a mixture of the dye and the dehydrogenase at room temperature. This lag period may be due in part to incomplete removal of traces of O_2 and consequent cyclic reduction by succinate and reoxidation by residual O_2, despite several evacuations and flushing with rigorously purified N_2, since the reaction of leucophenazine methosulfate with O_2

is a very rapid one.   It should be mentioned, however, that a lag period is also evident in the manometric phenazine method when it is carried out at 20 to 25°; this lag lasts only about 2 minutes when the enzyme is in the main compartment (in dilute solution) but may last 10 minutes or so if a concentrated solution of the enzyme is in the side

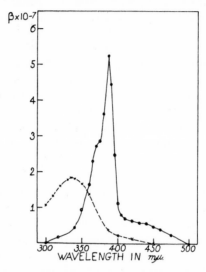

Fig. 6. Absorption spectra of phenazine methosulfate and of its reduced form. Solid line, oxidized dye at pH 7.6; dashed line, dye reduced by highly purified lactic dehydrogenase from yeast in the presence of lactate at pH 7.6 (from (6)).

arm.   No lag is detected in the usual manometric method at 38°. It appears that this type of lag period may reflect an activation process which the enzyme undergoes in the presence of agents which combine with the active center (24a).   The activation is rapid at 38° and in dilute solutions and slow at lower temperatures and in the concentrated state.   Since the usual manometric assay is carried out at 38° and the enzyme is in a dilute solution in the vessel during the temperature equilibration period, a lag would not be detected, whereas it would be evident in the spectrophotometric test which is usually carried out at 19° to 25° and requires only a very brief temperature equilibration.   In accord with this interpretation preliminary tests of the spectrophotometric method at 38° revealed little or no lag phase.*

3. The Ferricyanide Method

A. GENERAL PRINCIPLES

Since the introduction of the method by Quastel and Wheatley (39), ferricyanide has been widely used for the estimation of succinic dehydrogenase activity (reaction (3)). The reduction of ferricyanide may be followed either manometrically by CO_2 evolution from $NaHCO_3$-CO_2 buffers or spectrophotometrically, taking advantage of the differences in the spectra of ferricyanide and ferrocyanide. Either method entails the advantage of greater sensitivity, compared with the manometric phenazine methosulfate test (manometrically 2 moles of CO_2 are registered in the ferricyanide reaction per mole of succinate oxidized) but they also suffer from two decided disadvantages. First, ferricyanide, a well-known —SH inhibitor, oxidizes the essential —SH groups of succinic dehydrogenase (4). This type of inactivation may partly account for the very low activity of certain preparations of the soluble dehydrogenase in the ferricyanide assay. The addition of protective proteins, such as crystalline serum albumin (17), to some extent appears to minimize this effect and the inclusion of massive amounts of serum albumin may increase the activity of the primary dehydrogenase from animal tissues 3- or 4-fold in this assay. Even in the presence of albumin, however, the activity of all soluble preparations of the dehydrogenase tested in this laboratory was very much lower in the ferricyanide test than in the phenazine methosulfate assay. This circumstance somewhat offsets the greater sensitivity of the ferricyanide reaction. The second disadvantage is that the sites of action of ferricyanide in the succinoxidase chain remain to be cleared up. As correctly predicted by Tsou (53), ferricyanide indeed reacts with the primary dehydrogenase (24,36,40, 47) but the apparently higher activity of this reagent as compared with phenazine methosulfate in certain preparations of the succinic dehydrogenase complex studied by Green et al. (16,17) raises the question as to whether the primary dehydrogenase is the only point

* An alternate possibility is that the lag period may be a reflection of a stepwise reduction to the semiquinone, since recent evidence suggests the formation of a relatively stable semiquinone on reduction of the dye by hydrosulfite or by the dehydrogenase (35).

322   T. P. SINGER AND E. B. KEARNEY

in the chain where ferricyanide can accept electrons. This uncertainty poses obvious limitations to the reliability of succinic dehydrogenase assays based on the ferricyanide reaction when components of the electron transport chain other than the dehydrogenase are still present.

B. MANOMETRIC ASSAY

Reagents.
Sodium or potassium succinate, 0.2 M, as in 2.B.
Potassium ferricyanide, 1 M, in glass distilled water.
Potassium bicarbonate, 0.2 M, in glass distilled water.
Crystalline serum albumin, 3% prepared in glass distilled water and neutralized to pH 7.4 to 7.6.
Method.
The main compartment of a Warburg vessel receives the enzyme, 0.4 ml. 0.2 M NaHCO$_3$, 20 to 30 mg. (0.66 to 1 ml.) serum albumin, and water to make 2.5 ml.; the side arm receives 0.1 ml. 1 M ferricyanide, 0.1 ml. 0.2 M NaHCO$_3$, and 0.3 ml. 0.2 M succinate. The vessels are gassed for 3 to 4 minutes with 95% N$_2$–5% CO$_2$ and placed into the bath at 38°. After suitable temperature equilibration the contents of the side arm are tipped in and readings are taken every 5 minutes starting at 2 minutes after tipping. Unless the reaction remains linear for longer periods, the 2- to 7-minute period is used to calculate the activity. The reaction mixture may be scaled down proportionately for smaller vessels and the pH changed by varying the ratio HCO$_3$/H$_2$CO$_3$, as calculated from the Henderson-Hasselbach equation.

C. SPECTROPHOTOMETRIC ASSAY

Slater and Bonner (49) follow the reduction of ferricyanide at 400 mμ in a spectrophotometer equipped with cells of 1 cm. light path. A total volume of 3 ml. reaction mixture contains enzyme, succinate, suitable buffer, and ferricyanide (3 μmoles). The reaction is started by addition of the enzyme and the change in absorption is measured against a reference cell containing water. A blank (no substrate) is run simultaneously. In the case of crude preparations containing cytochrome oxidase 30 μmoles of neutralized KCN is included to inhibit this enzyme; this precaution is unnecessary with purified preparations of the dehydrogenase. In any case, the inclusion of serum albumin may be advantageous. For accurate results by either the manometric or spectrophotometric methods it is desirable to test a series of ferricyanide concentrations and to calculate the V_{max} by the double reciprocal method.

4. Assays Based on the Reverse Reaction

A. GENERAL CONSIDERATIONS

During the period 1938–1942, Fischer and colleagues (12,13) demonstrated the enzymatic reduction of fumarate in the presence of certain reduced dyes of low potential as electron donors, as catalyzed by partially purified preparations of brewer's yeast. They elaborated a colorimetric assay based on these observations. Since their preparations failed to catalyze the oxidation of succinate with methylene blue as acceptor, they apparently concluded that a separate enzyme, "fumaric hydrogenase," catalyzed this enzymatic event. Subsequent work in the authors' laboratory (43,46,47) has demonstrated that in preparations isolated from beef heart as well as from baker's yeast mitochondria the "fumaric hydrogenase" activity is due to succinic dehydrogenase acting in reverse. These observations provide alternative assay methods for succinic dehydrogenase by measurement of the rate of oxidation of suitable electron donors with fumarate as acceptor. The test may be safely applied to purified preparations of succinic dehydrogenase but its use with very crude preparations, particularly of microbial origin, is not recommended, since the existence of a unidirectional fumaric hydrogenase, distinct from succinic dehydrogenase, in sources other than those mentioned has not been disproved, much as it may appear unlikely on theoretical grounds. As a matter of fact, there is some rather suggestive evidence that *M. lactolyticus* may contain just such an enzyme (38,51).

B. SPECTROPHOTOMETRIC METHOD

The method involves the use of a modified Thunberg tube which fits the Beckman spectrophotometer. A simple device may be constructed by sealing onto a rectangular, 1-cm. light path cuvette a short, ground glass joint test tube equipped with one or two side arms, and fitting a stopcock ending in a ground joint on top of the test tube in order to permit evacuation.

In practice the dye, buffer, and enzyme are placed in the main part

324   T. P. SINGER AND E. B. KEARNEY

of the tube and fumarate, in a small volume, is added to the side arm.
The stopcock is put in place and the tube is evacuated, filled with
N_2 (Matheson "prepurified" N_2, slowly passed through a train of
alkaline pyrogallol to remove traces of O_2); the tube is then opened
and sufficient hydrosulfite is quickly added to the main part of the
tube to give nearly complete reduction of the dye. The tube is then

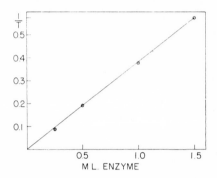

Fig. 7. Relation of succinic dehydrogenase concentration to activity in the
"fumaric hydrogenase" test. Abscissa, enzyme added (0.17 mg./ml. solution of 70% pure beef heart succinic dehydrogenase); ordinate, reciprocal
time (min.$^{-1}$) for reoxidation of leucodiethylsafranin. The latter is the
time required for the transition from optical density = 0.05 (92% reduction)
to optical density = 0.30 (54% reduction) in the Klett colorimeter, equipped
with a green filter. Conditions: leucodiethylsafranin, 3.6×10^{-5} M;
phosphate, 5×10^{-2} M, pH 7.6; total volume, 3 ml., temperature, 30°.
The blank was zero and the initial rate was linear. Dry fumarate (100 μ-
moles) was present in the side arm of a Thunberg tube. The tubes were
evacuated prior to the addition of just sufficient hydrosulfite to reduce the
dye, and following repeated evacuation, they were filled with pure N_2 (from
(43)).

once again evacuated, filled with N_2, and the evacuation and gassing
with N_2 are repeated. After a suitable period of temperature equilibration readings are taken at the appropriate wave length, depending
on the dye used, to insure that no reoxidation of the leuco dye is
occurring, then the fumarate is tipped in, and readings are followed
against time until some two-thirds of the color reappears. The rate
is then calculated as the increase in optical density per unit of time
($\Delta E/\Delta t$) from the linear portion of the curve and it should be proportional to the enzyme concentration. An alternative method,

which does not require the use of zero-order kinetics in the calculation of the enzyme activity, is to plot the reciprocal time required for the transition between two fixed optical densities against the enzyme concentration, as in Figure 7; the resulting straight line should pass through the origin. Conversion of fumaric hydrogenase units to succinic dehydrogenase units requires knowledge of the ratio of succinic dehydrogenase to fumaric hydrogenase activities for the particular enzyme source at the temperature used. For succinic dehydrogenase from beef heart and baker's yeast the ratio of the forward over the reverse reaction at 20° to 23° is 9 (43). For comparative experiments, such as studies of the action of inhibitors or serial assays of certain types this calculation is usually unnecessary.

Regardless of the dye used as electron donor, certain practical problems arise in this method. First, the availability of an accurately thermostated cell compartment in the spectrophotometer is a great convenience. In its absence, recourse may have to be made to a correction of the activity from the temperature of the observation to the desired temperature by means of the temperature coefficient of the enzyme, a correction which is not always satisfactory (6a). Second, it is essential to perform assays at a series of dye concentrations and to use the V_{max}, calculated by the double reciprocal method, as the true activity (at infinite dye concentration). It has been observed, for instance, that at a fixed dye concentration the ratio of observed activity to V_{max} may change on storage of the enzyme without a concomitant change in the V_{max} (35). Third, in order to obtain accurate initial rates and to ascertain satisfactory anaerobiosis, the dye must be slightly (5 to 15%) oxidized during the initial observation period, i.e., before the substrate is tipped in. Since it is not always easy to add just exactly the right amount of hydrosulfite to give no more than 95% and no less than 85% reduction, it is convenient to add a slight excess of hydrosulfite and, after evacuation and gassing, admit traces of O_2 to permit reoxidation of the leuco dye, under gentle shaking, to the desired point. If the dye is entirely in the reduced form at the time of tipping of the fumarate a lag period is usually observed, which corresponds to the depletion of the excess hydrosulfite. Under such conditions experimental artifacts may often register. Thus while iron does not appear to participate in the reduction of fumarate by succinic dehydrogenase (46) and added Fe^{2+} may be actually inhibitory, with fully reduced diethylsafranin as electron donor, incomplete anaerobiosis, and a slight excess of hydrosulfite, added Fe^{2+} may appear to stimulate fumaric hydrogenase activity. The reason for this is that Fe^{2+} catalyzes the reoxidation of the dye by molecular O_2: the observed rate is then the sum of fumaric hydrogenase action *plus* the non-enzymatic reoxidation of the dye by O_2, as catalyzed by Fe^{2+}. If the enzyme or fumarate is omitted, no recolorization may occur at all, provided that the residual hydrosulfite is sufficient to reduce any oxidized dye, as fast as it is generated by the relatively slow, non-enzymatic reaction (46).

The experimental conditions for the spectrophotometric method are as follows: phosphate buffer, 0.05 M, pH 7.6 (for animal tissues), pH 7.7 (for baker's yeast); fumarate, 3.3 $\times$ 10^{-2} M, and enzyme so adjusted as to give a change in optical density in the range of 0.1 to 0.6 in 5 to 10 minutes; readings are taken every 15 to 30 seconds. If a recording spectrophotometer with kinetic scale is available, the rate may be increased. There is a fairly wide choice of dyes which have been used. Diethylsafranin is one of the original dyes recommended by Fischer *et al.* (12,13). It may be prepared from Janus Green B (diethylsafraninazodimethylaniline, National Aniline Co.) by the method of Cooperstein *et al.* (8). The oxidation of leucodiethylsafranin may be followed at 555 mμ, the point of maximum absorption of the oxidized dye (E molar = 49,000 (8)). The two disadvantages of this dye are its decided instability (it must be prepared fresh daily from Janus Green B) and the very poor quality of commercial preparations of Janus Green B, which introduces considerable amounts of unknown products into the reaction mixture. All attempts to purify the commercial dye have apparently met with failure (8). Among the impurities metal ions are certainly present, which fact suggests the inclusion of versene in the test system.

A related dye, safranin, has been widely used in this assay in Lynen's laboratory (34).

The most satisfactory dye for this test, in the experience of the authors, is flavin mononucleotide (FMN). The material of commerce (Hoffmann-La Roche or Sigma) is sufficiently pure to be used directly; it is highly soluble in water, and aqueous solutions may be preserved for long periods in the cold, provided that they are protected from light. The oxidized form exhibits a maximum at 450 mμ in neutral solutions (E molar = 12.2 $\times$ 10^3). The final molarity of FMN is varied in the range of 1.5 $\times$ 10^{-4} to 2 $\times$ 10^{-3} M and the maximal activity is determined by the double reciprocal method.

Another satisfactory electron donor is leucobenzylviologen, which, in contrast to the dyes above, is decolorized upon oxidation in the fumaric hydrogenase test.

C. MANOMETRIC METHOD

The reduction of fumarate to succinate may be readily coupled to the oxidation of molecular H_2 by purified bacterial hydrogenase, in the presence of suitable dyes as mediators (38). This coupled reaction has been made the basis of a very satisfactory manometric test

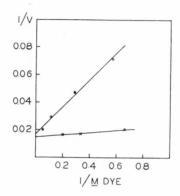

Fig. 8. Comparison of FMN (circles) and benzylviologen (crosses) in the manometric "fumaric hydrogenase" test for succinic dehydrogenase. Abscissa, $1M$ concentration of dye $\times 10^4$; ordinate, $1/\mu$l. H_2 uptake in 5 min. Each vessel contained 0.05 M phosphate buffer, pH 7.7, 0.03 M fumarate (side arm), an excess of purified hydrogenase from *Cl. pasteurianum*, dye as indicated, and a limiting concentration of highly purified succinic dehydrogenase from baker's yeast (from (50)).

in which the uptake of H_2 is measured. Comparison of this manometric and the spectrophotometric assays for the reduction of fumarate by highly purified yeast succinic dehydrogenase and FMN gave satisfactory agreement (50). For the purpose of the manometric test a purified preparation of hydrogenase (from *Cl. pasteurianum*) is used in excess and FMN or benzylviologen serves as mediator. The two dyes (and also diethylsafranin) give identical maximal velocities at any given concentration of succinic dehydrogenase (Figure 8).

III. ASSAY OF THE SUCCINIC DEHYDROGENASE COMPLEX

1. General Considerations

Both phenazine methosulfate and ferricyanide may be used for the assay of succinic dehydrogenase in particulate or solubilized preparations of the succinic dehydrogenase complex. The fumaric hydrogenase assay may be useful, provided that the precautions discussed in section II.4 are taken into account. In addition to these methods a number of other manometric or colorimetric methods have been proposed for the estimation of the dehydrogenase, which depend on the presence of suitable electron transfer proteins to catalyze the reaction between reduced succinic dehydrogenase and the dye employed. The methods which have found the widest application employ methylene blue, brilliant cresyl blue, 2,6-dichlorophenolindophenol or neotetrazolium as electron acceptors. Since none of these agents is thought to react at significant rates with the dehydrogenase directly, and since there are numerous claims that certain types of preparations of the succinic dehydrogenase complex (or of fractions derived therefrom) react with one dye but not another, it is clearly impossible to delineate the usefulness and range of applicability of these methods at this time. About all that can be said is that, historically, each of these methods has yielded valuable information on succinic dehydrogenase in relatively crude preparations but that they should be applied with great caution to appraising the succinic dehydrogenase *content* of cells or even to measuring the effect of various treatments on the dehydrogenase, since additional enzymes (besides the dehydrogenase) in all likelihood play a role in these methods. For these reasons only the methylene blue assay, which has enjoyed the widest use among these methods, will be considered in detail.

2. The Methylene Blue Assay

Of the many variants of the methylene blue method elaborated since its introduction by Thunberg (52) the present one is based on the experiments of Slater (48).

Reagents.

Sodium or potassium succinate, 0.2 M, in glass distilled water.

Phosphate buffer, pH 7.6, 0.3 M, in glass distilled water.

Cyanide, 0.1 M, neutral, in glass distilled water.

Procedure (cf. II.2.B).

Phosphate or other suitable buffer (0.5 ml.), enzyme, cyanide (0.3 ml.), and sufficient water are placed in the main compartment of a Warburg vessel to give a volume of 2.7 ml. The side arm contains 0.3 ml. succinate. The quantity of enzyme is adjusted so that the rate of O_2 uptake does not exceed the rate of diffusion of O_2 into the liquid phase in the vessel. After temperature equilibration for 8 to 10 minutes, the contents of the side arm are tipped in and the activity is calculated from the O_2 uptake during the period where the latter is linear with time. In purified samples devoid of cytochrome

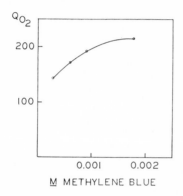

Fig. 9. The effect of the concentration of methylene blue on the activity of particulate succinic dehydrogenase from beef heart in the manometric methylene blue assay (from Slater (48)).

oxidase the addition of cyanide is not essential. If the enzyme is deficient in catalase and cyanide is omitted, it is advisable to include purified catalase in the reaction mixture. (Like phenazine methosulfate, methylene blue gives rise to H_2O_2 formation, but methylene blue does not inhibit catalase significantly.) With methylene blue, excess catalase, and no cyanide, 1 *atom* of O_2 uptake is registered per mole of succinate oxidized, while in the presence of cyanide (which inhibits catalase) 1 mole of succinate corresponds to 1 *mole* of O_2. Although the method just described is satisfactory for numerous experiments dealing with the effect of experimental conditions on the enzyme(s), it is to be noted that it does not measure the full activity of the dehydrogenase, since, as noted by Slater (48), the observed activity increases with increasing methylene blue concentration throughout the range that has been studied (Figure 9). For calculation of the V_{max} it is essential to vary the methylene blue concentration (e.g., from $3 \times 10^{-4} M$ to $6 \times 10^{-3} M$) and to plot the results graphically by the double reciprocal method.

The same considerations and experimental conditions apply to the spectrophotometric methylene blue method (6a), wherein the rate of decolorization of methylene blue is followed anaerobically in a Thunberg tube modified to fit a suitable colorimeter or spectrophotometer, except that the cyanide and catalase are omitted.

3. Other Electron Transport Agents

A. BRILLIANT CRESYL BLUE

Certain deoxycholate preparations from heart muscle can utilize, besides phenazine methosulfate, brilliant cresyl blue as acceptor for the oxidation of succinate, although they do not react rapidly with methylene blue or indophenol dyes (2). The manometric assay with brilliant cresyl blue is essentially the same as for methylene blue except that a $0.002 M$ final concentration of the dye is recommended (2).

B. 2,6-DICHLOROPHENOLINDOPHENOL

One of the methods current at the Institute for Enzyme Research for the assay of the succinic dehydrogenase complex is as follows. A spectrophotometer cuvette of 1-cm. light path and 1-ml. capacity receives 10 μmoles phosphate, pH 7.4, 0.5 mg. serum albumin, 2 μmoles KCN, 10 $u$moles succinate, 0.02 mg. 2,6-dichlorophenolindophenol, and enzyme in a total volume of 1 ml. Readings are taken at 600 mμ and the optical density, divided by 19.1, equals the μmoles of succinate oxidized (17). In the authors' experience it is advisable to include versene in the reaction mixture, since many preparations of the dye are contaminated with heavy metals.

C. NEOTETRAZOLIUM

The use of triphenyltetrazolium chloride for the colorimetric estimation of succinic dehydrogenase activity in particulate preparations has been described by Kun and Abood (33). Improvements on this method include the use of neotetrazolium (15) and the elaboration of a micromethod which permits the use of microgram amounts of tissue (20).

D. CYTOCHROME c

The rapid reduction of cytochrome c by succinate involves the entire chain of enzymes from succinic dehydrogenase to cytochrome c and is, therefore, a measure of the functioning of the complete succinic dehydrogenase complex. Green et al. (17) recommend the following assay conditions. A mixture of 10 μmoles of phosphate, pH 7.4, 10 mg. serum albumin, and the enzyme is incubated 5 minutes at 30° in a volume of 0.22 ml. At the end of that period 1 μmole KCN and 5 μmoles succinate are added and the volume is made to 0.9 ml. The solution is brought to 38°; 1 mg. cytochrome c is added in a volume of 0.1 ml. to start the reaction and readings are taken at 550 mμ in a thermostated spectrophotometer. The activity is calculated from the initial rate by using the figure 1.97×10^7 cm.^{2} mole^{-1} for the difference between the extinction coefficients of reduced and oxidized cytochrome c.

References

1. Axelrod, A. E., Potter, V. R., and Elvehjem, C. A., *J. Biol. Chem.*, *142*, 85 (1942).
2. Ball, E. G., in Gaebler, O. H., *Enzymes: Units of Biological Structure and Function*, Henry Ford Hospital International Symposium, Academic Press, New York, 1956, p. 433.
3. Ball, E. G., and Cooper, O., *J. Biol. Chem.*, *180*, 113 (1949).
4. Barron, E. S. G., and Singer, T. P., *J. Biol. Chem.*, *157*, 221 (1945).
5. Basford, R. E., and Bernard, B. de, *Federation Proc.*, *15*, 215 (1956).
6. Boeri, E., unpublished data.
6a. Bonner, W. D., Jr., in Colowick, S. P., and Kaplan, N. O., eds., *Methods in Enzymology*, Academic Press, New York, 1955, pp. 1, 722.
7. Bueding, E., Entner, N., and Farber, E., *Biochim. et Biophys. Acta*, *18* 305 (1955).
8. Cooperstein, S. J., Lazarow, A., and Patterson, J. W., *Exptl. .Cell Research*, *5*, 69 (1953).
9. Dickens, F., and McIlwain, H., *Biochem. J.*, *32*, 1615 (1938).
10. Edwards, S. W., and Ball, E. G., *J. Biol. Chem.*, *209*, 619 (1954).
11. Estabrook, R., and Mackler, B., *Federation Proc.*, *15*, 248 (1956).
12. Fischer, F. G., and Eysenbach, H., *Ann.*, *530*, 99 (1937).
13. Fischer, F. G., Roedig, A., and Rauch, K., *Ann.*, *552*, 203 (1942).
14. Glenn, J. L., and Crane, F. L., *Federation Proc.*, *15*, 262 (1956).

15. Glock, E., and Jensen, C. O., *J. Biol. Chem.*, *201*, 271 (1953).
16. Green, D. E., Basford, R. E., and Mackler, B., in McElroy, W. D., and Glass, B., eds., *Inorganic Nitrogen Metabolism*, The Johns Hopkins Press, Baltimore, 1956, p. 628.
17. Green, D. E., Mii, S., and Kohout, P. M., *J. Biol. Chem.*, *217*, 551 (1955).
18. Haynes, W. C., Stodola, F. H., Locke, J. M., Pridham, T. G., Conway, H. F., Sohns, V. E., and Jackson, R. W., *Bacteriological Proc.*, A36 (1956).
19. Hogeboom, G. H., *J. Biol. Chem.*, *162*, 739 (1946).
20. Jardetzky, C. D., and Glick, D., *J. Biol. Chem.*, *218*, 283 (1956).
21. Kearney, E. B., Massey, V., and Singer, T. P., *Federation Proc.*, *15*, 286 (1956).
22. Kearney, E. B., and Singer, T. P., *Biochim. et Biophys. Acta*, *17*, 596 (1955).
23. Kearney, E. B., and Singer, T. P., *Résumés des Communications*, 3rd Intern. Congress. of Biochem., Brussels, p. 54 (1955).
24. Kearney, E. B., and Singer, T. P., *J. Biol. Chem.*, *219*, 963 (1956).
24a. Kearney, E. B., and Singer, T. P., *Federation Proc.*, in press.
25. Kearney, E. B., Singer, T. P., and Zastrow, N., *Arch. Biochem. Biophys.*, *55*, 579 (1955).
26. Kehrman, F., and Havas, E., *Ber.*, *46*, 343 (1913).
27. Keilin, D., and Hartree, E. F., *Proc. Roy. Soc. London*, B125, 171 (1938).
28. Keilin, D., and Hartree, E. F., *Proc. Roy. Soc. London*, B129, 277 (1940).
29. Keilin, D., and Hartree, E. F., *Biochem. J.*, *41*, 500 (1947).
30. Keilin, D., and Hartree, E. F., *Biochem. J.*, *44*, 205 (1949).
31. Keilin, D., and Hartree, E. F., *Nature*, *176*, 200 (1955).
32. Kluyver, A. J., *Bactericlogical Proc.*, A35 (1956).
33. Kun, E., and Abood, L. G., *Science*, *109*, 144 (1949).
34. Lynen, F., personal communication.
35. Massey, V., unpublished data.
36. Morton, R. K., *Nature*, *166*, 1092 (1950).
37. Neufeld, H. A., Scott, C. R., and Stotz, E., *J. Biol. Chem.*, *210*, 869 (1954).
38. Peck, H. D., Jr., and Gest, H., *Bacteriological Proc.*, p. 54 (1954).
39. Quastel, J. H., and Wheatley, A. H. M., *Biochem. J.*, *32*, 936 (1938).
40. Singer, T. P., and Kearney, E. B., in McElroy, W. D., and Glass, B., eds., *Amino Acid Metabolism*, The Johns Hopkins Press, Baltimore, 1955, p. 558.
41. Singer, T. P., and Kearney, E. B., *Biochim. et Biophys. Acta*, *15*, 151 (1954).
42. Singer, T. P., Kearney, E. B., and Bernath, P., *J. Biol. Chem.*, *62*, 479 (1956).

43. Singer, T. P., Kearney, E. B., and Massey, V., in Gaebler, O. H., ed., *Enzymes: Units of Biological Structure and Function,* Henry Ford Hospital International Symposium, Academic Press, New York, 1956, p. 417.
44. Singer, T. P., Kearney, E. B., and Massey, V., *Arch. Biochem. Biophys.,* 60, 255 (1956).
45. Singer, T. P., Kearney, E. B., and Zastrow, N., *Biochim. et Biophys. Acta,* 17, 154 (1955).
46. Singer, T. P., Massey, V., and Kearney, E. B., *Biochim. et. Biophys. Acta,* 19, 200 (1956).
47. Singer, T. P., Zastrow, N., Massey, V., and Kearney, E. B., *Arch. Biochem. Biophys.,* 62, 497 (1956).
48. Slater, E. C., *Biochem., J.,* 45, 1 (1949).
49. Slater, E. C., and Bonner, W. D., Jr., *Biochem. J.,* 52, 185 (1952).
50. Smith, O., Gest, H., Singer, T. P., and Massey, V., unpublished data.
51. Smith, O., Peck, H. D., Jr., and Gest, H., personal communication.
52. Thunberg, T., *Skand. Arch. Physiol.,* 22, 430 (1909).
53. Tsou, C. L., *Biochem. J.,* 49, 512 (1951).
54. Wadkins, C. L., and Mills, R. C., results presented at the 47th Annual Meeting, American Society of Biological Chemists, Atlantic City, April 20, 1956.

AUTHOR INDEX*

A

Abbott, L. D., 236, 238 (ref. 1), 240 (ref. 1), 244, *252*
Abdul-Fadl, M. A. M., 260, 261 (ref. 2), 262 (refs. 1, 2), *281*
Abood, L. G., 330, *332*
Abu-Nasr, A. M., 106 (ref. 2), *137*
Albert, A., 145 (ref. 15), *168*
Allen, R. S., 90 (ref. 1), *95*
Allen, W. M., 147, 148, *168*
Almquist, H. J., 70, *95*
Ambrose, A. M., 3 (ref. 90), 7 (ref. 90), *42*
American Oil Chemists' Society, 103, 116, *138*
Ames, S. R., 43–98
Ammon, R., 173 (ref. 19), *210*
Anagnostopoulos, C., 277, *281*
Andersch, M. A., 267 (ref. 4), 271, *281*
Andersen, W., 204, *209*
Animal Nutrition Research Council, 55, *98*
Armstrong, 244, *253*, 259 (ref. 50), 269, 273 (ref. 50), *283*
Asimov, I., 258 (ref. 20), *282*
Asselineau, J., 131, *137*
Association of Official Agricultural Chemists, 12 (ref.1), *39*, 72, 85, 88, *95, 96*
Association of Vitamin Chemists, 8, 11 (ref. 2), 15, *39*
Atkins, M. E., 3 (ref. 7), 19 (ref. 7), 23 (ref. 7), 24 (ref. 7), 36 (ref. 7), *39*
Ault, W. C., 113 (ref. 8), *137*
Austin, C. R., 16, *39*
Awapara, J., 78 (ref. 12), *96*
Axelrod, A. E., 309 (ref. 1), *331*
Axelrod, B., 262, *282*

B

Babcock, M. J., 91 (ref. 24), *96*
Bacharach, A. L., 7 (ref. 39), *40*
Bagnoli, E., 213 (ref. 90), 230 (ref. 90), *254*
Bailey, G. F., 3 (refs. 7, 9, 75, 90), 7 (ref. 90), 11 (ref. 27), 17 (ref. 27), 19 (ref. 7), 21 (ref. 8), 23 (ref. 7), 24 (ref. 7), 26 (ref. 8), 36 (refs. 7, 75), *39, 40, 42*
Baliasnaia, A. I., 299 (ref. 19), *306*
Ball, E. G., 308, 309 (ref. 3), 310 (refs. 2, 10), 311 (ref. 2), 330 (ref. 2), *331*
Barber, M., 213 (ref. 3), 237 (ref. 3), *252*
Barron, E. S. G., 321 (ref. 4), *331*
Barrueto, R. B., 263, *282*
Basford, R. E., 310 (refs. 5, 16), 321 (ref. 16), *331, 332*
Bates, R. G., 172, 188 (ref. 2), *209*
Baumgarten, P., 224 (ref. 4), *252*
Baxter, J. G., 46, 48 (ref. 49), 49 (ref. 68), 50 (ref. 25), 74, 81 (ref. 67), 86 (ref. 49), *96, 97*
Beadle, B. W., 2 (ref. 98), 5 (ref. 98), 10 (ref. 4), 16 (ref. 4), 23, *39, 42*, 105, 110 (ref. 4), *137*
Beckman, A. O., 21 (ref. 34), *40*
Benotti, J., 272 (ref. 7), 273, *282*
Berk, L. C., 111, *137*
Berkhout, H. W., 10, *39*
Bernard, B. de, 310 (ref. 5), *331*
Bernath, P., 309 (ref. 42), 312 (ref. 42), 314 (ref. 42), 316 (ref. 42), *332*
Bessey, O. A., 90, *96*, 271 (ref. 8), *282*
Bevenue, A., 22 (ref. 12), 24 (ref. 12), 36 (ref. 12), *39*
Bickoff, E. M., 1–42, 49 (ref. 14), 86,

340   AUTHOR INDEX

Kernohan, G., 17, *40*
Kimble, M. S., 89 (ref. 50), *97*
Kind, P. R. N., 269, *283*
King, E. J., 244, 249, *252, 253,* 259
  (ref. 50), 260, 261 (ref. 2), 262 (refs.
  1, 2), 269, 273 (ref. 50), *281, 283*
King, H. K., 287, 303, *306*
Klein, R., 143, *168*
Kluyver, A. J., 311 (ref. 32), *332*
Knaffl-Lenz, E., 172, 173, *210*
Koch, W., 59, *96*
Koehn, R. C., 12 (ref. 23), *39*
Kohake, E., 11 (ref. 27), 17 (ref. 27), *40*
Kohout, P. M., 309 (ref. 17), 311 (ref.
  17), 321 (ref. 17), 331 (ref. 17), *332*
Kono, K., 237, 238 (ref. 46), 249 (refs.
  47, 48), 250, *253*
Koppeschaar, W., 266, *283*
Krause, R. F., 93 (ref. 51), *97*
Kraybill, H. R., 2 (ref. 98), 5 (ref. 98),
  42, 105, 110, 116, *137, 138*
Krebs, H. A., 288 (refs. 14, 15), 294–
  296, 300, 301 (ref. 14), 305, *306*
Kretchmer, N., 111, *137*
Krinsky, N. I., 93 (ref. 52), *97*
Kuhn, R., 13 (ref. 50), *40*
Kun, E., 330, *332*
Kuper, S. W. A., 213 (ref. 3), 237 (ref.
  3), *252*
Kurata, J., 251, *254*
Kurono, K., 213 (ref. 69), 234, *254*
Kutscher, W., 258 (ref. 52), 259, 260
  (ref. 54), *283*
Kyrning, S., 93, *97*

L

LaDue, J. S., 258 (ref. 47), *283*
Laine, T., 299, *306*
Lamp, B., 122, 130 (ref. 23), 131 (ref.
  23), 133, *138*
Lapworth, A., 242, *252*
Lawrie, N. R., 94 (ref. 54), *97*
Lazarow, A., 326 (ref. 8), *331*
Leadbetter, W. F., 262 (ref. 27), 272
  (ref. 27), *282*
Leftin, J. H., 145 (ref. 13), *168*

Lehman, R. W., 43–98
Lemon, H. M., 258 (refs. 20, 73), 263.
  282, 284
Léonis, J., 171–210
Lerner, F., 259 (ref. 29), 261 (ref. 29),
  262 (refs. 27, 29), 272 (ref. 27), *282*
LeRosen, A. L., 23, 35 (ref. 68), *41*
Levy, A. L., 203, 209, *210*
Lewis, J. I. M., 238 (ref. 14), 239 (ref.
  14), *252*
Lichstein, H. C., 305 (ref. 16), *306*
Lindahl, P. E., 217 (ref. 58), *253*
Linderstrøm-Lang, K., 171–210
Lingane, J. J., 173, 178, *210*
Linhardt, K., 267 (ref. 55), 268, *283*
Link, K. P., 229 (ref. 64), *254*
Lips, H. J., 112, 126, *138*
Little, R. W., 78 (ref. 55), *97*
Livingston, A. L., 3 (ref. 9), 11 (ref.
  10), 12 (ref. 10), 17 (ref. 10), 21
  (ref. 8), 24, 25 (ref. 10), 26 (ref. 8),
  39
Lloyd, A. G., 221 (ref. 15), 226, 227 (ref.
  15), 228 (ref. 15), *252*
Locke, J. M., 311 (ref. 18), *332*
Loewenstein, E., 48 (ref. 77), *98*
London, M., 258 (refs. 56, 58), 280
  (ref. 57), 281, *283*
Longsworth, L. G., 173, 177 (ref. 13),
  210
Lopez, J. A., 90 (ref. 13), *96*
Lovern, J. A., 105 (ref. 10), *137*
Lowenstein, J. M., 217 (ref. 59), *253*
Lowry, O. H., 90 (ref. 13), *96,* 271 (ref.
  8), *282*
Luckmann, F. H., 78 (ref. 56), *97*
Lundberg, W. O., 121–123, *137*
Lundquist, F., 258 (ref. 60), 262 (ref.
  59), *283*
Lynen, F., 326 (ref. 34), *332*
Lyons, F. B., 11 (ref. 29), *40*

M

McClure, L. E., 304, *306*
MacDonald, M. P., 140 (ref. 9), *168*
Macfarlane, Y. J., 86 (ref. 28), *96*

Sorensen, S. P. L., 172, 188, *210*
Sohns, V. E., 311 (ref. 18), *332*
Sols, A., 268 (ref. 71), *284*
Sommer, A., 258 (ref. 58), *283*
Spencer, B., 211–255
Sproul, E. E., 258 (ref. 39), 259 (ref. 39), *283*
Sprunt, D. H., 272 (ref. 61), *283*
Sreenivasan, B., 136 *138*
Stauffer, J. F., 286 (ref. 26), *306*
Stecklein, H. R., 236 (ref. 40), 247 (ref. 40), *253*
Steenbock, H., 2, *41*
Stephenson, M. L., 304, *306*
Stern, M. H., 47 (ref. 69), *95*
Stetter, H., 271 (ref. 40), *283*
Steyermark, P. R., 140 (refs. 18, 24), *168, 169*
Stickney, M. E., 21 (ref. 34), *40*
Stitch, S. R., 213 (ref. 101), 215 (ref. 101), 230 (ref. 101), 231 (ref. 101), *255*
Stitt, F., 3 (refs. 7, 75), 19 (ref. 7), 23 (ref. 7), 24 (ref. 7), 36 (refs. 7, 75), *39, 41*
Stodola, F. H., 311 (ref. 18), *332*
Stoll, A., 9, 13, *41*
Stone, S. S., 19 (ref. 91), *42*
Storer, R. V., 272 (ref. 72), *284*
Stotz, E., 308, 310 (ref. 37), 311 (ref. 37), *332*
Strain, H. H., 3 (ref. 77), 15, 16 (ref. 78), *41*
Strandberg, L., 227 (ref. 102), *255*
Stregevsky, S., 91 (ref. 24), *96*
Stubbs, A. L., 72, 74 (ref. 59), 86, *97*
Subbarow, Y., 267, *282*
Sumner, A., 2 (refs. 25, 26), *39, 40*
Suzuki, S., 226 (ref. 34), *253*
Swain, M. L., 113 (refs. 6–8), 114 (ref. 7), 115 (ref. 6), 116 (ref. 7), *137*
Swanson, W. J., 47 (ref. 6), 49 (ref. 7), 51 (refs. 6, 7), 60 (refs. 6, 7), 71 (ref. 8), 82 (ref. 9), *95*
Sweat, M. L., 140, 153, *169*
Szczypinski, A. J., 267 (ref. 4), 271, *281*

T

Takahashi, N., 226 (ref. 34), *253*
Talalay, P., 250 (ref. 103), *255*, 268 (ref. 45), *283*
Tanaka, S., 217, 236 (ref. 105), *255*
Tanko, B., 213 (ref. 106), 221 (ref. 106), *255*
Taylor, E. S., 305, *306*
Tessier, H., 112, 126, *138*
Thevenet, M., 213 (ref. 49), 230 (ref. 49), *253*
Thomas, J., 214 (ref. 23), 235 (ref. 25), 236 (refs. 23–25), 237 (refs. 25, 100), 239 (refs. 23, 25), 245 (ref. 23), 248 (ref. 25), *252, 255*
Thompson, C. R., 3 (refs. 9, 11, 75, 80), 5 (ref. 11), 6 (ref. 80), 12 (refs. 11, 79, 80), 17 (ref. 79), 19, 23 (ref. 11), 26 (ref. 79), 31, 33, 36 (ref. 75), 38 (ref. 79), *39, 41*, 93, *98*
Thorn, G. W., 140, *168*
Thorsteinsson, T., 258 (ref. 60), *283*
Thunberg, T., 308, 329, *333*
Tice, S. V., 288 (ref. 20), 296 (ref. 20), 299, 300 (ref. 20), 301, *306*
Todhunter, E. N., 69, *98*
Trunnell, J. B., 276, *282*
Tsou, C. L., 321, *333*
Tswett, M., 9, 14, *41*
Tucker, R. E., 91 (ref. 24), *96*
Tyler, F. H., 147 (ref. 17), *168*

U

Umbreit, W. W., 286 (ref. 26), 294, 302, 305 (ref. 16), *306*
United States Pharmacopeia, 53, 74, *98*

V

Vahlteich, H. W., 78 (ref. 56), *97*
Valk, W. L., 271 (ref. 64), *284*
Van Atta, G. R., 11 (ref. 10), 12 (ref. 10), 17 (ref. 10), 24, 25 (ref. 10), *39*
Vandenheuvel, F. A., 111, *138*
Viala, R., 236 (ref. 107), *255*
Virtanen, A. I., 299, *306*
Vlitos, A. J., 213 (ref. 108), *255*

SUBJECT INDEX

A

R

Reaction rates, measured in pH-stat, 198–209
Recorder for pH-stat, 178–181
Rehydration of plant material, 25–26
Retinene. *See also* Isoretinene; Neoretinene.
  properties, 49
Rhizobium leguminosarum, amino acid decarboxylase activity, 299
Rhodopsin in vitamin A assay, 70–71
Rosolyl phosphate, as substrate for serum acid phosphatase, 268, 269

S

Saponification in vitamin A purification, 82–83
Serum acid phosphatases, abnormal values, 279–280
  buffers, 267–268, 277–278
  in cancer of prostate, 258–260, 271–272, 279–281
  determination, 257–284
    by aminoantipyrene methods, 269–270
    by diazo methods, 270
    elimination of protein precipitation, 268–272
    by Fishman-Lerner method, 273–276
    nitrophenyl phosphate procedures, 271–272
    by phenol release, 266–268
    by phosphate release, 265–266
    sources of error, 276–279
    time requirements, 264–265, 278
  dilution effects, 276–278
  heterogeneity, 260–263, 277
  normal values, 279–281
  stability, 276
  substrates, 265–270
  tartrate inhibited, 262, 272, 273–276, 278
  unit of activity, 272
  rum albumin in protection of succinic dehydrogenase, 321, 322

Sinigrin. *See* Potassium myronate.
Snails, arylsulfatases in, 234
Solvent partition in vitamin A purification, 86, 91
Spectral constants. *See* Absorbance; Extinction coefficients.
Spectrophotometry in assays, carotene, 20, 23–24, 28–31, 36–38
  ketosteroids, 144–149, 150–151, 152, 157–159
  polyunsaturated fatty acids, 104–130
  succinic dehydrogenase, 319–321, 322–323, 323–327, 328–330
  sulfatases, 240, 241–242
  vitamin A, 46–48, 71–78
Stereoisomerism and vitamin A activity of carotenes, 5–6
Stereoisomers of carotene, determination, 22–24, 33–38
Steroids. *See* 17,21-Dihydroxy-20-ketosteroids.
Steroid sulfatase, assay, 215, 230–234
  occurrence, 213, 230
Stirrers for pH-stat, 182–183
Streptococcus faecalis, preparation of decarboxylase from, 290, 295–297
Succinic dehydrogenase, assay of complex, 328–331
  electron transport agents, 328, 330–331
  methylene blue method, 327–330
  assay of primary, 310–327
    ferricyanide method, 311, 321–323
    by fumarate reduction, 323–327
    manometric methods, 313–319, 322, 327, 328–330
    phenazine methosulfate method, 309, 310, 312–321
    spectrophotometric methods, 319–321, 322–323, 323–327, 328–330
  inhibition, 315–319, 321
  mechanism of action, 309–310
  protection, 315–319
  reaction with dyes, 310–312
Succinic oxidase system, 308
Sulfatases, assay of, 211–255

Methods of Biochemical Analysis

CUMULATIVE INDEX, VOLUMES I-IV

Author Index